D1087847

LEGAL ASPECTS
OF
ENGINEERING

LEGAL ASPECTS

OF

ENGINEERING

by RICHARD C. VAUGHN

Iowa State University

PRENTICE-HALL, INC.
Englewood Cliffs, N.J.

LIBRARY OF CONGRESS CATALOG CARD NO.: 62-9582

PRINTED IN THE UNITED STATES OF AMERICA
52757-C

Current printing (last digit):
12 11 10 9 8 7 6 5 4 3

PREFACE

This book was written for people in all fields of engineering. The lecture notes from which it evolved were used in classes composed of a variety of engineering students.

The topics treated are those with which any engineer is likely to be concerned. It is highly probable that the engineer will be an agent for someone. He will be concerned with the formation of contracts and performance under them. Many of the contracts concern sales; nearly all will concern property rights. It is quite possible that an engineer might be concerned with torts and with law cases involving either tort or breach of contract. He may find an acquaintance with patent law useful. Since many companies find it desirable to promote engineers to management and executive positions, the introduction contains a few comments on management and executive qualities. Engineering students are preparing themselves to enter a profession; for this reason a discussion of engineering ethics is presented in Chapter 4.

Legal cases are presented at the ends of most of the chapters to serve as illustrations of the various principles studied, and as examples of legal reasoning. Since legal reasoning is somewhat different from the reasoning involved in solving engineering problems, the jurists' opinions are preserved with a minimum of editing—only lengthy lists of case citations are omitted.

One note of caution seems appropriate—the product of the course in which this book is likely to be used will not, by virtue of the text or the course, be an attorney. However, the student should acquire enough familiarity with the law to know when he needs the services of a member of the bar.

The writing of a textbook is almost always the result of efforts by many people in addition to those of the author. I am deeply indebted to the following people for their aid and encouragement: to Donald B.

Wilcox for his encouragement, inspiration, and editorial comments; to Mark Shovar for his editing and guidance; to various members of the engineering staff at the University of Florida for their assistance; to many students in past classes of IG 463 who have added their comments; and last, but far from least, to Mrs. Vaughn and Evelyn Rawls, who deciphered my handwriting and turned it into a typed manuscript.

R. C. Vaughn

CONTENTS

vii

7

PARTIES 101

8

AGREEMENT 114

9

REALITY OF AGREEMENT 129

10

CONSIDERATION 139

11

LAWFUL SUBJECT MATTER 148

12

STATUTE OF FRAUDS 161

13

THIRD PARTY RIGHTS 169

14

DISCHARGE 178

LEGAL ASPECTS
OF
ENGINEERING

1
INTRODUCTION

The engineer is a problem solver. He possesses unique tools for stating problems in such a manner that they can be solved, and for giving answers. His facility at this results from screening, natural selection, and specialized training in problem-solving techniques. It is this ability to state and solve problems that employers hope to find when they hire an engineer; and it is because of the many uses for this knowledge that we presently have a very substantial demand for engineering graduates.

Most of the training offered to an engineer equips him to solve problems of a mathematical nature—problems which may readily be reduced to symbolic form. However, not all problems lend themselves to such an attack. The stress resulting from force application to a particular design of beam is easily stated in mathematical terms. It is a little more difficult, but still quite possible in most cases, to assume probabilities and solve for the number of parts to be run or warehouse space to be required for next year's production. It is exceedingly difficult, though, if not downright impossible, to state laws governing relationships between people in terms of x's and y's with proper coefficients and thereby solve legal or ethical problems. Most such problems involve the interpretation of man-made laws and the use of discretion and judgment in determining rights. Despite the difficulty in their solution, legal problems and problems involving human relations are no less important to a successful engineer than his ability to use La Place Transformations in solving a differential equation.

In most engineering jobs the engineer is part of a so-called "management team." Before turning to the aspects of law with which the engineer should be familiar, it may well be desirable to consider certain management skills which he should strive to acquire.

1

Engineering Management

To the vast majority of engineering graduates the first job secured is merely a steppingstone to higher things. Most people, including engineers, are ambitious. It is only natural that the engineering neophyte should raise his sights toward higher positions with greater economic rewards for the future.

Normally the engineer's first job requires a large amount of technical skill. As he moves up, the percentage of time in which he uses his technical skills usually decreases. Regardless of the ladder the engineer has chosen to climb—research, manufacturing engineering, consulting, sales, or any other—progression to higher levels depends upon at least four factors in addition to his engineering ability.

COMMUNICATION SKILLS. An idea possessed by an engineer may have very great latent value, but until it is used or communicated in some way, the idea is worthless to him. In addition, the very mental work necessary to put the idea in coherent word-form is in itself of value. Nearly everyone has had the experience of gaining new insight or of discovering added features of an idea when faced with the task of trying to explain it to someone else.

HANDLING PEOPLE. A promotion from a strictly technical position to something higher almost always leads to handling people. Being "boss" isn't easy. People can be forced to work under threat of being deprived of their paychecks, but such threats usually stifle initiative. The manager who takes time to explain to his subordinates "why" and keep them informed is likely to be more successful than one who does not.

SENSE OF COST. Most operations are undertaken with a profit motive. Even in those operations which are not expected to make a profit, cost is usually important. If the selling price of a company's product is unchanged, money saved in manufacturing or raw material cost represents added profit; conversely, added cost decreases profit. Many engineers have won promotions, and many consultants make their livelihoods on their ability to analyze operations and reduce costs.

KNOWLEDGE OF LAW. The engineer is not expected to become an attorney from exposure to one survey course in law, any more than an attorney could become an engineer by taking one survey course in engineering. However, the engineer should be cognizant of the probable effects of carelessness in dealing with others. He should know when he is in trouble and needs the advice of an attorney. The law background is a somewhat preventive asset; that is, because of a limited knowledge of law, it is intended that the engineer will be equipped to prevent costly lawsuits against his company. Meticulous reading of contracts before signing can be a sizeable preventive measure. It is often surprising how little attention is paid to contracts and supporting documents, particularly in view of the fact that these documents outline the rights and responsibilities of the parties.

Executive Qualities

In recent years there has been an increasing trend toward filling top management or executive positions with engineers. There has been recognition of the value of the engineer's analytical approach to executive problems.

While there is a good deal of truth to the often quoted comment that "there is always room at the top," those who get there usually must possess special abilities. Engineering training is beneficial to the executive aspirant, but so is a knowledge of many other fields.

What makes an executive? Why does one person achieve this goal while many others strive and fail? At first glance the behavior of one successful executive appears to have little in common with that of another who is equally successful. One is the brusque, bull-of-the-woods; another is as smooth as silk. However, upon closer examination certain similar behavior patterns become apparent. Each usually possesses the four above mentioned qualities of a manager, one or more to a high degree. There are other qualities, too, which are seen to be common to most top executives and which deserve consideration.

LEADERSHIP. The quality known as leadership is difficult to define. It is clearly evident in one person and strangely lacking in another. Psychologically, leadership indicates an identification of the leader with the group he leads—it is necessary that he be considered by the other members as one of them. Effectiveness as the leader also requires that he be somewhat superior to the others in the group in one or more qualities esteemed by them.

It is doubtful if anyone is truly a "born leader." It is more probable that the qualities are a result of training acquired both consciously and unconsciously—study and observation so ingrained that the leader's responses to various situations are almost as natural as breathing. Thus the term "born leader" has come to be used in reference to the leader who seems to do everything right at the right time in a very natural way.

The qualities of leadership seem to be enhanced by practice. Opportunities to practice the poise and purposefulness of leadership occur in virtually limitless ways. One of the main reasons that job application blanks nearly always contain space for listing organizational activities is to determine the amount of practice in leadership the candidate has had.

Two outstanding leadership characteristics are the ability to keep the ultimate goal uppermost in mind and the ability to pursue it enthusiastically. Enthusiasm is infectious—it rubs off on others. The relative success of dictators and would-be dictators attests to this. A speech delivered in a monotone makes dull listening; however, the same speech using virtually the same words but delivered enthusiastically can move people to action.

A leader does not need a leaning post—either literally or figuratively. *Leadership* stems partly from the ability to stand firm on principles. There is a popular misconception that a leader should not admit mistakes. Few people bat 1.000 on all their decisions. Not only must the leader admit his own mistakes; he must also take the responsibility for the mistakes of his subordinates, since their actions result from his direction or lack thereof. Scapegoating is a popular art, but few effective leaders in top management will stoop to it to avoid criticism.

DELEGATING. One of the characteristics of most top executives is a facility for delegating authority and responsibility to others. It is virtually impossible for anyone to rise to the top of a modern industrial organization without the ability to delegate. There is just not time to cover effectively and thoroughly all of the requirements of a top management job. The executive who delegates very little is robbing himself of time needed for adequate thought before making decisions. Also, failure to delegate routine tasks to others is a bar to his own promotion; if no one can be found who has performed a portion of the executive's task with the authority necessary to that performance, it is natural to leave the executive where he is.

Specialization is an inherent advantage of effective delegating. No one is a specialist in everything. By assigning some of his tasks to others, the executive can obtain the advantage of specialized treatment.

Delegation, as the term is used industrially, is something more than the mere assignment of a task to be performed. Delegation includes clothing the delegee with the necessary authority to carry out his assigned function. It is this parting with a portion of his authority which causes the shortsighted executive consciously or unconsciously to oppose delegation to others. It is this very aspect of delegating, however, that is valuable in contributing to the growth of assistants. The able executive realizes this and takes full advantage of it in helping others develop.

DECISIONS. All of us must make decisions involving a choice among alternatives. In this choosing we are not always correct. One attribute which seems characteristic of those people who reach top management is their ability to be right a higher percentage of the time than the average person. Of course, top management decisions are decisions on particularly difficult problems. Decisions run all the way from a single-variable problem such as the checking of a part with a go-no go gage to multi-variable problems where little, if anything, is fixed or known. Generally, routine decisions are delegated to others; the top manager is the one who makes the decision when major uncertainties are present. The man to make decisions such as these is a venturer—a man who will assume risks in his decisions. Generally, the greater the risk undertaken the greater the possible reward. The conclusion to expand a plant or install new production facilities based on an apparently expanding market is such a decision. No one can predict the future—the further into the future the planning, the more inaccurate it is likely to be.

Top management decisions generally consist of five elements: a gathering of facts; a recognition of limiting conditions; assuming facts and conditions as they are expected to be and recognition that these are assumptions; analysis of the facts, limits and assumptions; and decision. Many of the assumptions can be reduced to probabilities. If enough of this can be done the problem can be programmed for a computer, which will then give the executive some answers. However, the answers are based on assumptions and probabilities and it is still up to the executive to decide whether to go ahead or not. The risk is still his; not the computer's.

A few top executives possess such vast knowledge and ability at analysis and synthesis that they can make rapid-fire policy decisions which are nearly always right. However, such people are very rare. Generally, people in top management do not make hurried policy decisions. There is often grumbling from below because of apparently undue procrastination. Despite the grumbling, such delay is usually the course of wisdom, since the risks are frequently sizeable. A decision based on inadequate facts is hazardous, and delay in waiting for more facts is often inescapable. Even the rare management genius who makes correct decisions rapidly usually has had many years of experience in more methodical decision-making which equipped him for his present role.

DISCIPLINE. Discipline is a necessary component of any well-run organization. People must be taught; old habit patterns must be changed. Most top executives are past masters of the use of reward and punishment in changing the behavior of subordinates. To be effective, executive orders must imply some form of reproof for disobedience; rewards of some sort must follow outstanding performance if the effort required for the performance is to be continued.

The extent of reward or punishment necessary depends to a great degree upon the personal stature of the executive. If he is held in high regard by his subordinates, a word or so of reproof is often the equivalent of the proverbial "ten lashes."

In addition to his drives for food, water, and means of satisfying other basic needs, man has a whole host of derived needs, not the least of which is the need for recognition. Every person needs recognition or respect from others—lack of it causes loss of self respect and, eventually, diminished effort. Recognition is either tangible or intangible—both forms are required. Verbal praise sounds hollow after a while if it is not accompanied by some monetary reward. Similarly, financial increases without praise for accomplishments are incomplete.

It has often been stated that rewards should be public; criticism or punishment private. The truth in the statement is inescapable. Most top managers observe this principle in the interest of preserving their organizations.

These are only a few of the principles which guide a top executive in his management of discipline. Most of them he understands and observes without conscious thought when disciplinary occasions arise.

There are many elements or ingredients which make a person successful in top management. Only a few have been mentioned here. Nevertheless, these few are basic and must be mastered by executive aspirants.

The purpose of an industry and its management is to produce something. Converting time and raw material into goods and services requires production facilities. Assembly of the machines and equipment required to produce something is normally undertaken as an engineering project. Not only must the original facilities be planned and built; every design change or functional change of the product requires changing machines and equipment. The job of setting up production facilities becomes, then, not a "one-shot" enterprise, but an almost continuous re-planning and rearrangement. The burden of deciding when and how much to change—and what to change to—falls on top management; the job of planning and carrying out the details of rearrangement is assigned to the engineering department.

ENGINEERING PROJECTS

A large proportion of the capital wealth of our country has resulted from engineering projects. Civil engineering projects—roads, bridges, buildings and the like—are most familiar to the public. As a result, whenever the term "engineering project" is used, visions of a dam or cloverleaf are likely to come to mind. The value of civil projects cannot be denied, but contributions by other engineering fields are also significant, even though the public is not as aware of the activities or results.

Since the development and adoption of mass production methods in the United States, a new combining of engineering talents has taken place. People were needed to apply knowledge of civil engineering, mechanical, electrical, chemical, industrial, or other engineering fields to manufacturing problems. This combining of engineering talents to solve manufacturing problems has come to be known by many names, but the term "manufacturing engineering" seems more appropriate than most. Typically, manufacturing engineering is concerned with the process required to mass-produce some product. It starts with an analysis of someone's brain child and continues as long as there are engineering problems in the process.

Manufacturing Engineering

In any engineering project there are three phases or stages of development: 1) the idea, 2) the construction, and 3) making it work. The stages are fairly separable and a particular engineering group may have responsibilities in one or more of the stages.

IDEA. Just about everything we enjoy started as someone's idea or "screwball notion." Neither products nor the processes by which they are manufactured could have been made without someone's original idea. Not all ideas are practical, however. A large number of those which were adopted required alterations before they were acceptable. Many of the ideas have appeared attractive in the beginning only to be demonstrated as impractical by objective examination. This objective examination of a possible engineering project is known as a "feasibility study."

A feasibility study is a preliminary examination of an idea proposed. It is meant to answer such questions as: What will it cost to produce various quantities per year? Can we market enough to make a reasonable return on the required investment in productive facilities? How many can be sold at a given price? What processes will be better in the long run? The answers given determine whether it is desirable to go to the next stage—actually setting up to produce.

CONSTRUCTION. The job of turning someone's idea into a reality can be quite complex in a manufacturing situation. Planning is necessary. The planning requires imagination—a vision of the future; and the planning continues until everything is firmly in place. Even then, maintenance should be planned. Changes are easily made in the planning stage—it costs little to erase a machine location on a layout and place the machine in another location. Even rearrangements of the entire process are inexpensive at this point. It is here that questions pertaining to equipment sizes, locations, and added features must be answered and the answers justified if the process is to be successful. Layout changes after the process equipment has been placed are very expensive. For this reason, questions which should have been raised in the planning stage but were never brought up reflect on the process engineer's ability. A member of a manufacturing engineering department does not have to be omniscient, but it would help if he could be.

The process engineer designs a layout of the process, complete with machines and equipment, and writes specifications for the machines to function as desired. The specifications are then sent out, proposals received and contracts let to the successful bidders. The engineer is the owner's agent; as such he must supervise the building of machines or other structures to fit the layout and then supervise their installation.

Just as a good cook times everything so that nothing will be cold when it is served, the engineer must control times of completion of the elements of his layout. It is rare that a process is completed and functioning properly in the time which it apparently should take. It seems there is nearly always at least one contractor who is late. If the engineer is wise he will allow some time for this in his schedule.

MAKING IT WORK. It is probably safe to state that in every manufacturing process ever installed there were special problems to be solved before full-scale production could begin. The presence of "bugs" in a newly installed process is about as normal as any expectancy can be. The bugs must be removed before the process can be considered complete. The engineer who set up the process is the logical person to remove these bugs before the operation is turned over to the production people.

Law and Engineers

In any engineering project the engineer is the representative or agent of the owner. It is his function to act in the best interests of the owner— to get the best possible results with a minimum of delay and problems. The engineer must deal with the rights of others. His actions affect others' property rights or personal rights, arising from ownership of property, contractual obligations, torts, or crimes. He is a guardian of the owner's rights and, in a manner of speaking, of the rights of others with whom the owner deals. Since court proceedings are costly in both time and money, he should do all in his power to avoid entanglements which will lead to them. And, since violation of the rights of others is likely to lead to court, the engineer must know the characteristics of these rights if his preventive job is to be well done.

The relationships between the owner and his contractor are set forth in a series of documents drawn up by the engineer. The Instructions for Bidders, Proposal, General Conditions, Specifications, and Drawings comprise parts of the contract. Careless errors in the preparation of these documents can cause legal controversies or place the owner and engineer in indefensible positions when controversies arise. He must formulate the documents in such a way that the owner's position is protected, and do this without imposing undue hardship on the contractor.

In some respects the engineer's position is between the owner and the contractor. When disputes arise he is likely to be called upon to mediate or at least enter into the controversies. To do a reasonable job in this intermediate position the engineer must be acquainted with the legal rights and responsibilities of both parties. He does not have to be an attorney, but some knowledge of the law is essential. He should be able to recognize situations in which it is necessary to go to an attorney for legal counsel. A minimum knowledge of the law is required even for this; you can't very easily recognize legal troubles unless you have some knowledge of the rights involved.

There is a second reason for the engineer to acquire a knowledge of the law. He is a citizen as well as a representative of his employer or client. The law controls many of his day-to-day dealings with others. When he buys insurance or signs a chattel mortgage for the purchase of a refrigerator, his own rights and responsibilities should be clear to him. At the very least, the idea of reading the document before he signs should occur to him.

An engineer is a member of society as well as a person possessing technical skills. As an educated member of society and a professional person, his knowledge and abilities should extend well beyond his technical skills. One popularly accepted criterion of the cultured person is his ability to analyze and discuss news events with some perception. Much of the news presented to us on radio, television, newspapers, or magazines has legal significance. If the engineer is to be accepted and respected as a learned man in his community, his interests must be broad enough to justify this acceptance. A minor acquaintance with legal lore is a step in this direction.

REVIEW QUESTIONS

1. Why should an engineer have an acquaintance with the law?

2. Name at least three more qualifications an engineer should possess for success in management. Name at least three additional qualities of successful executives.

3. What are the stages of an engineering project? What would each stage be composed of in the proposed manufacture of, say, tie clasps?

4. What is manufacturing engineering?

2 DEVELOPMENT OF LAW

Our activities are regulated by laws. As we live and work we become familiar with many laws, particularly those having to do with the physical world, the laws of nature. We know that if we are near the earth when we drop something it will fall to the earth in obedience to the law of gravity. We can even predict accurately how fast the object will fall and where it will strike the earth if we consider the laws of motions and the retarding forces. Such natural laws form a particular kind of universe of laws. They are not man-made laws, only man-discovered. The law would exist even if we passed a legislative act against it. It is interesting to note that such an act was once attempted by a state legislature, which tried to set the value of π as 3.000 to make calculations involving the diameter and circumference of a circle more convenient.

In this text we are concerned with *man-made laws*, the laws governing the relationships between people. As we will talk about it here, "law" is a set of rules and principles set up by society to restrict the conduct and protect the rights of its members.

A person living by himself in such a way that he had no contacts with others would have no use for man-made laws. Add another person and the need for law becomes apparent. Each of the two has rights which might be infringed upon by the other. In fairness, each must control his behavior in such a manner that the other's rights are protected. In such a simple society the relationships would not be complex and simple rules would be sufficient.

Man is gregarious; our social instincts are highly developed. Judging from the steadily increasing percentage of urban residents in our population, our social tendencies appear to be increasing, either from the strength of the pull or from the ease of succumbing to it. As we become more of an urban society we require more laws and restrictions of greater complexity to govern properly the behavior of the membership.

Beginnings of Law

Laws began as social customs. It was considered proper to behave in a certain manner in a particular circumstance. At first the tribal chief and later the priest was charged with the preservation of these customs, including punishment for infractions. In the hands of the priests the idea that laws were of divine origin was fostered. Thus many of our early laws, as well as the present Mohammedan system, were said to have resulted from divine manifestations.

DIVINE LAWS. Two codes of divine laws have made a contribution to the law of our Western civilization. The first of these was the Code of Hammurabi (about 2000 B.C.), based on the idea of an "eye for an eye, and a tooth for a tooth." Early justice in this country was sometimes not far removed from this concept, and our present sentence of death for first degree murder is similar.

The second set of divine laws which influenced our law is the Ten Commandments. Present influence of these laws in our legislation and court decisions is easily found. However, as rules these Mosaic Laws have one outstanding feature—they are short and simple. Each person is presumed by the court to know the laws under which he lives. It is necessary that this presumption be made; if it were not, anyone could plead ignorance of the law and thereby avoid it. Yet how true is this presumption? How many U.S. citizens know the local ordinances under which they live? Or the state statutes? Or the federal laws? Or even the rights guaranteed or the restrictions imposed by the Constitution and Bill of Rights? Yet a child can be taught the Ten Commandments, and he will be able to recall many of them when he reaches adulthood, even though he may have had little contact with them in the intervening years.

CIVIL LAW. Two great systems of law are used in the Western nations. The English common law is used in most of the English-speaking countries; Roman Civil Law is used in the remainder of Western societies. Civil Law (sometimes called the Continental system) originated about 450 B.C. as the Law of the Twelve Tables. This was the law of the Roman Empire as it expanded and contracted during the next ten centuries. During that time statutes were passed and meanings clarified in court decisions. Under the Emperor Justinian in the 6th century these laws were all boiled down to their essentials and published as the *Pandects*. This Civil Law spread to other countries and became the foundation of the legal systems of continental Europe.

In operation, Roman Civil Law and English common law are quite different, though in practice the results are usually about the same. Civil

Law is based on written codes or statutes, the court's task being to apply the correct statute to the particular set of facts in the case. Common law is built on cases—prior decisions in similar factual situations.

Most of the law brought to the United States by its early settlers was common law. However, in the states settled by the French and Spanish settlers, remnants of Civil Law may be found. Thus, in Louisiana, Texas, and California principles of Civil Law have had some influence.

The term "civil law" has come to have a dual meaning. It means a code of law based upon the Roman codes. As it has come to be used today, it also describes our system of private law, as opposed to criminal law. When the term is used in the remainder of the text it will refer to the system of private law.

Enforcement

A man-made rule to govern the behavior of individuals in a society has little practical value unless there is enforcement of the rule. Enforcement takes place in one of three forms: Punishment. Fines or imprisonment are the usual means of punishing someone who has committed a crime; Relief. In actions involving private rights the relief sought is usually money damages for the person who has been harmed at the hand of another, or prevention of future harm; Social censure. Frequently the strongest enforcement factor is the fear of social ostracism—the fear of public opinion. Although, strictly speaking, public opinion is not a recognized legal means of enforcement, its existence and strength cannot be denied.

Few of us possess a formal knowledge of the laws which govern our actions. Yet we obey them. Even the worst of criminals obeys nearly all the laws almost all the time. We comply unconsciously. The laws become a part of each member of the society in which we live—they have been a part of our lives since earliest childhood. Thus, even though we may not know the specific laws to which we conform, we do conform, and we are aware when others do not. Often we are not aware of the definite rule violated or the rights infringed. The attempt is made here to bring such an awareness to the reader.

COMMON LAW AND EQUITY

Types of Laws

Our laws are of four basic types: constitutional, statute, common law, and equity. The terms constitutional law and statute law almost speak for themselves.

Constitutional law sets up the operation of a government, including its powers and limitations. It states fundamental principles in the relationship between citizen and state, including rights which may not be infringed.

A statute is a law stating the express declaration of the will of a legislature in the subject of the statute. A state law prohibiting gambling and setting forth a maximum penalty of $500 or six months in jail for nonobservance would be an example of statute law. Similarly, federal laws such as the Interstate Commerce Act, and municipal laws (or ordinances) regulating traffic are statutes.

COMMON LAW

Our law, as we originally obtained it, was the common law brought over from England by the colonists. It is still our law; it is used when no statute or constitutional law covers the particular legal problem involved. Along with equity it forms a foundation for our legal system.

Origin

Before the Norman conquest of England the law that existed was local law. Each town or shire had its own law and each differed somewhat from the others. The king took an interest in the law only in a very exceptional case.

The Norman conquerors were organizers. Under them a national council, known as the King's Council, was established to make laws and decide cases. Eventually, the council evolved into Parliament and a system of king's courts.

In the first century or so following the Norman Conquest, what we know as common law began. It arose from the practice of judges to write their opinions, giving the general principles and the reasoning they followed in deciding cases. When the facts were similar, other judges tended to follow these past opinions.

STARE DECISIS. Abiding by previous decisions is known in legal terminology as stare decisis. The main feature of common law is that the law itself is built on case decisions. When a case is decided, that decision becomes the law for that court and other courts within its jurisdiction [1] in deciding similar future cases. In the cases in this text you will see many references to previously decided cases. Many other references have

---

[1] A court's jurisdiction, in the manner used above, indicates the area in which the court may operate. For example, the jurisdiction of the Supreme Court of Ohio is the State of Ohio, and a common law decision by the Ohio Supreme Court would be binding on all other courts in Ohio.

been omitted to allow easier reading of each case. The judge, by using the precedent cases lays the foundation for the decision which he will render.

About 200 years after the Norman Conquest a justice named Henry Bracton compiled the decisions which had been rendered under the king's court systems. This began case reporting. These and later decisions formed the common law of England and, eventually, of nearly all of the United States.

Shortly before the American Revolution, Sir William Blackstone, an English jurist, completed his *Commentaries on the Laws of England*. In this lawbook, the first major contribution since the time of Bracton, Blackstone clarified and made intelligible the English common law. An American jurist, James Kent, made a similar contribution in this country about sixty years later. Common law is defined in Kent's Commentaries as "those principles, usages, and rules of action applicable to the government and security of persons and property, which do not rest for their authority upon any express or positive declaration of the will of the legislature." In both books the principles of common law were extracted from decisions on record. These two books formed the basis for recent developments of common law in both countries.

It is frequently stated that courts do not make the laws, that they merely enforce them. The statement is largely true of constitutional law and statute law, but not for common law or equity. As decisions are made for new types of cases, new interpretations of law are made by the court; and the law is amplified in this way continuously.

BUSINESS CUSTOM. In deciding cases the courts make use of business custom. For instance, as well be mentioned later, silence on the part of one to whom an offer is made usually cannot constitute acceptance. However, if there has been a history of dealings between persons, or if there is a practice in a particular business such that silence constitutes acceptance, the court will consider this and decide accordingly. Terminology peculiar to a trade is given its trade usage interpretation in court.

Change

Frequently one hears the complaint that the law is behind the times, that it is slow to change in a rapidly changing world. The complaint is fairly well founded; the law is slow to change. However, it is usually far better to have a law or fixed principle upon which one can depend, than to have a law or principle which may this time decide one way and the next time another way.

The law does change, slowly, to reflect changes in society and changes in technology. By way of illustration we can look back a few years to necessary changes made when the automobile took over personal transportation from the horse and buggy. Similarly, we can look ahead to changes which are likely to be needed when space travel becomes a commercial reality.

Common law changes in two basic ways: by overruled decisions and by passages of statutes.

OVERRULED DECISIONS.   When a case goes to court, the attorneys for both of the parties in the case have usually done some research on the law involved. It is likely that both will be armed with decisions in previous cases on which the judge in the present case is expected to base his decision. Let us assume that one of the cases used is based on facts quite similar to those in the case at hand. Let us further assume that the decision in the precedent case was handed down by the state supreme court. If the present case is in a lower court and the facts of the case are in all ways the same, the judge should follow the prior decision. However, since there are nearly always differences in the facts of two cases, let us assume that the judge, on the basis of slightly different facts, did not follow the precedent case and an appeal resulted. The case at hand is finally taken to the state supreme court. If the supreme court justices see the facts in the two cases as being essentially the same, but render a decision different from the decision rendered in the precedent case, the precedent case has been *overruled*. The law has been changed. There is no effect as to the parties in the earlier case; that case was decided by the law of that time. The law was not changed until the state supreme court changed it in the process of overruling. In the interest of retaining stability in the law, courts are quite reluctant to overrule prior decisions, but at the same time they recognize that nothing is as permanent in this world as change itself.

STATUTES.   One of the many reasons for passage of a statute is dissatisfaction with the law in a particular field. Frequently, when decisions have for some reason become quite muddled in dealing with a problem, an appeal is made to the legislature for a law to clarify the issues involved. Passage of a statute voids the common law covering the same point within the legislature's jurisdiction. The statute must not, of course, conflict with the Constitution of the United States or with the state constitution involved. If, when a case arises, the courts find that a statute conflicts with the constitution, the constitution is protected and the statute eliminated.

Limits of Remedy

In the beginning the common law was administered by *royal writs*. These writs were orders, in written form, to a sheriff or other officer to administer justice in a particular way or to summon a defendant before the royal justices. We still use writs—written and sealed court commands or mandates ordering that some specified thing be done. Following a court judgment, a writ of execution, for instance, may be issued to an officer, telling him to take possession and sell some of the loser's property to satisfy the judgment.

During the first two or three centuries following the inception of the King's Court in England, the law underwent a hardening process. The writs accepted by a common-law court and the remedies offered became standardized and limited. The limitations of common law still exist today. There are three remedies available: money damages, return of real property, and return of personal property. If none of these remedies will suffice, the case is not a common-law case; the common law court has no remedy.

EQUITY

The limited remedies of common law brought about the fourth basic type of law, equity. Consider an example. Black, a contractor, is hired to build a structure for White. During the excavation, Gray, next door, notes an impending separation of his house from its foundation. The walls start to crack and the ceiling begins to bulge. At this point, at common law, Gray has no remedy. At common law he would have to await whatever damage might be forthcoming and sue to get compensation for it. However, in equity he can do something about it *now*. He can obtain a temporary injunction or a restraining order to prevent the excavation next door until something more appropriate can be done to prevent his house from sliding into the hole.

Origin

With the limiting of common-law writs (the Provisions of Oxford, 1258, put an end to the making of any new kinds of writs) certain injustices could take place without any relief being offered by the courts. Common law could not, and still cannot:

1. Prevent a wrong from taking place.
2. Order persons to perform their obligations.
3. Correct mistakes.

It soon became apparent that these gaps in the law had to be filled.

COURTS OF CHANCERY. With the King's Court system the king had become established as the "fountain of justice." As such, he could offer redress beyond that available in the common-law courts. In unusual cases the king was petitioned and settled the case with "unusual" remedies. When the load became too heavy for the king the task of hearing the unusual cases was delegated to his chancellor and, eventually, to vice-chancellors. From this the new courts took on the name of courts of chancery.

In the United States, courts of equity exist in three ways. In some states there are separate court rooms and judges for equity. In other states, the court rooms are the same and the judge is the same as in dealing with other types of law, but the procedure is different. In still other states and in the federal court system, law and equity have been completely combined.

UNUSUAL REMEDIES. The remedies available in a court of equity are quite different from those offered in common law. They are *in personam* remedies; that is, they are directed to a person, whereas common law acts *in rem,* or upon a thing. Probably the most common and well-known equity remedies are the injunction and specific performance. The list of equity remedies, though, is quite long and includes divorces, mortgage foreclosures, accountings, reformation of contracts, and many others. In fact, an equity court can act in any way necessary to secure a right or remedy a wrong. The very word "equity" implies that justice will be done and, if a remedy must be invented to serve the purpose, this will be done.

The *injunction* exists in two general forms: temporary and permanent. A temporary injunction (a restraining order or injunction *pendente lite*) is readily obtainable for cause. Any attorney, as a member of the bar in the court's jurisdiction is also an officer of the court. As such, he can request a temporary injunction from the court. As soon as the judge signs the temporary injunction, it is an act in contempt of court for anyone who has knowledge of the order to fail to obey it. The object of a temporary injunction is to hold the status quo until a hearing can be held on the merits of the case. The complaint may be dismissed at the hearing, or some other type of remedy may be given, or a permanent injunction may result when the facts are heard. If a permanent injunction is issued, the order is effective as long as the cause of the injunction exists.

Specific performance usually arises in connection with contracts involving land. Land is considered to be unique; no one piece of land is exactly like another. When a contract is made for the sale of a piece of land and the seller refuses to deed the land to the buyer, he may be forced to do so by an order for specific performance from a court of equity. Property other than real estate is treated the same way only when it is recognized as being unique; e.g., an antique or a rare painting.

Equity is reluctant to give a remedy which will require continuous supervision over an extended period. In some cases such remedies have been given, but where another remedy will suffice, such other remedy is preferred.

The remedies afforded in equity courts are not limited to equity remedies. Once a cause of action is legitimately in an equity court, the court will settle all the issues involved, including the remedies afforded at common law in addition to the equity remedy. For instance, an equity decree might include money damages for injuries already suffered in addition to an injunction against further injury. Equity, however, will not give a remedy which is directly contrary to common law; neither will equity act when an adequate remedy exists under a statute or under common law.

Features of Equity

Certain features of equity law are different from those of common law.

REQUIREMENTS.   In most actions the plaintiff does not have the right to choose whether the case will be decided by the rules of equity or common law. There are two basic requirements for equity which will determine where the case will be settled and both of these requirements must be met: 1) it must be shown that the remedy at law would be inadequate, and 2) there must be a property right involved.

The showing that the remedy at law would be inadequate can be made in several ways, but generally it is shown that: a) there is a threat of irreparable injury to the plaintiff. For instance, under a short-term lease the property owner is ordinarily entitled to return of his property in virtually the same condition as leased. Threatened extensive alterations or removal of trees or shrubs by the leaseholder could be cause of an injunction based on impending irreparable injury; b) no remedy at law would permanently solve the problem involved; the cause of action would remain for a later suit. A common example of this is the situation in which a survey shows that one person has built a structure which is now found to rest partly on his neighbor's land; c) money damages would be incalculable or insufficient as a remedy. A nuisance, such as smoke or noise, making a home untenantable would be basis for getting into equity jurisdiction with this reason.

The showing of a property right being involved is the second requirement. Early equity cases adhered strictly to this requirement, but the more modern interpretation includes also personal rights (such as the right of free speech or freedom of assembly).

SPEED.   A court of equity generally acts more rapidly than does a court of law. As previously pointed out, a temporary injunction may be obtained with very little delay. In addition, there is usually no jury involved in equity cases, which eliminates the necessity for a time-consuming selection of members and deliberation over the evidence.

PRIVACY. Since there is no jury involved, a case in equity may be decided more privately. This feature is particularly significant when a case involving a trade secret is tried. If a jury were to hear the facts, there would be twelve more people to hear the secret. The secret would become virtually public information.

INJUSTICES. There are occasions when equity decisions appear to work injustices on defendants. Black owns an industrial plant bordering a stream. The plant discharges waste materials in the stream. White owns property downstream from the plant, which also borders the stream. White's property is far enough downstream so that the water purifies itself before it gets to his property. White has never been injured as a result of the waste discharge into the stream, and does not use the stream except as a location of the boundary of his property. White brings suit to enjoin waste disposal into the stream by Black. A court of equity would be likely to enjoin the waste disposal, even though no one has been injured by it. If the court were to allow the waste disposal to continue, it is possible that, with the growth of the plant, harmful contamination could result. Also, the possibility exists that someone else might later obtain and use property between Black's plant and White, and be injured by the pollution of the stream. If the court dismissed the suit and the contamination became harmful, the dismissal could stand in the way of future relief, giving Black an apparent right to continue. Therefore, the court would have to find some solution other than outright dismissal of the case. Any solution other than dismissal is likely to add to Black's cost of operation.

Principles:

There are many equity principles and maxims which form the background for equity decisions. Five prominent equity maxims are listed below:

1. For every right a remedy.
2. He who seeks equity must do equity.
3. He who comes to equity must come with clean hands.
4. Equity regards substance rather than form.
5. Equity aids the vigilant, not those who sleep on their rights.

HOLZWORTH v. ROTH

101 N.W. 2d 393 South Dakota (March 2, 1960)

Rentto, Judge.

This suit in equity commenced on July 18, 1958, claimed a breach of the covenants of title in a series of standard form warranty deeds by which the title to Lot 37, Harmony Heights Addition in Spearfish, South Dakota, went from the Lampert Lumber Company to the Holzworths, as ultimate grantees. Those named as defendants are the grantors in this series of deeds. They interposed numerous objections to the suit, one of them being that in the circumstances of this case a suit in equity did not lie.

During the time that these named defendants successively owned the property, between June 26, 1956 and April 26, 1957, the construction of a residence thereon was commenced and carried on. Eight of the laborers and materialmen contributing to this improvement were not paid so they filed mechanics' liens.[2] Six of them were filed for improvements commenced during the period when these defendants were the owners, and two for improvements started after the plaintiffs acquired their title. Subsequently on October 22, 1957, two of these lien claimants instituted an action to foreclose their liens naming the other six lien claimants and Martin Holzworth as defendants. This is urged by the plaintiffs as a breach of the covenants of title. None of the grantors in these various deeds were made parties to this foreclosure action nor does it appear that they had notice of it. Whether it was further prosecuted and with what results does not appear in this record. However, plaintiffs still occupy the premises.

In the suit here involved the Holzworths as the ultimate covenantees asked that the defendants be required to remove the mechanics' liens or pay the amount thereof. The defendants by motion for judgment, by their answer, and by a requested conclusion of law directed the trial court's attention to their objection that a suit in equity was not the proper remedy. The trial court overruled this contention and entered judgment requiring the defendants to remove the various liens or pay to the plaintiffs an amount equal to any judgment entered in the lien foreclosure action. From this judgment the defendants appeal.

In this state the distinction between actions at law and suits in equity is abolished by statute. . . . All relief is administered through one proceeding termed a civil action. However, this statutory abolition of distinctions applies only to the form of action, and not to the inherent substantive principles which underlie the two systems of procedure. . . . In other words, the essential and inherent differences between legal and equitable relief are still recognized and enforced in our system of jurisprudence. . . . One of these principles is that if the primary right which is the foundation of the litigation is legal in nature and there is a remedy at law, the action is one at law. . . . Equity has jurisdiction in such cases only if the legal remedy is not full, adequate and complete.

---

[2] Note—a mechanic's lien is a claim established against property to secure priority of payment for work done to improve that property; it may be established by almost any unpaid person who had a hand in the improvement.

When property is conveyed by our standard form warranty deed, SDC 51.1403 writes into it these covenants on the part of the grantor, his heirs and personal representatives:

that he is lawfully seized of the premises in fee simple, and has good right to convey the same; that the premises are free from all incumbrances; that he warrants to the grantee, his heirs, and assigns, the quiet and peaceable possession thereof; and that he will defend the title thereto against all persons who may lawfully claim the same.

They spell out the obligation on the part of the grantor, his heirs and personal representatives arising out of the agreement between the parties. A breach of any of them is in effect a breach of their contract for which an action for damages will lie.

Significantly the chapter of our statutes concerned with damages for breach of contract, . . . prescribes the measure of damages to be allowed on breach of the covenants contained in our standard form warranty deed. . . . It seems to us that an action for breach of these covenants is clearly an action at law. . . . We think it follows that equity has no jurisdiction in this case if the remedy at law is full, adequate and complete. . . .

Concerning the jurisdiction of equity the question of adequacy of the remedy at law appears in two aspects. Where the suit is properly cognizable in equity the existence of an adequate remedy at law may justify a court of equity in refusing to entertain the matter. . . . On the other hand, where the matter is legal in nature the absence of an adequate remedy at law is necessary to confer equitable jurisdiction. This is the aspect in which it is here involved. Accordingly, the burden of establishing this is on the plaintiffs.

We are unable to find that such inadequacy was urged by them or that it exists. On this feature the record is silent except as it is referred to in the contentions of the defendants. The complaint does not plead the inadequacy of an action at law nor are there any factual allegations from which such conclusion is inferable. In the findings and conclusions proposed by plaintiffs and adopted by the court this matter is not mentioned. Nor did the plaintiffs in either their brief or argument in this court make a claim of such inadequacy. In the absence of fraud or some other unusual circumstances rendering the remedy at law inadequate equity will not interfere in this type of case. . . . Since it does not appear that plaintiffs' remedy at law was inadequate we must hold that equity is without jurisdiction.

Their remedy at law would have been even more efficient if Holzworth, who was a defendant in the lien foreclosure proceeding, had given these defendants notice of it and requested them to come in and defend the title they had warranted. This is called "voucher to warranty". . . . After such notice and request the judgment in that proceeding would be binding on them if they did not defend it. . . . That he neglected to utilize this privilege is of no help in getting this matter into equity. . . . The trial court should have dismissed this suit.

Reversed.

FRANKLIN v. SING-WILKES, INC.

112 S.E. 2d 618 Georgia (Jan. 8, 1960)

DUCKWORTH, Chief Justice.

This case is here on an exception to an order granting a temporary injunction after a hearing on a petition to enjoin certain lawful acts, wherein the purpose of said acts are for the illegal purpose of harassing the defendant by making continued calls and complaints to the police of the City of Thomasville about alleged noises and other breaches of the peace emanating from the petitioner's business in Thomasville. The allegations show that the complaints are not for the purpose of prosecuting the commission of any crime or violation of city ordinances, but for the purpose of harassing the petitioner in its lawful business to cause it to discontinue its night-service-station operations at this particular station. By cross-action the defendants sought an injunction to prevent certain noises and disturbances originating at said service station. The order excepted to enjoined the defendants, until the further order of the court, from interfering with or harassing the petitioner's employees and customers as prayed in the petition. The prayers of the petition sought among other things to prevent the defendants from making telephone calls to the police department and making prosecutions and suing out warrants against the petitioner's employees in the operation of said station and its customers. At the hearing it was stipulated that approximately 8 cases had been made against a person or persons for alleged breaches of the peace at the service station, involving noise. These cases had been disposed of in the Recorder's Court of Thomasville but are now pending on appeal in the superior court. The evidene and the stipulations showed that the property, which had been residential, has been zoned for business; that the noises around such station are the usual noises made by the operation of such a business; that since the beginning of the business, the petitioner's officers and employees and the defendants have been in continuous altercation and discussion over the operation of the service station; that one of the defendants had made the statement that, if the petitioner did not close at night he would see if he couldn't get him closed; that the arrests of customers and employees had hurt the petitioner's business; and that the defendants had called the police complaining of noises of tire changing, loud talking, air compressors running, and other varied noises and that cases had been made by the police after being so summoned. *Held:*

1. This court has repeatedly held that where the evidence is conflicting at an interlocutory hearing to determine whether or not the lower court should grant or deny a temporary injunction, it can not be said that the court abused its discretion in either granting or denying the injunction. . . . It follows that the court did not err in granting a temporary injunction against the defendants and in refusing to grant the temporary injunction prayed for in the cross-action.

2. The exception to the failure of the court to rule on and sustain the demurrers to the petition, after a hearing thereon in which the court reserved its rulings thereon, is treated as abandoned since counsel for the plaintiff in error has failed to argue it either in the brief or orally before this court. Furthermore, the exception is to no judgment and hence presents nothing for a decision.

Judgment affirmed.

REVIEW QUESTIONS

1. Why do we need man-made laws? What purpose do they serve?

2. What are the four basic types of laws in our legal system? What does each consist of?

3. What is the meaning and significance of the term *stare decisis*?

4. How do changes in common law take place?

5. What factors led to the establishment of equity as a separate system of law?

6. What types of remedies are offered by common law? By equity?

7. A owns a factory which emits large quantities of foul smelling smoke. People in a nearby housing development are annoyed by the odors whenever the wind shifts to an unfortunate direction. B, a resident in the housing development, has lodged a complaint against A for public nuisance. In what kind of court would the case be likely to be tried in your state? Why? What would be the probable result of the legal action?

8. What are the two general requirements for equity jurisdiction? How might these requirements be met?

9. In *Holzworth v. Roth* the decision of the trial court was reversed with the statement that the case should have been dismissed. Does this mean that Holzworth must give up his attempt to recover for the apparent injustice he has suffered? What else can he do?

10. In *Franklin v. Sing-Wilkes, Inc.,* why was this an equity case? What property or personal rights were involved?

3 COURTS, TRIAL PROCEDURE, AND EVIDENCE

The fact that one person accuses another of a wrong does not mean that the accusation is correct. Since the beginning of civilization the problem of determining the truth of an accusation has existed. Court trials with a judge, a jury, and attorneys for both plaintiff and defendant have not always been used. Probably the earliest form of trial was *trial by battle*. Accused and accuser (or their representatives) faced each other in battle, with the outcome determining the justice of the accusation. In many of the early civilizations trial by battle was replaced either by *trial by ordeal* or *trial by jury*. The codes of Hammurabi required trial by ordeal. For certain acts the accused was to be thrown in the divine river. If the river held him (if he couldn't swim), the guilty verdict and punishment took place at the same time. Trial by jury, in one form or another, existed in many ancient civilizations. Our present jury trial system developed with the common law. Its continuance in criminal and civil cases is guaranteed in the sixth and seventh amendments of the United States Constitution.

COURTS

In the United States we have a system of courts for each state as well as a system of federal courts. The systems are somewhat similar. In both the federal and state systems there is an ultimate tribunal, a supreme court. At the next lower level are the appellate courts (in the federal system and some state systems) which handle appeals from the lower courts.

The lower courts are the district courts, in the federal system, and usually county courts in the state systems.

Federal Courts

SUPREME COURT. The United States Supreme Court is our highest tribunal. It is our final court of appeal. Article 3 of the Constitution gives us our Supreme Court and whatever inferior federal courts Congress may from time to time require. The jurisdiction (as to types of cases) is limited in the Constitution to nine categories. The only cases which may originate in the Supreme Court are those involving ambassadors, public ministers, and consuls, or in which a state is a party. In these the Supreme Court has original jurisdiction; all other cases go to the Supreme Court by appeal.

Cases are appealed to the Supreme Court from either United States Courts of Appeal or from state supreme courts in the normal course of events in an appealed case. However, cases may go directly from any court to the U.S. Supreme Court if the question to be settled involves the U.S. Constitution, or is of very great public interest. Appeal is made by a petition to the court for a writ of *certiorari*. If the petition by the appellant is successful, a writ of certiorari will be issued to the lower court demanding that the case be sent up for review. Only a very small portion of such petitions are successful—something like one out of twenty.

The nine men who preside as our U.S. Supreme Court have the final say as to what our law shall be. They do not, of course, make formal statutes—this is the function of the legislative branch of the government. But the interpretation of what was meant by the Constitution or the wording of a statute is a highly significant function. The interpretation given by the Supreme Court determines the lawful interpretation to be used in future cases in lower courts.

COURTS OF APPEAL. Eleven United States Courts of Appeal exist. Appeals on federal questions are normally settled by the three justices who preside over each court. These courts were first established by Congress in 1891 because of the burden of appeals upon the United States Supreme Court. They function as appeal courts only and do not conduct trials. Issues between parties are appealed on the basis of a conflict in the law, the facts of the issue having been decided previously in a lower court.

DISTRICT COURTS. The trial courts of the federal court system are the United States District Courts. The districts presided over by the 100 or so U.S. District Courts are formed in such a way that no state is without a Federal District Court. The number of justices in a U.S. District Court is determined by statute and is based on the amount of federal legal controversy arising in the district.

For a case to be tried in a federal court, it must:

1. Arise from the U.S. Constitution, federal laws, or treaties of the United States, or

2. Affect ambassadors, other public ministers and consuls, or

3. Arise in admiralty or maritime jurisdiction, or

4. Involve two or more states as parties, or

5. Involve the United States as a party, or

6. Be between citizens of different states with the amount in controversy greater than $10,000, or

7. Be between citizens of a state who claim land grants in another state, or

8. Be between a state and a foreign country, or

9. Be between U.S. citizens and a foreign country or its citizens.

Most of the controversies handled involve federal statutes or the Constitution.

Common examples of cases tried in United States District Courts are: bankruptcy, admiralty, patent, copyright and trademark, restraint of trade, tax cases, and cases involving infringement of personal rights. Many other cases arise from decisions of administrative boards (e.g., National Labor Relations Board) which operate as quasi judicial entities and look to the federal courts for enforcement of their orders. Claims against the federal government may be filed either in a U.S. District Court or in a U.S. Court of Claims if the amount in controversy is less than $10,000. If the amount is greater than $10,000 the suit must be filed in a court of claims.

The U.S. Court of Claims is a special court in the federal system. Other special courts include the U.S. Customs Court, the U.S. Tax Court, and the U.S. Court of Customs and Patent Appeals.

State Courts

State court systems are far from uniform throughout the United States. Not only do the systems differ from state to state, but the names of the courts differ as well. A few generalities, though, can be stated.

Each state has a final court of appeal, usually called the supreme court of the state. Nearly always the highest court confines its work to appeals of cases tried in lower courts. Courts of intermediate appellate jurisdiction are interposed between the supreme court and lower courts in many states.

The next lower tier of courts consists of the trial courts of general jurisdiction, known variously as circuit courts, courts of common pleas, county courts, superior courts, or, in New York, the supreme court. Probate courts or surrogate courts handle cases of wills, trusts, and the like. Such courts are limited in geographical jurisdiction to a particular county, district or other major political subdivision of the state.

At the lower end of the judicial hierarchy are various municipal courts. Police courts, justices of the peace, small claims courts, juvenile courts, and recorders courts are common examples of these courts of very limited jurisdiction.

Jurisdiction

The jurisdiction of a court means its right or authority, given either by a legislature or constitution, to hear and determine causes of action presented to it. A court's jurisdiction relates to geographical regions (as to location of persons and subject matter), to types of cases, and possibly to the amount of money concerned.

Courts have jurisdiction over property, both real and personal, located within their assigned geographical limits. Even though the owner may not be available, his property may be taken in satisfaction of a judgment. A court has no authority over property lying outside its territorial limits. Let us assume that a Tennessee court has awarded Black $5,000 as a result of a damage action against White. If White does not pay and cannot be made to pay in satisfaction of the judgment, justice for Black is rather hollow. The Tennessee court could take and sell that part of White's property which could be found in Tennessee until the judgment was satisfied. However, it could not touch any of White's property in, say, Georgia.

A court has jurisdiction over all persons found within its geographical limits, whether the persons are residents or not. Jurisdiction over a person is exercised by serving that person with a summons or other legal process —a defendant would be served with a summons; a witness with a subpoena. How service may be made is a matter clarified by each state's statutes. Generally, a sheriff or other officer is directed to serve the process upon the person; however, if the person cannot be found there is usually an alternate means of service. In certain types of cases, such as quieting title to real property, divorce, probate of a will, and others where the thing involved is within the court's jurisdiction, a process may be served even though the person on whom it is to be served is outside the court's jurisdiction. The means by which this is done is known as constructive service. This service on an absentee is made by publication of the process in a local paper. In most damage actions, though, absence of both defendant and his property acts as a serious obstacle—action against him would be pointless unless some recovery could be anticipated.

Jurisdiction of courts is also limited as to types of cases which they have authority to handle. A probate court, for instance, ordinarily has no authority to handle criminal cases; criminal courts usually do not handle civil suits.

A monetary limitation is placed upon many of the courts. Justice of the peace courts and small-claims courts are limited to cases involving no more than some statutory limit—usually one or two hundred dollars, but up to $1000 in some states.

TRIAL PROCEDURE

Jury trials involve a great deal of human interest. Newspaper articles, television shows, and movies are often built upon courtroom activities. With these sources available it is a rare individual who has no concept of courtroom procedure.

Trial at Law (as opposed to equity)

Although courtroom procedure has become pretty common knowledge, the preliminaries and the aftermath are not so well known. Let us assume that you are involved in a controversy in which you have been injured in some way and, apparently, are entitled to damages—how do you go about taking the controversy to court? The most obvious and correct answer is to see a competent attorney. But what steps does he take?

COMPLAINT.   If, after hearing your story, the attorney decides that you have a reasonable cause of action, his first step will be to draw up and file a complaint in the court where the remedy is sought. Although *complaint* is the common term, it is often called a petition or declaration. The complaint has a two-fold function:

1. To state the facts constituting the cause of action as clearly and concisely as possible, and
2. To demand the remedy sought by the plaintiff.

SUMMONS.   Following receipt of a complaint, the court issues a summons to the defendant. The summons is simply a notice to the defendant that he is about to be sued. A copy of the complaint may or may not accompany the summons, depending upon the jurisdiction. If the complaint does not accompany the summons, it is made available to the defendant by the clerk of the court. If the defendant is served a summons but does not answer it, the result is a judgment against him by default.

DEFENDANT'S ANSWER.   The defendant has a statutory time in which to answer the complaint lodged against him and avoid a judgment by default. There are three usual answers made by the defendant: demurrer, motion to dismiss, and counterclaim.

The demurrer alleges that even if the factual situation is proved to be as stated in the complaint, these facts are insufficient to support the legal action. A demurrer, then, raises a question of law; do the facts alleged give the plaintiff a cause of action at law?

The motion to dismiss quarrels with the facts. The defendant may point out specific defects of a factual nature in the plaintiff's complaint.

A counterclaim usually admits the facts stated in the complaint, but alleges other facts and, on the basis of these, demands damages from the plaintiff. The plaintiff is then given an opportunity to make a *reply* or *replication* to the counterclaim.

An issue must be framed before a trial can be held. There must be a question of fact or of law, or questions of both, to be settled by the trial. The pleadings are not complete until an issue has been presented. When an issue is clear, the case is ready to go to trial.

THE JURY. Parties to a court conflict at law have a choice as to whether or not they will have a jury decide the facts of the case. Both parties may agree to submit all the issues, including issues of fact, to the judge. If there are questions of fact (e.g.: "Did the plaintiff act reasonably?"), both parties must be in agreement if they are to dispense with the jury.

A trial jury is known as a *petit* jury. It usually consists of twelve persons, but, by statute in several states, a petit jury may consist of fewer people for civil cases or for crimes less than capital offenses. Selection of the individual members of the jury involves both attorneys and the judge. Grounds for challenging prospective jurors are established by statute. The two opposing attorneys may use these grounds to disqualify prospective jurors being examined for jury duty. Generally, the established grounds for disqualifications are those which show a financial or blood connection between the prospective juror and one of the litigants. In addition to disqualifying a juror on established grounds, each attorney may usually disqualify a limited number of prospective jurors arbitrarily by exercising the right of peremptory challenge. The judge supervises the qualification proceedings. When the jury has been impaneled the case is ready for trial.

COURTROOM PROCEDURE. When the pleadings are complete, the case has come up on the court's docket, and the jury has been chosen and sworn in, the trial begins. Following opening statements by the attorneys, witnesses are sworn in and the evidence is examined. Each attorney sums up his case to the jury, the judge charges the jury, and the jury retires to reach a verdict. In his charge to the jury the judge sums up the case and instructs the jury as to the issues to be decided by it. After reaching a verdict the jury returns to the courtroom and the foreman (usually the first juror chosen) announces the decision. The judge then gives the judgment which is the official decision of the court in the case.

NEW TRIAL OR APPEAL.   Within a certain, statutory time after the judgment has been rendered, a new trial or an appeal may be requested. Generally, a new trial is concerned with error in the facts of the case and an appeal is concerned with a misapplication of the law.

A successful motion for a new trial may be made upon the basis of an almost unlimited number of circumstances. It is argued that if a new trial is not granted, there will be a miscarriage of justice. The following are only common examples of reasons given for requests for new trials:

1. Unfairness or trickery in selection of members of the jury.

2. Prejudice stemming from financial or blood relationship between a jury member and a party to the trial.

3. Misconduct by a jury member, e.g., sleeping during the trial, or gambling on the outcome.

4. Error by the judge in failing to allow evidence which should have been admitted, or in admitting evidence which should have been excluded.

5. False testimony (perjury) of a witness.

6. Unforeseen accident preventing the appearance of a witness.

7. Improper statement in the charge to the jury.

If the motion to the trial court for a new trial is unsuccessful, appeal may be made to a higher court to order a new trial.

Either party may appeal a decision in a civil case; only the defendant may appeal from an adverse criminal judgment. Appeals are based on questions of law—the trial court has decided issues of fact.

Reasons for appeal are presented to the appeal court in a "bill of exceptions." Stated here are objections or exceptions taken to the rulings of the trial court. These objections are usually concerned with objections to and rulings on the admissibility of evidence, errors in the conduct of the trial, and instructions by the judge. Evidence presented and testimony taken are usually included along with the judge's instruction to the jury.

The appellant (the appealing party) is usually required to post an appeal bond upon taking the case to a higher court. The reason for the appeal bond is to insure that the appellant will pay court costs and damage to the appellee if the trial court decision is upheld.

In addition to the bill of exceptions and the bond, appellant must present a "brief" of the case to the appellate court. The brief contains a statement of the case from the appellant's position and a list of errors forming the basis of appeal.

Equity Suits

Equity acts when common law or statutes offer no remedy. Equity procedure is different from that of common law. The judge decides both questions of fact and questions of law. There is no jury unless the judge specifically requires a jury recommendation on a question. Even then, the verdict of the jury is only a recommendation and the final conclusion as to fact rests with the judge. If factual questions are long and involved, the judge may appoint a "master" to take testimony and make recommendations.

Equity terminology is somewhat different from that used in common law. The first pleading (complaint or declaration or petition in common law) is usually known as either a bill or a complaint in equity cases. The court's judgment is known as a decree.

Equity acts in personam. By the decree, a person is directed to do or not to do a certain thing. The decrees are either interlocutory or final. An interlocutory decree reserves the right of the court to act again in the case at some later time. Appointment of a receiver for a corporation is an example of such a decree.

Cases

In both common law and equity the doctrine of stare decisis is followed. Similar prior cases are followed in deciding present issues. Since cases must be known to be followed, it may be in order to consider for a moment how cases are recorded and reported.

The West Publishing Company, St. Paul, Minnesota, publishes reports of state cases which reach the appeal courts, and all federal cases. The case of *Manning v. Public Service Elec. & Gas Co.*, 156 A 2d 260, 58 N.J. Super. 386, 1959, appears at the end of this chapter. In this case Manning and Public Service Elec. & Gas Co. were plaintiff and defendant in the trial court. Without reading the case, though, there is no way to tell who was originally plaintiff and who was then defendant, since the case has gone to a higher court. In the lower court, the case reads plaintiff v. defendant; in the appeal court the case usually reads appellant v. appellee, and either the plaintiff or defendant may be appellant. In this case Manning is appellant and he happens to have been plaintiff in the trial court. The case is located according to a numbering system. The numbers 156 A. 2d 260 following *Manning v. Public Service Elec. & Gas Co.* indicate one place where the case may be found. This case begins on page 260 of the 156th volume of the second series of case-reporting books for the states covered in the Atlantic Reporter. In like manner,

58 N.J. Super. 386 refers to page 386 of volume 58 of the New Jersey Superior Court Reports.

The case reporters used by the West Publishing Company for reporting state cases divide the United States into seven districts. Each district covers several states. In addition to the Atlantic Reporter, there is the Pacific Reporter, the South Western Reporter, the Southern Reporter, the South Eastern Reporter, the North Western Reporter, and the North Eastern Reporter. The cases reported in these reporters are state cases which have been appealed from lower court decisions. The reason for this is that appeal decisions become controlling law for that type of case in that state's courts. A particular decision in an appealed case may even be the basis for decisions on similar cases in other states or in the federal courts.

Another set of reporters covers federal case decisions. The Federal Reporter reports U.S. Circuit Court of Appeals cases; U.S. District Court opinions are found in the Federal Supplement; Supreme Court decisions are reported in the Supreme Court Reporter. Federal special court cases and decisions of administrative boards are found in other series of West volumes.

Cases are reported in the West publications in three sections. A short summary of the facts is followed by a list of the legal points brought out in the case; then the full text of the judge's opinion is given.

EVIDENCE

Evidence is used to prove questions of fact. The facts, as presented by the contestants in a law case, often stray somewhat from the truth. The truth may be shaded a bit in the presentation. Each contestant must be willing to prove that what he said is true. The judge or jury then has the task of determining the true situation. Evidence is the means of establishing proof.

In a criminal case the evidence must prove guilt "beyond any reasonable doubt" for the defendant to be found guilty. A civil case, by contrast, is won or lost on the comparative weight of the proof.

The burden of proof in a criminal case is always assumed by the state. In a civil case the burden usually rests on the plaintiff to prove his charge but, under certain circumstances, may shift to the defendant; one such circumstance occurs when a counterclaim is made.

Real Evidence and Testimony

Evidence may be classified in many ways. It is classed as real evidence if it is evidence which the judge or jury can see for themselves. For example, a fire extinguisher shown in court to be defective would be real evidence; so would a defective cable or a ladder which broke because of a defective rung. Testimony consists of statements by witnesses of things which have come to their knowledge through their senses. Testimony might be used to prove that a driver was operating his car unsafely, thus contributing to the cause of an accident.

Judicial Notice

Certain facts are so well known and accepted that the court will accept them without requiring proof. The court takes such judicial notice of logarithm tables, provisions of the federal or a state constitution, Newton's laws of motion, and the like. Evidence would not be required to prove that gasoline is combustible, but the presence of gasoline in a particular situation might require proof.

Witnesses

Determination that a witness is competent to testify is part of the court's (judge's) function. Competence is usually questioned on the basis of the witness's mental capacity or mental ability.

The witness is required to testify only as to information having some bearing on the case at hand. If the testimony given under examination or cross examination gets too far afield, either the opposing attorney or the judge may object. Wandering by the witness under examination is likely to result in an objection from the other counsel on the basis that the testimony is "incompetent, irrelevant, and immaterial." Each of the three words has a particular meaning in a trial court.

Incompetency refers to the inadmissibility of the testimony. As a matter of law, certain testimony may be excluded. Testimony as to the terms of a written agreement would be incompetent if the terms are apparent from the contract itself.

Irrelevancy refers to the lack of relationship between the issues of the case and testimony requested or given. In a case involving machinery specifications, a question pertaining to an engineer's home life would hardly be relevant.

Immaterial evidence is evidence which is insignificant. The color of tie worn by a salesman when he sold a piece of machinery would be immaterial.

The right of a witness not to testify on certain matters is known as *privilege*. According to the Fifth Amendment to the U.S. Constitution, no person may be compelled to testify against himself. Communications between certain people need not be revealed in court. Examples of such privileged communications are those between husband and wife, doctor and patient, and attorney and client. Neither party may be made to testify unless the privilege is waived by the party affected by the trial.

Conclusive evidence is evidence which is incontestable. It is evidence which can in no way be successfully challenged. The existence of a written contract is conclusive evidence that someone wrote it.

Prima facie evidence is something less than conclusive. It is rebuttable. It is capable of being countered by evidence from the opposing side but, if allowed to stand, is sufficient to establish some fact. A signature on a written document would be evidence of this nature.

Direct and Circumstantial

Direct evidence goes to the heart of the matter in question. It is evidence which, if uncontested, would tend to establish the fact of the issue. A witness to a signature could establish the fact of signing by a particular party.

By contrast with direct evidence, circumstantial evidence attempts to prove a question of fact, for instance, as to the authenticity of a claimed oral contract. Circumstantial evidence might be taken to show that the person now denying the contract would not have acted as he did at some past time unless he had entered into the contract. A net of circumstances is often woven to show a high probability that a particular version of an issue is true.

Best or Primary Evidence

The court will require the best evidence possible in a particular case; that is, the highest and most original evidence available. "Secondary" evidence will not be used unless, for some reason, the primary evidence is not obtainable. In a case involving a written document, for instance, the document is the best evidence of its existence and provisions. If the original document were destroyed or lost, a copy of the document or testimony as to its existence and contents would be admissible. The document, itself, would be best or primary evidence; the copy or testimony would be secondary.

Hearsay

Hearsay evidence is second hand. It is testimony as to something that the witness has heard another person say. Most hearsay evidence is objectionable to the court for three main reasons: first, because the person whose observation is quoted is not present in the court to be seen by the jury; second, the original testimony was not under oath; and third, there was no opportunity for the original testimony to stand the test of cross examination.

There are a few exceptions to the exclusion of hearsay evidence by the court. Statutes vary somewhat in this respect from state to state. Hearsay is sometimes permitted where other evidence is completely lacking. Hearsay testimony as to dying declarations is usually admissible. A prominent exception to the hearsay rule is the *res gestae* statement.

Res Gestae

In common English, the term *res gestae* is interpreted to mean "things done." In courtroom procedure res gestae refers to allowable hearsay testimony as to spontaneous utterances closely connected with an event. Consider an industrial accident situation in which the victim was killed. If, just before the accident occurred, the victim shouted that the safety device didn't work, testimony to that effect by a fellow worker might be allowed as res gestae. The statement explains the cause.

Parol Evidence Rule

Parol evidence is oral evidence. It is not admissible for use in changing the meaning of a document which sets forth rights and responsibilities. It is the court's job to interpret the meaning of a contract or other written instrument. Only in cases where the terminology is ambiguous or incomplete or where unfamiliar trade terms are used will the court allow testimony to get to the heart of the matter.

The parol evidence rule is confined to interpretations of wording of a document; it does not apply to a question of the validity of the instrument. In a question as to the reason why a person entered into a contract—for instance, a claim of duress—oral evidence would be allowed. Similarly, an attack as to the legality of consideration offered would permit testimony.

Opinion Evidence

During the taking of testimony in a trial, the objection is occasionally heard that the "counsel is asking for a conclusion of the witness." An ordinary person appearing on the witness stand is not allowed to give his opinions or conclusions in evidence. Such is the rule but, as with many other rules of law, there are exceptions. In some instances the nature of the testimony requires that opinions be given—otherwise the evidence will not be clear. In fact, just about any perception of anything is a conclusion based upon sensory responses and experience.

The main thing objected to in opinion evidence is that logical deduction or reasoning is being required of a witness. If such reasoning and conclusions are required in the progress of a trial, an expert from the field of knowledge involved should be called upon to give his opinion as to facts or the meaning of a series of facts. If an opinion is necessary it is desirable to have the best possible opinion. Engineers are qualified by training and experience to act as expert witnesses in certain types of cases. Occasionally it is by giving expert testimony that members of engineering faculties obtain fees enabling them to afford to remain teachers.

THE ENGINEER AS AN EXPERT WITNESS

Most opinion evidence is excluded from a trial; the opinion of an average person acting as a witness is inadmissible. Opinion implies conjecture and the law looks with disfavor upon indeterminate factual situations. Nevertheless, such factual situations do arise and the truth in them must be determined as closely as possible. Such questions as the adequacy of design of a structure or the capabilities of a specially designed machine often must be answered.

Expert

Attorneys and judges are usually quite learned men. Knowledge of the law requires a broad general knowledge of many specialized fields in order to understand the factual situations presented in cases. Most lawyers, though, would admit that their knowledge of a particular technical field is quite general and that, therefore, they would be incapable of drawing intelligent conclusions on complicated technical questions. For such purpose an expert is needed.

An "expert" was once facetiously defined as "any person of average knowledge from more than fifty miles away." Such a criterion would hardly stand up in a court of law. An expert is a person who, because of technical training and experience, possesses special knowledge or skill in a particular field which would not be possessed by an average person. Qualification before the court as an expert witness is part of the expert testimony. The prospective expert witness can expect to be asked questions as to his background, projects in which he has been involved, his training, whether he is registered, and other questions of a similar nature. The court then determines if he is qualified to give expert testimony.

Expert Assistance

There are three important ways in which an expert may assist an attorney in a case involving a technical matter: 1) advice and consultation regarding technical matters in the preparation of the case; 2) assistance in examining and cross-examining technical witnesses; and 3) expert testimony on the issues involved.

ADVICE AND CONSULTATION.   In engineering, as in other technical fields, it is necessary that a person be thoroughly familiar with the technical concepts in order to explain them to laymen. A jury is made up of a cross section of a community (or some near approach to that). Part of the engineer's function as expert witness will be to present to his attorney and to the judge and jury the facts of the case in such a manner that laymen can understand them. The minimum requirements for this are technical proficiency and the ability to effectively communicate the knowledge.

The basis of any effective presentation is investigation. The engineer as an expert witness should be so thoroughly familiar with the facts of the case that nothing the opposition can propose will come as a surprise to him. Drawings and specifications may have to be carefully read, materials tested, and building codes or other laws examined. All should be analyzed for the presence of flaws if the engineer is to do an effective job. Assistance in the preparation of the attorney's brief requires the best of an engineer's investigative powers.

The engineer's obligation to his client and attorney requires an objective approach to the case. Not only should the facts to substantiate his client's claim be present; opposing facts should also be shown. There are two sides to any controversy. In the interest of winning the case, opposing arguments must be considered and rebuttals prepared.

TRIAL ASSISTANCE.   In a case involving technical fields, both parties normally obtain experts to aid them and testify in their behalf. In addition to assistance in preparation of a case and testimony in court, the expert may also be valuable in suggesting questions to be asked by the attorney. *Direct* examination questions have been prepared in advance, but most *cross*-examination questions and *redirect* and *recross* questions must be planned during the course of the trial. A flaw in the technical argument posed by the opposition might escape an attorney's notice but should not escape the notice of a technical expert in that field. The question suggested may be aimed at the opposition by way of cross-examination; or they may be in the form of direct questions to be asked of the expert when he is put on the stand to counter the opposition's evidence.

TESTIMONY.   The judge, attorneys, and jurors are laymen as far as the technical expert's field is concerned. The expert, therefore, must present his information in a simplified manner so that it will be readily understood by laymen. Such presentation is quite akin to teaching. A simple foundation must first be laid and then the complexities based on it. The preparation of such a presentation is not always easy. It necessitates comparison of technical principles with everyday occurrences; the use of pictures, slides, models, and drawings to make a meaning clear. A large number of hours of preparation is required for an hour of effective presentation. Each part of the presentation must be as nearly perfect as possible —incapable of being successfully questioned by opposing counsel.

It is almost essential that the expert witness be present at the entire trial if he is to do an effective job on the witness stand. Prior evidence established by opposing counsel may require alterations in the expert's presentation and changes in the attack on the opposing witnesses.

Honesty in answers is one of the prime requisites of any witness under examination. The opposing attorney will look for (with expert assistance) any point upon which he can attack the expert's testimony. Once found, and properly worked on, a small loophole in the presentation can destroy the effect of laboriously developed testimony. If the engineer does not known the answer to a particular question, the least damaging answer is a simple "I don't know." If the question involves prior testimony, the witness may request the reading of that prior testimony before answering the question. If the question requires calculations or a consultation between the witness and his attorney or other experts, time for such calculation or consultation may be requested from the court.

The demeanor of the expert witness on the stand is important. His appearance and answers to questions posed should inspire confidence in his ability. A professional appearance, professional conduct, and a professional attitude toward the entire proceedings come through clearly to the others in the courtroom. During cross-examination the opposing counsel will usually try to belittle or pick apart testimony damaging to his case; usually, the more damaging the testimony, the greater the effort to reduce it to a shambles. Failing this, the attorney may attempt merely to enrage the witness in hopes that an opening in the testimony may occur. Calm and considered answers by the witness are the best defense against the opposing counsel's attack. Courtesy and self-control must be exercised.

Reference use of writings by acknowledged authorities in the technical field is advisable. Often it seems that a quotation excerpted from a textbook has more weight than an oral statement by the author if he were on the witness stand.

DEPOSITIONS. There are occasions when a witness may be unable to attend a trial to give his testimony. On such occasions his testimony may be taken in some place other than the courtroom prior to the trial. The testimony is taken under oath and recorded for use in the trial. Both opposing attorneys must be present and the rights to direct examination, cross-examination, redirect and recross are the same as they would be in the courtroom. At the time of the trial the deposition is read into the court record and becomes part of the proceedings. A deposition is generally considered to be less effective than testimony given in open court where jurors can see and hear the presentation. However, there are times when it is the only means available and is far preferable to the alternative of omission.

TO TAKE THE CASE OR NOT.   An engineer who is asked to be an expert witness should decide whether or not he really believes in his prospective client's position. The quality of support rendered by the engineer in the case will often depend upon how firmly he believes in the case. On the witness stand the engineer will be required to tell the truth of the case as he sees it. Conviction that his client is right often becomes apparent from the manner in which the testimony is given.

FEES.   The fee to be charged by the engineer for acting as an expert witness in a case should correspond to the fee which he would normally charge for other important consulting work. It should be based on the amount of his time which will be required and the relative importance of his role in the proceedings. In *no* case should the fee be contingent upon the outcome of the case. Double or nothing is closer to gambling than it is to payment for services. Contingency fees are seriously frowned upon by the court as tending to cause inaccurate testimony; opposing counsel will not hesitate to take full advantage of this arrangement if it appears.

In every section of the United States there are minimum fees for professional engineering services. In most states these fees are published by the state society of professional engineers. A typical minimum charge is $100 per day in addition to such expenses as required travel and hotel accommodations. However, the minimum varies considerably in the various geographical sections of the United States.

MANNING v. PUBLIC SERVICE ELEC. & GAS CO.

156 A. 2d 260, 58 N.J.Super. 386 (Dec. 4, 1959)

FOLEY, J.A.D.

In this negligence case plaintiff appeals from a judgment entered in the Law Division on a jury verdict of no cause of action.

On May 24, 1956 plaintiff, a masonry worker in the employ of Puratex Stone Co., was engaged in resurfacing the front of a building situated on the westerly side of Grand Avenue in Palisades Park, New Jersey. The work required him and a co-worker to operate from a scaffold which was suspended at its northerly end by ropes attached to the upper part of the building and at its southerly end was rested on the railing of a fire escape platform. In order to supply these workmen with mortar, two other men mixed it on the ground and then raised it by means of a rope and pulley apparatus. Plaintiff, in reaching for a bucket thus raised, received a severe shock when the bucket came in contact with an adjacent uninsulated high tension wire which was maintained by the defendant. The wire carried approximately 4,000 volts. The shock stunned him and he lost his balance and fell to the ground. Defendant had no knowledge that work was being performed in the vicinity of its high tension wires until after the accident occurred.

The theory of liability advanced by plaintiff was that defendant was negligent (1) in having violated the requirements of the National Electrical Safety Code (hereinafter referred to as the Code) with respect to the installation and maintenance of uninsulated high tension wire, and (2) in having violated a common law duty to exercise a high degree of care to install and maintain the wire in such manner and at such place as to avoid foreseeable injury to those who themselves were in the exercise of reasonable care. The Code was adopted by the Board of Public Utility Commissioners pursuant to R.S. 48:2-23 and was in force at the time of the accident. Pertinent provisions follow:

Sec. 23. Clearances.

. . .

234. Clearances of Conductors of One Line From Other Conductors and Structures.

. . .

C. Clearances from Buildings.

. . .

4. Conductors Passing By Or Over Buildings.

(a) Minimum Clearances. Unguarded or accessible supply conductors carrying voltages in excess of 300 volts between conductors shall not come closer to any building or its attachments (balconies, platforms, etc.) than listed below, except that this rule should not be interpreted as restricting the installation of a trolley contact conductor over the approximate center line of the track it serves.

. . .

Table 4. Clearances of supply conductors from buildings.
(All voltages are between conductors)

Voltage of supply conductors	Horizontal clearance Feet	Vertical clearance Feet
300 to 8,700	3	8

In connection with the construction of this regulation *section 20, subsection 202* has bearing:

Sec. 20. Scope, Nature and Application of Rules.

. . .

202. Minimum Requirements.

The rules state the minimum requirements for spacings, clearances, and strength of construction. More ample spacings and clearances or greater strength of construction may be provided if other requirements are not neglected in so doing.

Note: Some of these minimum values are exceeded in much existing construction; service requirements frequently call for stronger supports and higher factors of safety than the minimum requirements of these rules.

There is no dispute as to the relative position of the essential objects. The platform of the fire escape, suspended at the southern end of the building, extended horizontally three feet from the building to a railing. In addition, there was a seven-inch horizontal extension created by a decorative bow which was attached to the exterior of the railing. The railing extended vertically from the base of the platform 37 inches. Of this, four inches were composed of another decorative curved structure. The boom of the aforementioned hoisting apparatus was attached to the roof at the northern end of the building and extended 22 inches out from the front of it. The bucket was approximately 30 inches at its widest point. The wire, part of a four wire system, was: four feet eleven inches from the face of the building; approximately two feet from the outermost edge of the fire escape; and was six feet three inches in a vertical plane from the top of the railing excluding the elevated bowed decorative portion of four inches. The face of the building was in a north-south plane and the wires, running parallel thereto, were supported by poles erected along the curb in front of the building. The scaffold was 18 inches wide and approximately 20 feet long. Plaintiff and the hoisting mechanism were at the northern section of the scaffold at the time of the accident. The fire escape at the southern section was in no way involved in plaintiff's activities. The wires in question were 33½ feet above the ground, thus satisfying another section of the Code which required a minimum height of 20 feet.

The initial problem presented to the trial court was one of construction of the Code. Specifically, the question was: Do the "minimum clearances" provided in section 23, *subsection* 234, require *both* a horizontal clearance of three feet and a vertical clearance of eight feet from the building, or was it intended that these should be considered as alternative requirements, in the sense that the vertical clearance applies only to wiring passing over the "building or its attachments (balconies, platforms, etc.)," all other installations, including that here involved, being subject only to the necessity of a three-foot clearance from the side of the building and structures attached thereto? The court reached the latter conclusion, held as a matter of law that the defendant's installation conformed with the Code requirements since the wire was in excess of three feet from the side of the building at the point where plaintiff was working, and expressly charged the jury to this effect. Thus the court removed violation of the Code as a ground on which the jury might predicate liability and confined the determination of defendant's negligence to whether or not defendant had violated its common law duty as above set forth.

It is urged by the plaintiff that the elimination from the case of the alleged violation of the Code constituted a judicial usurpation of the function of the jury. It is argued that upon the basis of certain conflicts in the expert testimony to which we will hereinafter refer the jury should have been permitted to decide whether the Code contemplated as minimum requirements both a horizontal clearance of three feet and a vertical clearance of eight feet, rather than either the one or the other. But this contention runs afoul of the principle that within their allotted sphere the rules and regulations of a state administrative agency duly promulgated under properly delegated powers have the force and effect of law . . . from which it follows that the construction of such rules and regulations is subject to the fundamental concept that the interpretation of a statute is for the court, not the jury.

No doubt this branch of the plaintiff's argument is founded on the fact that one of the plaintiff's experts, Isaac Stewart, testified that the wire was in violation of the Code because it was less than eight feet above the guard rail of the fire escape and less than three feet from the ornamental or decorative bows attached to the railing. He expressed the opinion that the Code compelled compliance with both horizontal and vertical requirements despite his admission that it is permissible to run a wire over the top of a building, provided it is not less than eight feet above the roof or an attachment thereto. It is obvious that in such circumstances the required horizontal clearance of three feet could not be met. In practical effect, Mr. Stewart's interpretation would mean that if a power company found it necessary to install a high tension wire three feet from the side of a skyscraper, it would be obliged to run the wire eight feet above the top of the building, notwithstanding that the Code fixes the minimum height as 20 feet above ground level. The theory advanced by Mr. Stewart was rejected by plaintiff's other expert, Solomon Fishman, as is demonstrated by his answers to interrogation by the court:

The Court: If it is 8 feet above the building, it can go right over the top of the building, isn't that right?
The Witness: Yes, sir.
The Court: And it would comply with the requirements.
The Witness: Yes, sir.
The Court: And if it is 3 feet away from the nearest fixture on the building, it needs only to be 20 feet high, even though the building might be 40 feet high. Is that right?
The Witness: Yes, sir.

The experts called by defendant also testified that the installation was in conformity with the Code by reason of compliance with the minimum horizontal clearance of three feet.

It is not unusual for experts called by opposing sides to differ concerning the safety of a given facility, conformity with standards of construction or installation, or even as to the standard itself. In such circumstances their conflicting opinions usually are for jury consideration. Had the court determined here that the intent of the Code was that every installation of uninsulated wire should meet the minimum clearance requirements both horizontally and vertically, the expert testimony tending to support such conclusion would have been the subject of consideration by the jury in its appraisal of the connection between noncompliance with the Code and defendant's duty to exercise a high degree of care in plaintiff's behalf. But that is not the point. As we have said, it was the duty of the court to interpret the Code, that is to say, to determine the meaning of it. Conflicts in the expert testimony relating to the meaning of the Code were for resolution by the court alone, and thus did not raise a jury question of defendant's ultimate responsibility.

The purpose of judicial interpretation is the discovery of the true sense of the form of words which are used, taking all parts into consideration, and if fairly possible, giving them all effect. Whether the subject matter of such interpretive inquiry be an agreement between parties, a statute, or a constitution, the object is the thought which it expresses. . . . In this instance the objectives sought to be attained are set forth in the Code itself:

214. Isolation and Guarding.
   A. Current-carrying Parts.

To promote safety to the general public and to employees not authorized to approach conductors and other current-carrying parts of electric supply lines, such parts shall be arranged so as *to provide adequate clearance from the ground or other space generally accessible, or shall be provided with guards* so as to isolate them effectively from accidental contact by such persons. (Emphasis added)

We are satisfied that the trial court's construction of the Code which necessitated its removal from the case as a ground of liability was sound.

On the oral argument plaintiff asserted that independently of the alleged violation of the Code a jury question of defendant's responsibility was presented by the evidence relating thereto. This point was not made in the appellant's brief but it was argued in opposition to defendant's motion for a judgment of involuntary dismissal at the trial, and it was referred to in the court's charge. We shall consider it.

The thesis offered is that since the Code merely provides minimum clearance requirements, compliance with the same was not an absolute defense to the action; rather, it was for the jury to say whether or not under all the circumstances displayed by the evidence the defendant discharged its duty to the plaintiff in locating the wire where it did. We are in accord with the contention that compliance with the Code does not necessarily preclude a recovery in this type of case. By analogy, this view is supported by the established rule that, while ordinarily the adoption and use by well regulated companies satisfies the duty of care owed, nevertheless the care which must be exercised over the construction and maintenance of a highly destructive agency requires more than the use of mere mechanical skill and approved mechanical appliances. It includes also circumspection and foresight with regard to reasonably probable contingencies. . . .

But recovery upon the basis of the infraction of a common law duty depends upon a showing that the defendant acted improperly, or failed to act at all, in a situation where an accident such as occurred here was reasonably foreseeable. The test of liability is whether under the particular circumstances the injury ought reasonably to have been anticipated. . . . It is not disputed that the wire in question was strung more than 50 years ago with the permission of the municipality and in accordance with the provisions of R.S. 48:7-1 *et seq.*, which permit utility companies to use public streets for the purpose of erecting poles to sustain necessary wires and fixtures. There is no evidence that in the half-century intervening between the installation and the accident the wire had been a source of danger to any person. Moreover, the court may judicially notice that this installation differed not in the slightest from the countless miles of uninsulated high tension wires which furnish the lifeblood of industry, commerce and public convenience, here and elsewhere. Notwithstanding, it is suggested that the defendant was bound to foresee that as time passed it would become necessary to repair the side of the building adjacent to the wire, and that such work would involve the use of a scaffold which would bring workmen in close proximity to it. The argument is lacking in logical appeal for several reasons. In the first place, if this contingency be regarded as having been reasonably foreseeable by defendant, seemingly the importance of it must have occurred to the framers of the Code and have been reflected in the clearance requirements contained therein. Furthermore, according to the testimony, the outer edge of the scaffold on which plaintiff was working was in excess of three feet from the wire; and it is entirely clear that the injury resulted not from plaintiff's contact with the wire but from his contact with the bucket which had been energized by the wire. But, more importantly, by legislative enactment any notion of the obligation of a power company to foresee the performance of work of the kind here involved is dispelled, absent proof of actual knowledge in the power company that such work was to be undertaken. *Section* 5 of the High Voltage Lines Act, *L.* 1948, *c.* 249 (*N.J.S.A.* 34:6-47.5), which was adopted shortly after *Beck v. Monmouth Lumber Co., supra,* was decided provides:

> Notification to power company and responsibility for safeguards.
>
> When any operations are to be performed, tools or materials are to be handled, or equipment is to be moved or operated, within six feet of any high-voltage line, the person or persons responsible for the work to be done, shall promptly notify the operator of the high-voltage line of the work to be performed and such person shall be responsible for the completion of the safety measures, which are required by sections two and three of this act, before proceeding with any work which would impair the aforesaid clearance.

The statute is penal in character, violators being subject to fine or imprisonment or both.

It stands without question that the notification required by the statute was not transmitted to the defendant. If by any process of reasoning it is inferable that defendant should have foreseen that work within the prohibited area might at some time be in contemplation, there is no rational basis to infer that the defendant should have foreseen that it would be commenced without notice in direct violation of the statutory mandate.

It is our conclusion, therefore, that since there was neither evidence of violation of the Code nor evidence of a reasonably foreseeable risk of harm in defendant's lawful installation and maintenance of its wires, the motion for involuntary dismissal should have been granted.

This disposition makes moot appellant's second point that the court erred in its interpretation of *N.J.S.A.* 34:6-47.5 as it bore upon the workmen's duty to comply with its provisions. Because any view expressed by us as to our interpretation of the statute in this connection would be *dicta* we leave resolution of this interesting question to a case in which it is squarely in issue. Likewise other criticisms of the court's charge are of no consequence, in view of our decision that the case should not have been submitted to the jury.

In affirming we observe that the submission of a case to a jury which arrives at the same result the court should have reached as a matter of law furnishes no ground for reversal. . . .

Affirmed.

REVIEW QUESTIONS

1. Describe the federal court system. Describe the court system in your state.

2. Assume that you have been the unfortunate victim of someone's negligence. What steps will be taken by you or your attorney in an attempt to get compensation for the loss you have suffered?

3. Distinguish between the proof required in a criminal case and the proof required in a civil case.

4. How would you prove the existence and terms of an oral agreement if there were no third parties present to overhear the agreement?

5. Why does a court hold in disfavor:
    a. Oral testimony as to the meaning of a written document?
    b. Hearsay testimony?
    c. Expression of an opinion by a witness?

6. Why is circumstantial evidence so often used in criminal trials?

7. In the case of *Manning v. Public Service Elec. & Gas Co.,* assume that Manning had hired you to be expert witness for him. What could you do for him as an expert witness?

4 ETHICS

An engineer is a professional person; the occupation he has chosen is one of the newer professions. Until quite recently the only callings of sufficient dignity and dedication to public service to be termed "professions" were law, medicine, and theology. These three "learned professions" are still looked upon by the public as the pinnacle of professions. Because of the intimate contact between members of these professions and the public it is doubtful that this concept will ever change.

Engineering has existed as a separate calling for about a century and a half. Considering the short span of its existence, the progress of engineering toward top professional standing is quite striking. Certainly there was engineering prior to a hundred and fifty years ago, as the ancient pyramids, the aqueducts of Rome, and other engineering works mutely testify; but the designing and building of these structures was not known as engineering. Most of the early engineering was done by or for the military.

Civil engineering was first to be recognized as a separate calling. Around 1750, John Smeaton, an English engineer, made the first recorded use of the term "civil engineering." In 1818 the Institution of Civil Engineers was founded in Great Britain; it defined engineering as "the art of utilizing the forces of nature for the use and convenience of man." With the development of new fields of technological knowledge since then, many other fields of engineering have been established.

A separate, recognized field of learning and the presence of societies of its members do not make a profession. A man does not have professional status merely because he has graduated from a school and joined a society. Perhaps it is best to consider for a moment the meaning of the term "profession."

It is not difficult to find definitions of "profession." Webster's Dictionary says it is "the business which one professes to understand and to practice for subsistence; a calling, occupation, or vocation distinguished from a trade or handicraft." Black's Law Dictionary calls it "a vocation, calling, occupation or employment involving labor, skill, education, special knowledge and compensation or profit, but the labor and skill is predominantly mental or intellectual rather than physical or manual."

While each of the above definitions serves a purpose, each is brief at the expense of completeness. Probably one of the best and most complete definitions was given by the United States Congress in the Labor Management Relations Act as amended in 1947 (the Taft-Hartley Law). In this act Congress defined the term "professional employee."

Professional Employee

The term "professional employee" means:

a) any employee engaged in work (1) predominantly intellectual and varied in character as opposed to routine mental, manual, mechanical, or physical work; (2) involving consistent exercise of discretion and judgment in its performance; (3) of such a character that the output produced or the result accomplished cannot be standardized in relation to a given period of time; (4) requiring knowledge of an advanced type in a field of science or learning customarily acquired by a prolonged course of specialized intellectual instruction and study in an institution of higher learning or a hospital, as distinguished from a general academic education or from an apprenticeship or from training in the performance of routine mental, manual, or physical processes; or

b) any employee, who (1) has completed the courses of specialized intellectual instruction and study described in clause (4) of paragraph (a), and (2) is performing related work under the supervision of a professional person to qualify himself to become a professional employee as defined in paragraph (a).

The four requirements stated in the Taft-Hartley Law are repeated in some form by most people who attempt to define a profession. In addition, various other criteria are frequently added to the list above: a) registration requirements for practicing the professions; b) representation of members and control of activities by a professional society; c) the public service nature of the occupation; and d) adherence to a code of ethics.

State Registration Laws

The state laws of each of the United States require that an engineer be registered before being allowed to practice professional engineering in the state. Registration in any one state does not give the engineer a right to act as a professional engineer in another state; however, many states have reciprocal agreements whereby registration is much simplified if the engineer is already registered in another state.

The primary purpose of the state engineering registration laws is to protect the public from shoddy engineering practices. To this end, it is necessary that the prospective licensee convince a board of examiners that he is qualified to practice professional engineering. The usual method for this is a scrutiny of the individual's past engineering work and training by the board, in addition to a qualifying examination. This examination commonly lasts two days and is either oral and written or entirely written. It usually covers the basic sciences and specialization in a particular field of engineering. Full registration as a professional engineer allows the licensee to act as a professional engineer within the state and to resort to the courts to collect fees for his services. Penalties in the form of fines and/or confinement are specified for practicing without a license.

According to at least one court decision [1] engineering became a profession upon enactment of the state registration law. Such a landmark is, perhaps, convenient in legal interpretations within a state. However, professions do not magically spring into existence on the day when a law is passed. Obtaining acceptance of a field of knowledge as a profession is a never-ending job, and efforts to maintain high standards of service to the public must continue and grow as the profession grows.

Professional Societies

Each of the recognized branches of engineering has formed at least one society of its members. In addition to these there are three organizations which are concerned with all engineers.

E.C.P.D. The Engineers Council for Professional Development was formed in 1932. The E.C.P.D. is active in four major areas: 1) accreditation of engineering curricula for engineering degree-granting institutions. Periodically (at least once every five years) each engineering curriculum is scrutinized by E.C.P.D. representatives to determine content and effectiveness; 2) development, adoption and maintenance of codes of ethics for engineers; 3) development of techniques of vocational guidance; and 4) development of means to aid the transition of young engineers from campus atmosphere to work situations.

N.S.P.E. The National Society of Professional Engineers, formed in 1934, is concerned with the social, economic, political, and professional interests of all engineers. N.S.P.E. activities were largely responsible for the passage of engineer registration laws in the various states, public recognition of engineering as a profession, and recognition of the value of engineering activities.

---

[1] H. C. Downer and Associates, Inc. v. The Westgate Realty Company, No. 4892, Court of Appeals, Ninth Judicial District, Ohio, Nov. 25, 1959.

E.J.C. The Engineers' Joint Council consists of the presidents and secretaries of the engineering societies. It is concerned primarily with the educational, scientific, and technical aspects of engineering.

Professional Life

A degree in engineering is a foundation; a life career in the engineering profession can be built on it. An engineer can reasonably expect to be treated as a professional person by his client or his superior. However, complete public recognition of engineering as a profession has not yet occurred. The service rendered by a doctor, an attorney, or a member of the clergy is obvious to the public. A person experiencing a strange pain seeks out a doctor for diagnosis and cure. One who has been accused of a crime requires personal contact with an attorney. A family undergoing matrimonial difficulties may turn to a member of the clergy for aid. The public has little knowledge, though, of the engineer whose work makes crossing a bridge or riding an airplane safe and convenient. The engineer's work is just as vital and his contributions are as great as those of the other professions—a member of the public can be just as dead from an accident caused by mechanical malfunction as from cancer. The engineer's contribution is unseen; it is for this reason, among others, that the engineer must act as a professional person if he is to establish and maintain the respect accorded professional people.

The medical doctor must keep abreast of new developments and the lawyer must peruse recent cases to improve the service rendered. Similarly, an engineering education is never finished. The engineer has a duty to his client and his profession to learn the new developments in his field. Unquestionably, the professional person's day-to-day bread-winning efforts are important to him; but so is the extra time on evenings and weekends required to read technical periodicals and to attend engineering society meetings. A lathe operator or maintenance man in a shop may work from 7:00 A.M. to 3:30 P.M. and forget his job and everything connected with it at the end of the day. For the dedicated professional the day does not end when the office doors close behind him. There is always more to learn.

CANONS OF ETHICS

DEFINITION. According to Webster's Dictionary, the word ethics is defined as: "The science which treats of the nature and laws of the actions of intelligent beings, these actions being considered in relation to their moral qualities; the science which treats of the nature and grounds of moral obligations; the science of human duty."

Ethics are the ground rules of our moral conduct. They consist of our attitudes toward honesty, integrity, trust and loyalty; they are exhibited in our day-to-day contacts with others. No laws compel an engineer to take an interest in community affairs or to give a completely unbiased report of the results of an investigation. The manner in which the engineer will act depends upon his own moral code or ethics.

Establishment of Moral Patterns

Our code of ethics or sense of moral duty is not something acquired by reading a passage in a textbook and then deciding to abide by what was stated. Rather, it is a summary of experiences and observations gained throughout one's life.

Perhaps we each inherit a predisposition toward a certain type of moral behavior. This, though, is rather doubtful. Certainly we are influenced by what happens after birth—by the environment in which we mature. Examples set by parent or guardian, by friends, by classmates, by teachers and professors all contribute their share. Punishment for censured acts and praise for achievements are the building blocks for individual codes of ethics. All these help to make up the student's moral structure; to these will be added the experiences and observations on the job.

In 1947 the E.C.P.D. adopted the Canons of Ethics presented below. In 1957 the N.S.P.E. added the rules of Professional Conduct. These canons and rules are not meant as a body of inflexible laws, to be observed "or else." Rather, they are meant as guidepost, to be worked into and be the basis for change of the engineer's moral standards. They have been in existence in various stages of development for several decades and have been found to be of value in dealing with others. They are our professional standards.

CANONS OF ETHICS FOR ENGINEERS
AND RULES OF PROFESSIONAL CONDUCT

Foreword

Honesty, justice and courtesy form a moral philosophy which, associated with mutual interest among men, constitutes the foundation of ethics. The engineer should recognize such a standard, not in a passive observance, but as a set of dynamic principles guiding his conduct and way of life. It is his duty to practice his profession according to these Canons of Ethics.

As the keystone of professional conduct is integrity, the engineer will discharge his duties with fidelity to the public, his employers and clients, and with fairness and impartiality to all. It is his duty to interest himself in public welfare and to be ready to apply his special knowledge for the benefit of mankind. He should uphold the honor and dignity of his profession and avoid association with any enterprise of questionable character. In his dealings with fellow engineers he should be fair and tolerant.

Professional Life

Canon 1. The engineer will co-operate in extending the effectiveness of the engineering profession by interchanging information and experience with other engineers and students and by contributing to the work of engineering societies, schools and the scientific and engineering press.

Rule 1. He will be guided in all his relations by the highest standards.

Rule 2. He will not lend his name to any enterprise about which he is not thoroughly informed and in which he does not have a positive belief.

Rule 3. He should seek opportunities to be of constructive service in civic affairs and work for the advancement of the safety, health and well-being of his community.

Rule 4. He will not offer to pay, either directly or indirectly, any commission, political contribution, or a gift, or other consideration in order to secure work, exclusive of securing salaried positions through employment agencies.

Can. 2. He will not advertise his work or merit in a self-laudatory manner and he will avoid all conduct or practice likely to discredit or do injury to the dignity and honor of his profession.

Rule 5. Circumspect advertising may be properly employed by the engineer to announce his practice and availability. The form and manner of such advertising shall satisfy in all respects the dictate and intent of the Canons. Only those media shall be used as are necessary to reach directly an interested and potential client or employer, and such media shall in themselves be dignified, reputable and characteristically free of any factor or circumstance that would bring disrepute to the profession or to the professional using them. The substance of such advertising shall be limited to fact and shall contain no statement or offer intended to discredit or displace another engineer, either specifically or by implication.

Rule 6. Telephone listings shall be limited to name, address and telephone number under each branch listing in which he qualifies.

Rule 7. He will not allow himself to be listed for employment using exaggerated statements of his qualifications.

Relations with the Public

Can. 3. The engineer will endeavor to extend public knowledge of engineering, and will discourage the spreading of untrue, unfair and exaggerated statements regarding engineering.

Rule 8. He will avoid belittling the necessity for engineering services.

Can. 4. He will have due regard for the safety of life and health of public and employees who may be affected by the work for which he is responsible.

Rule 9. He will regard his duty to the public welfare as paramount.

Can. 5. He will express an opinion only when it is founded on adequate knowledge and honest conviction while he is serving as a witness before a court, commission, or other tribunal.

Can. 6. He will not issue ex parte statements, criticisms or arguments on matters connected with public policy which are inspired or paid for by private interests, unless he indicates on whose behalf he is making the statement.

Rule 10. He will not advocate or support enactment of community laws, rules, or regulations that he believes are not in the public interest.

Can. 7. He will refrain from expressing publicly an opinion on an engineering subject unless he is informed as to the facts relating thereto.

Relations with Clients and Employers

Can. 8. The engineer will act in professional matters for each client or employer as a faithful agent or trustee.

Rule 11. He will not undertake or agree to perform any engineering service on a free basis.

Rule 12. He will be conservative and honest in all estimates, reports, statements, and testimony.

Rule 13. He will advise his client when he believes a project will not be successful.

Rule 14. His plans or specifications will not be such as to limit free competition, except with his client's consent.

Rule 15. He will associate himself only with projects of a legitimate character.

Rule 16. He will not solicit or accept employment to the detriment of his regular work or interest.

Rule 17. An engineer in private practice may be employed by more than one party when the interests and time schedules of the several parties do not conflict.

Can. 9. He will act with fairness and justice between his client or employer and the contractor when dealing with contracts.

Rule 18. He will insist on contractor compliance with plans and specifications.

Can. 10. He will make his status clear to his client or employer before undertaking an engagement if he may be called upon to decide on the use of inventions, apparatus, or any other thing in which he may have a financial interest.

Rule 19. Before undertaking work for others in connection with which he may make improvements, plans, designs, inventions or other records which may justify copyrights or patents, the engineer should enter into a positive agreement regarding the ownership.

Rule 20. When an engineer or manufacturer builds apparatus from designs supplied to him by a customer, the designs remain the property of the customer and should not be duplicated by the engineer or manufacturer for others without express permission.

Rule 21. A clear understanding should be reached before the beginning of the work regarding the respective rights of ownership when an engineer or manufacturer and a customer may jointly work out designs and plans or develop inventions.

Rule 22. Designs, data, records, and notes made by an employee and referring exclusively to his employer's work are his employer's property.

Rule 23. A customer, in buying apparatus, does not acquire any right in its design but only the use of the apparatus purchased. A client does not acquire any right to the ideas developed and plans made by a consulting engineer, except for the specific case for which they were made.

Can. 11. He will guard against conditions that are dangerous or threatening to life, limb or property on work for which he is responsible, or if he is not responsible, will promptly call such conditions to the attention of those who are responsible.

Rule 24. He will not complete, sign, or seal plans and/or specifications that are not of a design safe to the public health and welfare. If the client or employer insists on such unprofessional conduct, he shall call building authorities' attention to the case and withdraw from further consulting business or service on the project.

Can. 12. He will present clearly the consequences to be expected from deviations proposed if his engineering judgment is overruled by non-technical authority in cases where he is responsible for the technical adequacy of engineering work.

Rule 25. He will not apply his signature of approval or seal on plans that do not meet accepted engineering standards.

Can. 13. He will engage, or advise his client or employer to engage, and he will co-operate with, other experts and specialists whenever the client's or employer's interests are best served by such service.

Rule 26. He will not undertake responsible engineering work for which he is not qualified by experience and training.

Can. 14. He will disclose no information concerning the business affairs or technical processes of clients or employers without their consent.

Can. 15. He will not accept compensation, financial or otherwise, from more than one interested party for the same service, or for services pertaining to the same work, without the consent of all interested parties.

Rule 27. He will not accept financial or other considerations, including free engineering designs, from material or equipment suppliers for specifying their product.

Can. 16. He will not accept commissions or allowances, directly or indirectly, from contractors or other parties dealing with his clients or employer in connection with work for which he is responsible.

Can. 17. He will not be financially interested in the bids as or of a contractor on competitive work for which he is employed as an engineer unless he has the consent of his client or employer.

Rule 28. He will not accept personal consideration in any form. This assures that his recommendations for the award of a contract cannot be influenced.

Can. 18. He will promptly disclose to his client or employer any interest in a business which may compete with or affect the business of his client or employer. He will not allow an interest in any business to affect his decision regarding engineering work for which he is employed, or which he may be called upon to perform.

Relations with Engineers

Can. 19. The engineer will endeavor to protect the engineering profession collectively and individually from misrepresentation and misunderstanding.

Rule 29. The engineer will insist on the use of facts in reference to an engineering project or to an engineer in a group discussion, public forum or publication of articles.

Can. 20. He will take care that credit for engineering work is given to those to whom credit is properly due.

Rule 30. Whenever possible, he will name the person or persons who may be individually responsible for designs, inventions, writings, or other accomplishments.

Rule 31. He will not accept by voice or silence, credit rightfully due another engineer.

Rule 32. He will not sign or seal plans or specifications prepared by someone other than himself or an employee under his supervision.

Rule 33. He will not represent as his own the plans, designs, or specifications supplied to him by a manufacturer or supplier of equipment or material.

Can. 21. He will uphold the principle of appropriate and adequate com-

pensation for those engaged in engineering work, including those in subordinate capacities, as being in the public interest and maintaining the standards of the profession.

Rule 34. He will not undertake work at a fee or salary that will not permit professional performance, according to accepted standards of the profession.

Rule 35. He will not accept work in the geographic area in which he practices or intends to practice at a salary or fee below that recognized as a basic minimum in that area.

Rule 36. He will not accept remuneration from either an employee or employment agency for giving employment.

Rule 37. When hiring other engineers, he shall offer a salary according to the engineer's qualifications and recognized standards in the particular geographical area.

Can. 22. He will endeavor to provide opportunity for the professional development and advancement of engineers in his employ.

Rule 38. He will encourage attendance at professional or technical society meetings by his engineer employees.

Rule 39. He should not unduly restrict the preparation and presentation of technical papers by his engineer employees.

Rule 40. He will encourage an employee's efforts to improve his education.

Rule 41. He will urge his engineer employees to become registered at the earliest possible date.

Rule 42. He will assign a professional engineer duties of a nature to utilize his full training and experience, insofar as possible, and delegate lesser functions to subprofessionals or to technicians.

Rule 43. He will not restrain an employee from obtaining a better position with another employer by offers of short-term gains or by belittling the employee's qualifications.

Can. 23. He will not directly or indirectly injure the professional reputation, prospects, or practice of another engineer. However, if he considers that an engineer is guilty of unethical, illegal, or unfair practice, he will present the information to the proper authority for action.

Rule 44. He will report unethical practices of another engineer with substantiating data to his professional or technical society, and be willing to appear as a witness.

Can. 24. He will exercise due restraint in criticizing another engineer's work in public, recognizing the fact that the engineering societies and the engineering press provide the proper forum for technical discussions and criticism.

Rule 45. He will not review the work of another engineer for the same client, except with knowledge or consent of such engineer, or unless the connection of such engineer with the work has been terminated.

Can. 25. He will not try to supplant another engineer in a particular employment after becoming aware that definite steps have been taken toward the other's employment.

Rule 46. He will not attempt to inject his services into a project at the expense of another engineer who has been active in developing it.

Can. 26. He will not compete with another engineer on the basis of charges for work by underbidding, through reducing his normal fees after having been informed of the charges named by the other.

Rule 47. The practice of engineering is a learned profession, requiring of its members sound technical training, broad experience, personal ability, honesty and integrity. The selection of engineering services by an evaluation of these qualities should be the basis of comparison rather than competitive bids.

Rule 48. Competition between engineers for employment on the basis of professional fees or charges is considered unethical practice by all professional engineering groups. Hence, the announced intent of an owner or governmental body to request such competitive bids removes from consideration many engineers who may be the best qualified to be entrusted with the proposed work.

Rule 49. It shall be considered ethical for an engineer to solicit an engineering assignment, either verbally or written. Such solicitation may be in the form of a letter or a brochure setting forth factual information concerning the engineer's qualifications by training and experience and reference to past accomplishments and clients.

Should the engineer be asked for a proposal to perform engineering services for a specific project, he should set forth in detail the work he proposes to accomplish and an indication of the calendar days required for its accomplishment. The engineer's qualifications may be included if appropriate. Should such a statement be deemed necessary, the proposed fee shall be equal to or more than the fees recommended as a minimum for the particular type of service required, as established by fee schedules or practice in the geographical area where the work is to be done. Where a fee cannot be established in this manner, the ethical fee shall be equal to actual cost plus overhead plus a reasonable profit.

Rule 50. He will take a professional attitude in negotiations for his services and shall avoid all practices which have a tendency to affect adversely the amount, quality, or disinterested nature of professional services; such as charging inadequate fees for preliminary work for full services, competing for an engineering assignment on a price basis, spending large amounts of money in securing business or consenting to furnish monetary guaranties of cost estimates.

Can. 27. He will not use the advantages of a salaried position to compete unfairly with another engineer.

Rule 51. While in a salaried position, he will accept part-time engineering work only at a salary or fee not less than that recognized as standard in the area.

Rule 52. An engineer will not use equipment, supplies, laboratory, or office facilities of his employer to carry on outside private practice without consent.

Can. 28. He will not become associated in responsibility for work with engineers who do not conform to ethical practices.

Rule 53. He will conform with registration laws in his practice of engineering.

Rule 54. He will not use association with a non-engineer, a corporation, or partnership, as a "cloak" for unethical acts; but must accept personal responsibility for his professional acts.

Miscellaneous

Rule 55. An engineer who is in sales or industrial employ is entitled to make engineering comparisons of the products offered by various suppliers, but will avoid aspersions upon their character, standing, or ability.

Rule 56. If, in sales employ, he will not offer, or give engineering consultation, or designs, or advice other than specifically applying to the operation of the equipment being sold.

Rule 57. No engineer in the employ of equipment or material supply companies will tender designs, plans, specifications, advice or consultation to operations beyond the limits of a machine or item of material or supply, except as is required for proper functioning of the particular item.

Rule 58. He will not use his professional affiliations to secure the confidence of other engineers in commercial enterprise and will avoid any act tending to promote his own interest at the expense of the dignity and standing of the profession.

Rule 59. He will admit and accept his own errors when proven obviously wrong and refrain from distorting or altering the facts in an attempt to justify his decision.

Rule 60. Any firm offering engineering services must, in conformance with the laws of the state in which it operates, have its operations under the direction and responsibility of registered professional engineers.

Rule 61. He will not attempt to attract an engineer from another employer by methods such as offering unjustified salaries or benefits.

Law and Ethics

There is no penalty at law for a violation of ethics. Neither the examining boards nor the courts have any rights or responsibilities in the ethical practices of engineers. Whatever formal reproof there is for moral misbehavior must come from the societies. In the short history of the engineering profession there has not yet been developed a society equivalent to the American Medical Association or the local and state bar associations for handling ethical infractions. Nearly all the societies are concerned with ethical practices, but few seem deeply concerned. At present, enforcement efforts vary from apparent tacit condonation of the unethical in some sections of the United States, to very active policing in others. However, the need has been generally recognized and it is likely that systems for detecting, investigating, and holding hearings on unethical practices will soon be developed and vigorously maintained throughout the United States.

Despite the present lack of uniformity in formally policing ethical practices, informal penalties for infractions exist everywhere. The limit of formal penalties is removal of membership in an engineering society. While loss of membership in a society can be quite harmful to an individual member, the informal penalties are often much more severe. Loss of a job on a weak excuse or social censure within a community are often mute testimony of the presence and effectiveness of informal penalties.

Codes of professional ethics are not necessarily meant to be of practical value to an individual; yet, in most cases they are. The person who is honest and loyal in his adherence to a code of ethics in dealing with others often finds that, as a result, others are honest and loyal in dealing with him. Adherence to ethics tends to inspire confidence and admiration of colleagues, clients, and employers.

Gifts and Favors

Strict interpretation of the Canons of Ethics indicates that anything offered to an engineer by a present or prospective contractor should be shunned. This would seem to include all manner of gifts, favors, or evidences of hospitality. If a ball-point pen or a cigar is acceptable, why not a set of golf clubs or a silver tea service? If there is no stigma attached to a free lunch, then why not an evening of nightclubbing at the vendor's expense? If an inexpensive favor is to be condoned, where shall the line be drawn?

It must be recognized that the "ivory tower" approach is unpopular in many circles. Numerous companies exist in which buyers and engineers seldom buy their own lunches, where pen and pencil sets and other gifts are accepted with no qualms. In such places an engineer's refusal of such "advertising" marks him as a bit odd. Perhaps minor gifts and favors should be accepted; maybe even those larger than "minor." However, the engineer should consider well what is at stake when he does accept them.

Whenever the engineer accepts a gift or favor or hospitality from a contractor or potential contractor the engineer's freedom of action is inhibited. The obligation to deal with the particular contractor may not be very evident—many times it acts only as a subtle reminder. Nevertheless, at least slight inhibition of completely free action does result. The engineer is a person, a human being capable of being persuaded even against his best engineering judgment. Influence of this nature is against the best interests of the engineer's company. In recognition of this many large companies have adopted policies restricting or eliminating receipt of gifts from vendors.

It has been said that everyone has a price. Perhaps this is true. However, we in the engineering profession feel that an engineer's integrity cannot be bought—there is no price tag. If the engineer cannot afford to buy his own lunch or pocket knife he should look to a new employer for economic improvement, not to his present employer's vendors.

Recruiting Practices

In recent years there has been a shortage of engineers. It is occasionally contended that anyone with a reasonable pulse and a diploma certifying him to be a graduate of an engineering curriculum is eligible to be hired as an engineer. This demand for engineers is not likely to change a great deal in the forseeable future.

As might be expected, this unprecedented demand for engineers has led to some peculiar and even reprehensible recruiting practices. Proper use of the talent and problem-solving ability of qualified engineers can make or save money for a company; therefore, pressure is brought to bear on those whose duty it is to acquire such people. The results are not always in keeping with the highest ethical practices. It is, for instance, considered quite unethical for a company to contact an engineer working for another company in an effort to lure him away. If the engineer makes the first move, though, the resulting job change is considered to be above reproach. Often the efforts used to cause the engineer to make this first move are ludicrous (from an objective point of view).

A company's loss of engineers may sometimes be laid at its own doorstep. A distressingly large number of companies have a tendency to overlook contributions made by an engineer. If a methods or design change is made by an engineer, resulting in a sizable saving to the company, he often feels that there should be some recognition for him as a result of his achievement—after all, he could have accepted his paychecks and performed only as his boss required. The company, on the other hand, feels that the engineer is paid for both periods in which the engineer's contributions are outstanding, and many other periods in which seemingly little was accomplished. As a result of these conflicting views, engineers often become dissatisfied and are easy marks for competing offers. Most companies find that some form of tangible recognition (salary increase or bonus) along with words of praise for an outstanding job will inhibit such dissatisfaction.

The engineer owes a duty of full service to his employer. For the first few months after a new engineer is hired on a staff his contributions are not likely to be very great; yet his employer has invested time and money in him. If the engineer quits before he has repaid this investment, the company loses money. As a result of frequent "job-hopping," the engineer may find that even though a demand for engineers exists, he will have a rough time getting another job.

To aid in the development and maintenance of high ethical standards in college recruiting of engineers, the American Society for Engineering Education formulated a code of ethics. This code of ethics, "Recruiting Practices and Procedures—1959" was endorsed by the E.C.P.D. and has been distributed to placement offices on engineering college campuses. It outlines the responsibilities of the employer, the college, and the student applicant in an attempt to secure fair treatment of each by the other two.

The Ethics Tool

The professional engineer is taught to be an ethical person. His code of ethics is as much a tool as his knowledge of the grain structure of steel or the deflection of a beam. Proper use of the tools he possesses will give him a rewarding career; improper use leads to frustration and disaster.

REVIEW QUESTIONS

1. A process engineer was about to recommend the purchase of equipment for a new manufacturing process for his employer. A vendor calling upon him told him of a new and, apparently, cheaper means of accomplishing the same end result. The engineer was familiar with the type of work in question, but had never heard of the new process. The vendor invited him to go (at the vendor's expense) to several places in which the new process was used. Should the engineer go to see the new process? At the vendor's expense? What canons or rules have a bearing on the situation?

2. If the engineer took the trip mentioned above and the vendor suggested an evening at a local night club to avoid the boredom of a hotel room (with the vendor picking up the night club tab), should the engineer accept or decline? Why?

3. In going through the files on a process in which his employer finds himself in trouble, an engineer finds several instances of very poor judgment and miscalculation by his predecessor, who set up the process. Most of the present problems in the process are caused by the previous

engineer's errors. The previous engineer left the company and is now working for another firm. The present engineer's assignment is to improve the process. How should the improvements be justified to the employer? What, if anything, should the engineer say or do about his predecessor's mistakes? What canons or rules apply?

4. About a month ago an engineer made an outstanding improvement in a process. His company produces approximately 300,000 parts per year through the process and direct labor saving alone amounts to approx. $.10 for each part. The foreman of the department in which the process is located has complimented the engineer on his achievement, but no one else in the plant has done anything more than mention it to him. What, if anything, should the engineer do?

5. Summarize, in a few words each of the four requirements for a "professional employee."

6. Just before Christmas an engineer receives a package from a vendor with whom he has dealt in the past. The engineer is now concerned with work entirely outside the field of the vendor's interest. The package contains an eight-place setting of sterling silver. Should the engineer keep the gift or return it? Why?

7. An engineer is approached by a friend of his who argues stoutly for joining an engineer's union. It is pointed out that promotions will be based largely on seniority, that wages will be paid according to the class of work undertaken (which is likely to improve the engineer's economic situation), and that overtime will be paid for all work in excess of forty hours per week or eight hours in a day. Should the engineer join the union or not? What are the counter arguments?

5

TORTS AND CRIMES

Numerous man-made laws and rules regulate the behavior of people. The field of law may be broken down into many categories and the categories may be further subdivided. One major breakdown is that shown below:

I. Criminal Law.
II. Civil Law:
   A. Torts.
   B. Breaches of Contract.

An individual unlawful act must be either a public wrong or a private wrong; possibly both. An unlawful act which injures the public is a crime; one which injures one individual or a group of individuals less than the general public is a civil wrong. Civil law, or the law of private rights, is divided into torts and breaches of contract. More will be said about breaches of contract later. The intent here is to cover a few broad, general concepts in criminal law and torts.

Most engineers are concerned with contracts. However, they must also work with other persons and others' property. Most have some function in a management, either as consultants or as employees. For these reasons a brief treatment of the law as it pertains to public and private rights is presented here.

In the United States we have many rights and freedoms. We can do just about as we please up to the point where the things we do infringe upon the rights or freedoms of others. A crime is an anti-social act but, of course, not all anti-social acts are crimes. Relief of internal pressure by means of a loud belch is generally considered to be an anti-social act, but it is not yet a crime. Society is injured when a crime is committed. The main purpose of trying a person accused of a crime and punishing him if he is guilty is to prevent recurrences of the criminal act.

One main distinction between a criminal action and a civil action is that the state undertakes prosecution for a crime. On the other hand, when a civil wrong has been committed, the plaintiff must bring his own action. A criminal action is undertaken to punish the wrongdoer; a civil action is pursued to get compensation for a loss suffered or to prevent a loss from being suffered.

The same act may constitute at once a tort and a crime—as such it gives rise to both a civil and a criminal action against the person who committed the act. In fact, it takes a little thought to find a tort which may not be a crime and a crime which would in no way be a tort.

CRIMINAL LAW

A crime is an act which is prohibited by either common law or a statute. In states where a criminal code has been adopted all crimes are statutory. As time passes and society becomes more and more complex we tend to increase the number of laws defining certain acts as crimes. When a criminal statute is made it is generally necessary to answer at least three questions in the statute: 1) What is the act (or omission) which is to be prohibited? 2) Who can commit the crime (or, conversely, who cannot)? and 3) What is the punishment for commission of the act? Under common law there is both a physical and a mental component of a crime. The mental element is known as "criminal intent." In a common law case it is frequently necessary to prove intent as an element in the criminal act. Many state statutes remove the necessity for this proof on the basis that the act speaks for itself and that a person will intend the natural results of his acts.

Under common law a child under seven years of age is incapable of entertaining criminal intent. Between ages seven and fourteen the child is presumed incapable, but the presumption may be rebutted under certain circumstances. Insane persons and idiots are not criminally responsible for their acts. A corporation cannot be guilty of crimes involving malice or intent. Drunkenness might seem to be similar to insanity, but it is rarely a valid excuse. The law usually holds drunkenness to be a voluntary state preventable by proper foresight.

Punishment for a criminal offense ordinarily takes one of the following forms: 1) death; 2) imprisonment; 3) fine; 4) removal from office; 5) disqualification to hold and enjoy any office of honor, trust, or profit under the constitution or laws of the state.[1]

---

[1] California Penal Code.

Degrees of Crime

TREASON. The highest crime is treason. It is defined in the Constitution as: "Treason against the United States shall consist only in levying war against them, or in adhering to their enemies, giving them aid and comfort. No person shall be convicted of treason unless on the testimony of two witnesses to the same overt act, or on confession in open court."

FELONY. The second level of crime consists of felonies. Early common law punished felonies with a sentence to death. Now a felony is generally defined as an act which is punishable by death or imprisonment in a penitentiary. Every citizen has a duty to do everything in his power to prevent the commission of a felony and to prevent the escape of a felon after the crime has been committed. One who fails to act in a reasonable manner to prevent the crime or the escape of the criminal is, himself, guilty of a misdemeanor. The law does not require a person to walk into a blaze of gunfire—he must only do everything he reasonably could be expected to do under the circumstances.

MISDEMEANOR. The lowest level of crime is known as misdemeanor. It consists of all prohibited acts less than felonies. Traffic violations are examples of misdemeanors, as are zoning law violations and breaches of the peace. Punishment for misdemeanor usually consists of fine or jail sentence or, generally, anything less than death or imprisonment in a penitentiary.

TERMS OFTEN MISUNDERSTOOD. "Compounding a crime." This term refers to an agreement between a person who has committed a crime and another who has knowledge of the crime to the effect that the latter will not report the act. For example, one who has been robbed might agree with the person who robbed him that he will not report the theft if his property is returned. Compounding a crime is a criminal offense in itself. Society has been offended by the commission of the crime and no citizen has the right to deprive society of the opportunity to punish the criminal.

"Double jeopardy" is another misunderstood term in criminal law. The fifth amendment to the Constitution provides (in part): ". . . nor shall any person be subject for the same offence to be twice put in jeopardy of life or limb. . . ." A person is put in jeopardy when a valid indictment has been lodged against him, he has been tried, and jury verdict has been given. It is not double jeopardy however when, by a single act, a person violates two laws and is subsequently tried for violation of both of them. Many state laws prohibit acts which are also prohibited by federal laws. Both governments may have laws forbidding the sale of narcotics, for instance. If a person is acquitted in Federal Court on a charge of violating the Federal Narcotics Law, he may still be tried in a state court for violation of the state law.

TORTS

A tort is an offense against an individual, in the form of injury to his personal rights or his property rights. Prosecution is generally undertaken by the plaintiff to obtain compensation for the injury suffered. Or a decree may be sought to prevent harm to personal or property rights.

Just as the law undertakes to prevent acts against society by prosecution of one who has committed a crime, the law also provides procedures to redress wrongs to an individual. Such wrongs fall into two general categories—torts and breaches of contract. Breach of contract cases arise when there has been an agreement of some sort between the parties involved. These will be treated in Chapters 14 and 15. Tort actions arise from duties and natural rights which exist between parties. The driver of a car, for instance, has a duty to avoid hitting others while he is driving. If he is negligent in his duty and, as a result, injures another, a tort action is available to the victim to make the driver pay for the damage done.

In criminal law it is frequently necessary to prove the existence of the element of intent to commit a crime. In tort cases, particularly where negligence is involved, proof of intent is not likely to be as important. It is only necessary to prove three things in a tort action: 1) that the defendant owed the plaintiff a duty; 2) that this duty was breached by the defendant; and 3) that the damage resulted from the breach of this duty. Whether or not the tort-feasor (the one who committed the tort) intended his act to result in injury is beside the point.

RES IPSA LOQUITUR.   In most tort cases the plaintiff can point to specific negligent acts by the defendant to make out his case. In some instances, however, it is difficult or impossible to show defendant's specific acts or omissions. When this is true the plaintiff may still make out his case based on the doctrine known as *res ipsa loquitur*. Essentially this means "the thing speaks for itself." To use this doctrine, plaintiff may show that the injury would not occur unless someone were negligent; that defendant had control of the instrumentality causing the injury; and that plaintiff in no way contributed to the injury. The result is not proof, but circumstantial evidence which presents to the jury a logical inference to be accepted if they find it reasonable. Defendant, of course, has an opportunity for rebuttal, which may take one of several forms, but usually consists of showing that he actually used the care which he should have used.

Occurrence

In general there are three ways in which a tort may arise: through malfeasance, misfeasance, or nonfeasance on the part of the tort-feasor.

A tort is said to arise from malfeasance when the tortious act is one which the tort-feasor should not ordinarily be allowed to commit. Deliberate destruction of a company's reputation and good will by publication of falsehoods is an example of such torts.

Misfeasance results from an act which one would ordinarily be allowed to do, but which is done at such a time or place that it injures another Assume that you are driving down a highway and your left front tire blows out forcing you into the opposite lane in the path of an oncoming car. Ordinarily you do not violate any rights if your tire blows out—you can have a blowout whenever you wish. However, if the blowout is the direct cause of injury to another, the resulting injury is your responsibility. It was not the other car that caused the injury, but yours.

Nonfeasance takes place when one neglects to do that which he should have done to protect others from injury. When a construction crew leaves an excavation for an evening or week end, barriers are usually placed around the excavation. If the placing of barriers is neglected and, as a result, someone falls into the excavation, thereby injuring himself, his injury is the contractor's responsibility.

COMMON TORTS

Some of the more common torts will be treated under four general headings: 1) torts against a person; 2) torts against one's reputation; 3) torts against property rights; and 4) business torts.

Torts Against a Person

Assault and battery are two common personal torts. The first of these, assault, is a term quite frequently used improperly. The legal meaning of the term assault is a threat of violence. It consists of one or more acts intended by the tort-feasor to create apprehension of bodily harm in the victim. There must be an apparent present means of inflicting the bodily harm; for instance, a knife or a pistol (it would make no difference that the pistol was not loaded if the victim had reason to believe that it was). The tort of assault requires that the threat be concerned with immediate injury—not next week or "if I ever see you again." Harm from the tort of assault frequently occurs when the victim has a weak heart or when a pregnant woman receives the threats.

Assault ends and battery begins when the threat is carried out. Battery is the intentional and unlawful touching of another in an offensive manner. Battery is often incorrectly reported as assault; the two torts do often go together but there is a distinction between them.

False imprisonment occurs when one is intentionally confined within limits set by the tort-feasor. The victim must be aware that he is being confined and he must not have given his consent to the confinement. The means of imprisonment is incidental as long as the victim's personal liberty is restricted. For example, confinement of a person in a car which is traveling too rapidly for exit to be made safely would be imprisonment. A particular means of confinement might be imprisonment to one, but not to another; that is, an athletic young man might escape through a window, whereas a wheelchair cripple could not.

The right to have a court determine guilt or innocence in a criminal case or who should win a civil suit is sometimes abused. One party may bring suit against another merely as an annoyance to him. The tort involved in such an action is *malicious prosecution* (or *vexatious proceeding* if based on a civil case). The tort hinges principally on the presence or absence of "probable cause." If there were reasonable grounds to believe that the facts warranted the action complained of, this is a perfect defense against a suit for malicious prosecution. Usually, if a reputable attorney recommends an action at law after he has learned the true facts it can be assumed that there is "probable cause."

Torts Against Reputation

A person has a right to whatever reputation he earns in his day-to-day dealings with others. If false and malicious statements are published (orally or in writing) such statements may constitute *defamation.* Defamation occurs when false and malicious statements made about a person tend to expose him to public ridicule, contempt, or hatred. Even statements about a dead person can constitute a tort if they are false and maliciously tend to blacken the memory of him. Defamation occurs where a statement wrongly attributes a criminal act to a person. It also occurs in statements which tend to injure one in his job or profession.

Defamation takes two forms. Oral defamation is known as *slander.* Printed or written defamation or defamation by pictures or signs is known as *libel.* It is slander to falsely state that White is embezzling company funds; it is libel if the statement is written. In such an instance, slander would not occur if the statement were made only to White with no one else present. Someone other than White would have to hear the statement.

Libel results from printed matter. Even a radio or television broadcast of a speaker who reads a defamatory statement from a written article may constitute libel rather than slander. The damages recoverable for libel are usually greater than for slander because of the lasting impression created.

According to present day law, truth and privilege constitute complete defenses to defamation suits. Regardless of the malicious manner in which the statements are made, if they are true there is no defamation.

Privilege refers to the right of one person to defame another. A judge has this right and so does a sworn witness on the stand. Privilege is found when the otherwise defamatory statements are made in carrying out a judicial, political, or social duty. It arises from the necessity of making a full and unrestricted communication.

Torts Against Property

When one owns property, all he really owns is a set of rights. He has the right to possession of the property, to its use (as long as he does not infringe upon the rights of others) and the right to dispose of it. One can normally exclude others from using his property or from taking possession of it. Tort action frequently results from the invasion of these rights.

TRESPASS. The tort of *trespass to land* occurs whenever a person without license enters upon the land of another. Even simply walking across the lawn is a tort. The law, however, does not concern itself with trifles and a single instance of trespass such as the invasion of one's lawn probably would not be actionable. Even if it were, the result would be likely to be only nominal damages. An action for trespass is more likely when the trespass has been repeated numerous times or when material damage can be shown. Such damage to real property can be shown, for instance, where the foundation of a structure encroaches upon the property of another. Black builds a structure near the edge of his property line (according to a survey). White, the owner of the adjacent property, later has another survey made. The later survey shows part of Black's foundation to be on White's property. The court establishes White's survey as correct. An equity court (where such a case would be likely to wind up) has the right to order the removal of the foundation. It probably would not do so, however, realizing that it would only be placing a weapon in White's hand to force Black to pay an exorbitant price for a piece of White's land. It is more probable that the judgment would require White to sell Black the piece of land at the reasonable market value.

If trespass to land takes the form of numerous members of the public using the property as they desire, an easement may result. If Black, for instance, owns lakeside property and the public crosses his property to reach the lake he may eventually be prevented from excluding the public. The period of time for such a public easement to occur runs from 15 to 20 years in the various states. Public use to create the right of easement must be continuous. It is for this reason that one occasionally sees a road blocked off for one day per year.

The right to trespass upon another's land can be given by the person in possession. Such permission is known as a license or an easement. In addition, certain others may have a license to trespass. A caller at a home has the right to go as far as the door by a direct route. If a person must enter another's property to recover his own property he has a right to do so.

It is the person who is in possession of the land who has the right to exclude others from trespassing. In other words, those who rent or lease property have the right to exclude others from it (even the owner) as long as the property is leased by them.

Personal rights take precedence over property rights. One does not ordinarily have the right to shoot trespassers. The force used must be no more than sufficient to remove the person from the property.

ATTRACTIVE NUISANCE. Ordinarily, one who trespasses upon another's property assumes whatever risk may be inherent in the trespass. If the trespasser is injured by some hidden danger, he has little chance of recovery against the owner. But, just as is true with many other general rules of law, this one has its exceptions. Probably the most prominent exception is known as *attractive nuisance*, pertaining to children of tender age. It is of recent origin as legal doctrines go, and has been rejected by some courts, but the number and size of recoveries in the past decade or so prompts its consideration.

The doctrine of attractive nuisance began in the United States with a case involving injury to a child playing around a railway turntable. In the century or so since then, a multitude of property conditions and instrumentalities (including recently, swimming pools) have come to be considered attractive nuisances for children.

In jurisdictions where the attractive nuisance doctrine is supported, a property owner or occupant may be held liable for injuries sustained by children on his premises under the following conditions: if he knew or should have known of the attractiveness of the dangerous instrumentality or property condition to children and failed to reasonably guard against injury to them; or if he had reason to expect children to play there (e.g., having seen them play in the vicinity), and did not warn them or take other suitable precautions.

The owner's (or occupant's) risk of attractive nuisance liability is removed by taking reasonable precautions. He is not expected to foresee very unlikely events—only those which might befall a normal, inquisitive child; and he would not be expected to guard something of danger obvious even to a child. The doctrine is aimed at conditions which would be inherently dangerous to a child, but which he could not be expected to foresee. Thus, an unguarded piece of machinery could easily be an attractive nuisance whereas an open pit in a field would be less likely to be one. Generally, the attraction must be something unusual, uncommon, or artificial as against a natural hazard.

Attractive nuisance cases could involve children of any age, but children of an age between five and ten years seem particularly susceptible. The court also considers such things as the child's intelligence, his state of mental health, and other conditions as significant in such cases. The largest factor, though, is the presence or absence of proper precautions by the owner or occupant of the premises. And this question is rightly submitted to a jury.

CONVERSION.   The tort counterpart to the crime of theft is conversion. Conversion, though, includes more than just depriving the owner of his right to possession of his property. It also includes wrongful alteration of property and wrongful use of property by persons other than the owner. It may arise in instances of bailment, where something left with another is used or sold by the bailor. Black leaves a television set with White (as bailee) to be repaired. White sells the television set to Gray. White's tortious act is conversion for which Black may maintain a conversion action in court. A successful suit in conversion normally nets the true owner of the property the market value of the converted property and vests title in the converter when the judgment amount has been paid. The owner, though, has an election of two remedies available to him. He may sue on the tort of conversion or maintain an action in replevin to obtain the return of his property. If the owner desires return of his property prior to the replevin action, he may usually obtain it by posting a bond to be forfeited in case the property is found to belong to the other party.

NUISANCE.   Each of us has the right to use his property as he chooses as long as he does not, in some way, injure the person or property of another. If one's person or property is injured by another and the tort fits no other category, nuisance will usually cover it. Nuisance can be just about anything which interferes with the enjoyment of life and property. It may take the form of smoke or sulphur fumes; or it may be pollution of a stream; or excessive noise, to mention only a few types.

Nuisances are either public or private. A public nuisance is one which annoys or disturbs a substantial number of the persons in a community. A private nuisance produces special injuries to private rights of one or a very few people. Any citizen may successfully lodge a complaint about a public nuisance, but only the person injured can maintain a successful action on a private nuisance.

Black owns a factory in which semi-trailers are manufactured. Since the manufacture requires the use of rivets, the process is quite noisy. When Black first built the factory, several years ago, the building site was a cornfield and the nearest neighbor was some two miles distant. With the passage of time Black's trailer business expanded. Adjoining land was sold to a land development company and houses have been built and sold. Recent orders for trailers have forced Black to put on a third shift at the factory, from 11 P.M. to 7 A.M. Some of the new house

wners complained to Black about the noise; one (White) has instituted
a nuisance suit. In answer, Black contends that he was there first, that
an injunction would force him to close down his plant and deprive
workers of jobs, and that the noise just isn't great enough to injure anyone,
anyway. There are a variety of judgments which would be possible in
such a situation. As to Black's being there first and thus acquiring a right
known as a prescriptive right) to maintain the nuisance, it is doubtful
that this defense would succeed. Such a defense might succeed only if
White had full knowledge of the noise problem (as to degree and time
of day) and bought his house in spite of the noise. Proof by White that
the noise had increased in time and intensity would be likely to defeat
the defense. As to the hardship which would be imposed by an injunction,
the judgment would be different in various states. Certain of the state
legislatures have adopted policies tending to encourage business migra-
tion into their states. In such places the courts are very loath to take an
action which would result in hardship to an industry or company. The
"balance of hardship" doctrine would probably also be considered here—
is it a greater hardship to continue the operation under the circumstances
or to enjoin its continuance? Hardship in terms of job loss and loss of
income to the community would be weighed against the noise annoyance.
The likely result of such a case as the example presented is a decree requiring Black to do all in his power to abate the noise problem. Many
measures can be taken to attenuate such industrial noises.

Against Business Rights

In the United States the right to compete with others in a business
venture is protected by the government and the courts. Despite the likelihood that entrance into a particular field by an efficient newcomer may
injure or even eliminate an established concern, such competition is
favored. Usually the result is healthy. The general tendency is to encourage efficiency. The public benefits from the lower consumer costs
of the products manufactured.

Competition, though, leads to its own destruction. If all the less efficient concerns are driven from the field, a monopoly results. Since un-
regulated monopoly is usually associated with excessive prices, inefficient
operation, and other undesirable effects, laws exist to preserve competition.

Since the field of law treating competitive practices is very large, no
attempt will be made to cover the entire field here. Rather, a few of the
more prominent and well-defined business torts will be mentioned.

INDUCING BREACH OF CONTRACT. Although breach of contract is
treated under the law of contracts, inducing another to breach a contract
is a tort. According to the ancient common law, inducing breach of con-

tract was not actionable unless accompanied by violence or fraud. This concept was changed by the case of *Lumley v. Gye* [2] in which an opera singer was induced to breach her contract and work for another. Though no fraud or violence occurred, the court stated that a right of action for inducing breach of contract existed. Since that time the courts have become quite firm in their opposition to inducing a contract breach. It should be noted that merely advising a prospective buyer of the merits or properties of a product is not inducing breach of contract. The end result may be breach of contract, but the seller must have actively persuaded his customer to breach if he is to be justly accused of having a hand in it. Black has a contract to buy parts from the White Screw Machine Products Co. Gray offers to sell Black better parts at a lower cost. Black breaches his contract with White and signs a new contract with Gray. Black has breached a contract, but Gray cannot be said to have induced the breach of contract unless he actively advocated Black's breach.

FALSE DESCRIPTIONS. The presence of false or misleading advertising is often made apparent in our daily lives. Under common law the only remedy afforded a person injured by such advertising was an action for fraud or deceit. Federal and state statutes have modified the common law and the courts have become more liberal in this respect. The Federal Trade Commission Act seeks to prevent deceptive advertising as do many state acts. The Pure Food and Drug Acts, both state and federal, emphasize public protection in the area of food and drugs. Enforcement, though, is a major problem.

When false advertising is used to deprive a competitor of customers, his remedy in court is an injunction and an accounting for profits. To obtain this remedy he must show two things: 1) that his customers were lost to another; and 2) that it was by an unlawful means. Both are often difficult to prove.

Closely akin to false advertising is the disparagement of another's products. The tort resembles libel and is often called *trade libel*. Essentially, the law prevents a person from making false and misleading statements about a competitor's products. In addition to the preventive relief of injunction, damages for lost profits may be obtained if special damages can be shown. For any relief for disparagement to be forthcoming, the plaintiff must prove that:

1. The statements made by defendant were untrue.
2. The false statements were made as fact (rather than opinion).
3. The statements concerned the plaintiff's goods in particular—that is, defendant's statement that his goods were better than those of all competitors would not be disparagement.

---

[2] Ellis & Blackburn 216, 118 Eng. Rep. 749 (1853).

If the plaintiff has a case that will get him into equity jurisdiction and his evidence proves the three requirements above, he can usually get an injunction. To go beyond this and collect damages, the plaintiff must show special damage. He must show not only that his business in general has suffered, but that he has lost specific sales as a result of the disparagement.

Disparagement is a little more difficult than libel to establish. The burdens of proof fall upon the plaintiff where, in libel, the defendant often must bear part of the proof burden. Here plaintiff must prove that the statements made were untrue, whereas in libel the defendant would have the burden of proving statements true.

Just as in libel and slander, certain persons have the privilege of disparagement. If, in the interest of preserving life and health a doctor warns against the use of certain foods or drugs, he does so with privilege. The same is true if a family member warns another member of the same family against using certain things. In each case there is a personal interest to benefit others. Usually consumer's research organizations are extended the privilege of disparagement because of the public benefit from such services.

TRADE MARKS.   Property consists of many intangibles as well as tangibles. The good will attached to a trade mark or a trade name is an example of such intangible property. Trade marks and trade names are like other forms of property in that they can be bought, sold, and used by the owner as he chooses so long as he does not thereby injure someone else.

Trade marks are products of the industrial revolution. When goods were primarily manufactured for local sale, there was little need to identify the manufacturer. With specialization in manufacture and an expanded market, successful advertising required identification of the manufacturer's products in some way. The trade mark resulted.

Trade marks differ from other property in that part of their value stems from their unique design. They identify the products of one manufacturer. The intent of the trade mark is to distinguish the goods of one manufacturer from similar goods of all other manufacturers. Many distinctive marks are successfully used to identify products, but the more common the mark or expression used, the more difficult it is to make a trade mark out of it. It would, for instance, be difficult to obtain a trade mark right in the word "pencil" or "automobile" because of the common meaning of these words. The words Eagle "Chemisealed" and Ford, though, distinguish particular products of specific manufacturers.

Just as the descriptive terms pencil and automobile would be difficult to establish as trade marks, geographical names and family names present problems. The test of any of these three categories when used as a trade mark is whether the name has been used for sufficient time so that it identifies a specific product. A Cincinnati shaper is a product of one manufacturer; similarly a Ford car is the product of another. A company manufacturing, say dental materials, could use either Ford or Cincinnati to identify its products. A new company manufacturing automobiles, though, could not use the Ford name to identify its products, even though the owner might be named Ford. New competitors in a field have a right to identify themselves and the location of the manufacturer, but not in such a way that trade marks or trade names are infringed. If a new company in Cincinnati were to manufacture shapers they could not imprint the name Cincinnati on the side of the shaper in such a way that the prospective purchaser would be confused as to the manufacturer.

It is quite proper and common to use words ordinarily not connected with a description of the product in establishing a trade mark or trade name. The use of "Blue-bird" for a television set, for instance, would be lawful as long as it did not conflict with a similar name and product of another manufacturer. Many companies have made up their own words as trade marks or trade names. This is one of the safest means of identification.

Any trade mark or trade name may be lost if the word, after use, becomes established as a term descriptive of many products. "Aspirin" was once a trade name of only one product; so was "Cellophane."

The right to use a particular name for one's products is established by the first user of the name. A person who subsequently uses such an established name in the sale of competing products may be enjoined from continuing the use of the name. If the use of the mark or name was made intentionally in violation of another's right, damages may be recovered— even to triple damages under the federal law.

The market in which a second user of a trade mark advertises and sells is important in establishing the right to use a particular mark. As long as the second user does not harm the originator's market he is free to use a similar mark. That is, the simultaneous use of similar marks for goods to be sold in strictly local markets several thousand miles apart probably would not be cause for an injunction until the markets actually overlapped.

Common law and equity have established the right to the use of trade marks and trade names as well as penalty for abuse. Federal and state legislation (where statutes have been passed) have modified the established rules only slightly. The federal act, covering goods in interstate commerce, provides that the user of an identifying mark may register the mark. If the mark is used for five years after registration without protest, the one using such mark is presumed to be the first user and the mark is his. Registration of a mark continues for twenty years under the federal law. If a mark is still in use after a twenty year period, it is renewable upon application by the party using it.

TRADE SECRETS.   In the United States a person may obtain a patent [3] to protect certain of his ideas providing they are reduced to pictorial or written form. Many other original and profitable ideas may not be patentable, or the person may not desire to patent his idea for one reason or another. Obtaining a patent gives its owner exclusive right to use of the idea for a certain number of years. The law protects the owner's use of the patented idea against infringement.

An idea does not have to be patented to be protected by the courts— it may be protected as a *trade secret*. The protection is not based on the same reasoning in both patents and trade secrets. Patent protection is based on the government-induced incentive to create, the reward amounting to a protected monopoly. The owner of the patent may use his idea publicly without fear of lawful use of the idea by a competitor. The owner of a trade secret is not protected if a competitor obtains the secret by a lawful means, through study, research, or general observation. The protection afforded the holder of a trade secret is based upon breach of a trust or confidence.

Many things are classed as trade secrets. Customer lists, sources of raw material, ingredients, blue prints, and processes are only a few examples. An engineer for a company is in a position where he is particularly likely to obtain trade secrets. The law does not attempt to prevent persons from benefiting from experience gained while they work for an employer. Rather, the law tries to prevent the employee from passing on to others things which he knew *as secrets* of his employer. The employee must, of course, know that information passed along to him is a trade secret of the company for which he works if use of this knowledge is to be restricted.

A secret is, of course, something other than public knowledge. One who has an idea to sell must first obtain the promise of the prospective buyer to pay for it if he uses it. If the seller neglects to obtain such a promise, revealing his idea before getting a promise of compensation, he has no case if the prospective buyer uses the secret without paying for it. Black, conducting research on metals, finds a heat treatment which vastly improves the tone of bells. Black approaches White, a manufacturer of bells, to sell the idea to him. If White obtains the secret by lawful means without promising payment to Black, Black has no action available against White.

COPYRIGHTS.   A copyright does not preserve the ideas presented when the material is published. What is protected is the language used. Anyone is free to use and publish the ideas as long as the wording used is not identical with that in the previous publication. If a copyright pro-

---

[3] See Chap. 21, "Patents."

tected ideas, there would be little purpose in publishing a book and making public the ideas contained therein.

VENDOR'S AND MANUFACTURER'S TORT LIABILITY. Many products are normally used in such a manner that they would be dangerous if defectively made. For example, a defectively made rotary lawn mower blade could be dangerous in normal use. If such goods actually injure someone while being used properly, the seller may be held liable for the injury. Liability may go back to the manufacturer if it can be shown that he was negligent in making the goods. For recovery, the goods must have been used in the manner in which goods of that nature could be reasonably expected to be used. If the person using the goods uses them in a negligent manner, he cannot recover. It is not necessary for recovery in tort that the user of the goods be the buyer; usually injury resulting from normal use by another is actionable.

The basis for recovery for injury resulting from the use of faulty goods is negligence. It must be shown by the injured party that the defendant (either the seller or manufacturer) owed him a duty of care and that duty was neglected. If the injured party reasonably should have noted the defects, his recovery is barred.

Probably the leading case involving manufacturer's liability is *McPherson v. Buick Motor Co.*[4] In this case a customer purchased an automobile from one of Buick's retail sales outlets. While plaintiff was in his car a wheel suddenly collapsed. The resulting crash severely injured the plaintiff and he brought suit against the manufacturer, pointing out that the wheel had been made of defective wood. Buick's defense was that they bought their wheels from a reputable supplier, thus absolving Buick from responsibility for its defective manufacture. The Appellate Division upheld the plaintiff's position, stating that when a manufacturer makes and sells a product which is likely to be dangerous in normal use if negligently made, he must take care in its manufacture. And this care goes to the inspection of component parts even though they may have been made by another company.

Strict liability attends the sale of food and drugs. Even without proof of negligence, the manufacturer of things to be ingested by human beings may be held liable for damage done by his products.

Negligence

Most tort cases are based on negligence—someone did something negligently, or neglected to do something which he should have done. Black's Law Dictionary defines negligence as: "The omission to do something which a reasonable man, guided by those ordinary considerations

---

[4] 217 N.Y. 382 (1916).

which ordinarily regulate human affairs, would do." Negligence is present if harm could have been foreseen and prevented.

STANDARD OF CARE.   Negligence is the failure to behave in the manner in which a reasonable person would behave under the circumstances. In a tort action the plaintiff usually must show that the defendant owed him a duty of care. There is a general standard as to this duty of care; the standard developed over centuries of growth of the law. In addition, there are many circumstances which tend to modify the standard of care.

The general standard of care, as it has developed, is that care which would be exercised by a *reasonably prudent man* in like circumstances. The average or reasonably prudent man is one possessing normal intelligence, memory, capacity, and skill. He is a man who possesses no handicaps, either physical or mental, which would serve to set him aside as exceptional. It is, of course, easy to talk about an average person, much harder to find one. Most people have something other than average intelligence or average physical structure. Reaction time (for a visual stimulus, for instance) averages somewhere around 0.19 sec., but most people are either slower or faster. Nevertheless, there must be a standard established and then allowance made for the exceptions.

Modifications of the general standard of care are made to treat the exception. The standard of care required of a surgeon in removing an appendix would be considerably more strict than the standard required of a person whose only claim to a knowledge of medicine came from a course in anatomy but, who, because of an emergency, had to attempt the surgery. An engineer works under an exceptional standard of care when he designs or supervises the construction of a machine or structure. On the other end of the scale, people who are deficient mentally or impaired by a physical handicap cannot be held to the same standard as the average or reasonably prudent man.

GROSS NEGLIGENCE.   Doing something which should not be done or neglecting to do something which should be done, thereby causing injury to another, is negligence. When the act is done or neglected intentionally or with reckless disregard for the consequences, it ceases to be the common variety of negligence and becomes *gross* negligence. The likelihood of recovery by the victim is improved considerably if gross negligence can be shown. Contributory negligence by the victim is not a valid defense for the tort-feasor if gross negligence is proved.

ASSUMPTION OF RISK.   People do not always do what is best for them. Occasionally they assume risks for the experience or thrill of the very danger involved. If one is injured or dies as a result of the risk assumed (e.g., death of heart attack during a roller coaster ride) there can be no recovery.

The picture is a little more complicated where a person accepts employment in a risky occupation. For many years the holding of assumption of risk by the employee prevented recovery. Under the Workman's Compensation laws, though, the employer is deprived of this defense.

Assumed risks are only the risks normally and naturally involved with the undertaking. Going back to the roller coaster ride: if the roller coaster suddenly became unsupported, with the resulting crash killing and injuring people, recovery would be quite possible.

A person often assumes a risk (of sorts) when he becomes a volunteer as a "good Samaritan." If aid given to another who is in distress results in further injury to the distressed person, the volunteer is liable for such injury.

CONTRIBUTORY NEGLIGENCE. Assumption of risks ordinarily arises from a contractual situation of some sort, but *contributory* negligence comes from an improvident act of the injured party. It is essentially the lack of ordinary care which should be exercised by the victim under the circumstances. If negligence on the part of both plaintiff and defendant is involved in the case, the question becomes one of *comparative* negligence. Ordinarily contributory negligence bars recovery by the plaintiff. However, under comparative negligence if both parties were negligent and injury to plaintiff would have occurred anyway, recovery may be allowed but diminished by an amount by which plaintiff's neglect contributed to the total damage.

Proximate Cause

The main cause of most tort injuries is usually quite apparent when the facts are established. There are occasions, though, when more than one act or omission may be a cause of the injury. A motorist driving along a highway at night at a lawful speed may be so blinded by oncoming headlights that he will not see an object he is approaching. If he strikes another car in the rear, is he liable or would the person who failed to dim his headlights be liable? The question is one of *proximate* or *substantial cause*. The failure of the oncoming driver to dim his lights would probably be posed as a defense but with a probable lack of success. The driver, upon his failure to see properly, should have slowed down.

A proximate cause of a tort must be of such a nature that it was a substantial factor in the cause of injury. In other words, without the existence of the proximate cause, no tort would have resulted. There must be a direct connection between the cause and the effect; it must be part of a natural and continuous sequence. Black and White are engaged in the electrical repair of an overhead crane. Before starting the work Black turned off the electricity at the switch box. White is working as the ground man of the pair. Gray, requiring electricity for a job he is doing, throws the wrong switch at the box. Black, receiving a shock from the conductor drops a wrench on White, thereby injuring him. The immediate cause of White's injury was the force of the blow from the wrench dropped by Black. The proximate cause was Gray's action in throwing the wrong switch. If the case went to court, the probable result would be a finding for White and against Gray.

Justification

Under certain circumstances tortious conduct may be justified. A person is justified in trespassing upon another's land if he must do so to regain possession of some of his personal property. A person is justified in striking another if he must do so in self-defense. License (permission) may be given to commit an act which is tortious in nature—such as a license to trespass upon the land of another in making a survey. Legal authority may be given which allows the commission of tortious acts— as the authority a policeman may exercise.

While a tort may be justified in some way, the person committing the tort still must restrain himself from going beyond the limits justified. A person defending himself against the attack of another is justified in his defense up to the point where he becomes the aggressor. If he goes beyond the point of justification, he becomes answerable for the injury caused by his acts.

A tort may be justified by proving that the injury was caused by an inevitable accident. It must be shown that defendant did everything reasonable under the circumstances to prevent injury. Accidents resulting from natural causes such as lightning or storms or earthquakes are inevitable accidents.

Discharge of Torts

Discharge of the obligation to pay for damage by a tortious act may occur in several ways. It is apparent that not all causes of action find their way into court. Many are discharged by a simple agreement between the parties concerned that the injured party will not sue. The out-of-court settlement (accord and satisfaction) is a common means of discharge. Rather than take the case to court the tort-feasor agrees to pay the injured party for the damage done, thus avoiding court costs (in both time and money) and, often, lawyers' fees.

If the case goes to a jury a judgment results. The amount of the judgment in a tort case is generally made up of two elements: 1) the out-of-pocket cost to the plaintiff—such as medical cost, loss of wages, and the like, and 2) compensation for pain and suffering if such be involved.

Under common law only the injured party was allowed to bring a tort action. If the injured party died, the cause of action ended. This has been changed by the almost complete adoption of survival statutes, which allow others to sue in the name of the deceased.

Bankruptcy of the tort-feasor may act as a discharge of sorts for tort obligations. If tort action has been instituted or a judgment rendered or the obligation reduced to a contract before the bankruptcy proceedings are begun, the injured party shares in the bankrupt's estate as any other creditor. If no suit has been brought or contract made on the tort obligation, though, the tort-feasor's assets go to meet his obligations to his creditors. The injured party's cause of action remains after bankruptcy and he may elect to sue the tort-feasor for whatever remains.

If prompt action is not taken by the injured party, his cause of action may be lost to time. Most states have a statute of limitations for tort actions—the action must be instituted within so many years after the tortious act or the cause of action dies a legal death. Tort actions undertaken in a court having equity jurisdiction also run the risk of losing out to time. The equity term *laches* indicates a cause in which the plaintiff has "slept on his rights" too long. Stale causes are not popular, the feeling being that if the plaintiff wishes to pursue his cause of action he should do so without undue hesitation.

YELLOW CAB COMPANY OF NASHVILLE v. PEWITT

316 S.W. 2d 17, Tennessee (May 16, 1958)

Felts, Judge.

This was an action by Pewitt against the Yellow Cab Company and the Greyhound Corporation for damages for injuries to his person and to his automobile sustained from being struck by a cab of the former and a bus of the latter at the intersection of the Murfreesboro Road and the Elm Hill Pike in Nashville.

He was driving his car east on the Murfreesboro Road, intending to turn off to his left across its westbound traffic lanes into Elm Hill Pike. He signaled a left turn, cut his front wheels to the left, stopped his car at the center line, and was standing there signaling a left turn, waiting for westbound traffic to pass, when a cab of defendant Cab Company ran into the rear of his car and knocked it across the center line into the westbound traffic lanes, where it was struck by a westbound bus of defendant Greyhound Corporation.

The negligence charged was that the cab driver and the bus driver were each driving at an excessive, reckless, and dangerous rate of speed, not keeping a proper lookout ahead, did not have the vehicle under control, but struck plaintiff's car under the circumstances above stated; and that defendants were thus guilty of joint and concurrent negligence causing the harm sued for. Each of them pleaded not guilty.

The case has been tried twice. On the first trial the jury rendered a verdict for plaintiff against the Cab Company for $125,000 for personal injuries and $950 for property damage, and a verdict in favor of the Greyhound Corporation. Upon the Cab Company's motion, the Trial Judge granted it a new trial, but let the verdict stand and dismissed the case as to the Greyhound Corporation. To this latter action of the court the Cab Company saved a wayside bill of exceptions.

On the second trial there was a verdict for plaintiff against the Cab Company for $70,000 for personal injuries and $1,025 for property damage. The Cab Company moved for a new trial upon grounds of excessiveness of the verdict. The Trial Judge suggested a remittitur of $10,000 [5] which plaintiff accepted, and the judge overruled the Company's motion for a new trial and entered judgment for plaintiff against the Company for $60,000 for personal injuries and $1,025 for property damage.

From this final judgment against it the Cab Company brought the case to this Court by an appeal in the nature of a writ of error, and has assigned errors on the first trial upon the wayside bill of exceptions and errors on the second trial upon the amount of the verdict and judgment.

In such a case, where there are bills of exceptions saved upon successive trials of a case below, the established practice in the appellate court is to have, not a separate hearing on each trial, but one hearing upon the whole record of the case and to determine it by considering each trial separately and in the order in which it occurred.

Upon the first trial the Cab Company has assigned two errors, one upon an instruction given by the judge in his charge to the jury, and the other upon his overruling its motion to set aside the verdict not only as to it but also as to its co-defendant, the Greyhound Corporation, and to grant a new trial as to both of them. The instruction complained of was as follows:

The plaintiff, Pewitt, further contends that the defendant, Yellow Cab Company, is guilty of negligence in that it violated a certain state statute and that such violation was the direct and proximate cause of his alleged injuries. Now, the statute relied upon by the plaintiff, Mr. Pewitt, is Section 2682 (2687) of the Code of Tennessee, Subsection (b) as Follows:
"The driver of a vehicle approaching but not having entered at an intersection shall yield the right-of-way to a vehicle within such intersection in turning therein to the left across the line of travel of such first mentioned vehicle, provided the driver of the vehicle turning to the left, has given a plainly visible signal of his intention to turn."

It is urged that this statute could not here apply to the cab but only to the bus, since the bus was the approaching vehicle whose line of travel would be crossed by plaintiff's car turning left; and that this instruction was error against the Cab Company and in favor of its co-defendant, Greyhound Corporation, for which the Trial Judge should have set aside the verdict and granted a new trial as to both of them.

From the charge it appears that the paragraph here complained of was between two others in which the judge explained plaintiff's theory as to the Greyhound Corporation; and he doubtless intended this paragraph to be a part of such explanation, but by inadvertence used the name "Yellow Cab Company" instead of that of "Greyhound Corporation." In such case, it was counsel's duty

---

[5] Essentially reducing the judgment by $10,000.

to call the inadvertence to the judge's attention and ask him to correct it.

Assuming, however, that this instruction was positive and harmful error against defendant Yellow Cab Company, we think all the harm to it was removed when the Trial Judge set aside the verdict as to it and granted it a new trial; and that it has no interest or right to complain of his action in approving the verdict and dismissing the case to its co-defendant, Greyhound Corporation.

Defendants were charged with concurrent negligence causing plaintiff's injuries. As joint tort-feasors, each was jointly and severally liable for all the damages. Plaintiff could sue either alone, or both together or separately; and it was no concern of one whether the other was sued or not. The applicable principle is stated thus:

> If the concurrent or successive negligence of two persons, combined together, results in an injury to a third person, he may recover damages of either or both, and neither can interpose the defense that the prior or concurrent negligence of the other contributed to the injury. . . .

This principle was applied in the recent case of *Howard v. Haven,* 198 Tenn. 572, 281 S.W. 2d 480, where some, but not all of the wrongdoers were sued, and where on the trial the suit was dismissed as to all except one (a labor union) which was held for all the damages. Responding to objections on this account, Chief Justice Neil, for the Court, said:

> It is not material that Williams was not sued as a joint wrongdoer, as well as other members of the Union; nor is it important that the jury should find against one defendant and in favor of another, since all joint wrongdoers are liable jointly and severally for all damages. Nor can the one against whom the judgment is rendered escape liability on the ground that others were acquitted. . . .

Likewise in *McAmis v. Carlisle,* Tenn. App., 300 S.W. 2d 59, McAmis sued defendants as joint tort-feasors. The Trial Judge dismissed the action as to one of them and the other was adjudged liable for all the damages. It was held that the judgment defendant could not complain as to the dismissal of its co-defendant, Donald P. Rohan, d/b/a Yorktown Insulation Company. Judge Howard, for the Court, said:

> Nor do we find any merit in the defendant's contention that the trial judge committed error in dismissing the case against the defendant Donald P. Rohan, d/b/a Yorktown Insulation Company, because (1) the complaining defendant was not aggrieved thereby, and (2) the dismissal neither added to nor lessened its liability to the plaintiff. . . .

So, in the case before us, defendant Cab Company cannot complain of the dismissal of its co-defendant, since it was not aggrieved nor its liability affected thereby. This is true whether it was one of the joint tort-feasors, as charged, or was the sole wrongdoer, as implied by the jury's verdict acquitting its co-defendant.

Defendant Yellow Cab Company, however, contends that it has the right to complain of a plain error in the charge by which its co-defendant was discharged in this action; and that it is given this right by our third-party statute (T.C.A. sec. 20-120), construed with our statute (T.C.A. sec. 27-310) providing that any party to a judgment may appeal therefrom, the judgment remaining in full force against such parties as do not appeal.

This third-party statute was enacted in 1955 (ch. 145, Acts of 1955) and, while in force at the time this action was brought, it has since been repealed (ch. 33, Acts of 1957). As it then stood, it provided:

Whenever any person sued in a court of law on any cause of action cognizable therein shall deem that some other person, not a party to such suit, is primarily liable to the plaintiff, such person so made a defendant may file a cross-action against such other party, in which case the procedure shall be the same as though such cross-action had been filed against the original plaintiff; provided, however, that the filing of such cross-action shall not operate to delay the right of the original plaintiff to proceed against the original defendant when the cause shall be at issue as to such original defendant.

This says a defendant in an action at law, when he deems some other person "primarily liable to the plaintiff", may file a cross-action against such person, and the procedure shall be the same as if the cross-action had been filed against the plaintiff, though it shall not delay his right to proceed in his suit against defendant.

Whatever this may have meant, it seems to have been merely procedural. It does not appear to have created any new cause of action, or given the defendant any new substantive right. Nor does it appear to have changed the rule of joint and several liability of joint tort-feasors, or the rule of no contribution between them. So, we think this statute did not give defendant Cab Company any right to complain of the dismissal of its co-defendant.

This brings us to the Cab Company's assignment of error on the second trial upon the amount of the verdict. It insists that the verdict is excessive and so excessive as to indicate passion, prejudice and caprice on the part of the jury; and that the judgment, as reduced by remittitur, is still so excessive that a new trial ought to be granted or the judgment reduced by remittitur here.

Plaintiff was 41 years of age, living with his wife and three children in Nashville, able-bodied and in good health. He had no education or training for office or clerical work, but was a mechanic and had been continuously employed by Super Service Freight Lines for six and one-half years, and his regular wages were $103 per week. He was alone in his car on his way to work when the accident happened on the morning of November 11, 1954.

As above stated, he was driving east on the Murfreesboro Road, going to turn off to his left across its westbound traffic lanes into the Elm Hill Pike. He had reached this intersection, stopped at the center line, was standing there signaling a left turn, waiting for westbound traffic to pass, when defendant's cab struck the rear of his car with great force and knocked it across the center line into the westbound traffic lanes where it was struck by the other defendant's bus.

His car was demolished and he was seriously and permanently injured. He was taken from the scene in an ambulance to the hospital, and his surgeon and physician, Dr. Frank Fessey, saw him in the emergency room. He had a large open wound on his face and forehead, extending from the base of his nose up to his hairline. He was bleeding profusely, had lost a lot of blood, was unconscious, in a state of shock, his heart action depressed, and his circulation bad. His skull was exposed in the wound.

He had to be treated for shock before he could be examined. In addition to the wound on his head, he had suffered a concussion of the brain and of the spinal cord; both bones in his left arm were broken, the fracture extending into the wrist; the larger bone below his left knee, the tibia, was fractured, the fracture extending into the joint cavity; and the upper part of the hip joint that fits into the pelvic bone was fractured and dislocated, the back part of it being torn away. The doctors were unable to get the bone back in place by traction, and had to put the patient to sleep in an effort to get the hip joint in place, but it is still out.

He remained unconscious for about two weeks, due to the shock and concussion of the brain and the spinal cord. Though he was unconscious, it was still necessary to put him to sleep to manipulate the hip joint, because that much pain "was liable to throw him back in shock". The dislocated hip joint caused him intense pain in the hip and in the back over a long period, and it was necessary to give him opiates or sedatives for relief.

A plaster of paris cast was put on his body, extending from his arms down to and including his feet. A cast was also placed on his left arm. He remained in the hospital about six weeks or until December 24, 1954, when the doctor permitted him to be taken home in an ambulance and put to bed there. He was later taken back to the hospital for a week or so and brought back home, where he was confined to his bed for several months. Then for some six more months he was able to move about the house on crutches and later had to use a cane until May 1956.

He was wholly disabled from November 1954 to June 1956. Then he was permitted to go back to his former employer, and put upon light work. His loss in wages was $8,908.98, his doctor's bill $1,100, and his bills for hospital and medicines were $949.02, totaling approximately $11,000 of actual out-of-pocket loss, not counting the loss of his automobile. In addition to his pain and suffering, he has permanent injuries causing 25% permanent partial disability.

This case differs from a case of contract or property, where the damage or value is reasonably certain. In a case for personal injuries the law can only say that plaintiff is entitled to reasonable compensation for his bodily injuries, his pain and suffering, his disability, loss of earnings and expenses; it cannot furnish any fixed or certain standard for measuring such damages, but must leave the amount to the judgment of a jury guided by the facts and circumstances of the case. . . .

The amount of damages is primarily for the jury to determine, and next to the jury the most competent person to pass on the matter is the judge who presided at the trial and heard the evidence, and after he has approved the verdict, it is not for us to substitute our judgment for his or the jury's, but it is our duty not to disturb the verdict unless it is plainly so unreasonable as to shock the judicial conscience. . . .

This is especially true where the Trial Judge has suggested a remittitur to reduce the verdict to the amount he thought proper; and such action on his part is entitled to added weight in determining whether the verdict is excessive. . . .

Upon these authorities, and considering the serious and permanent injuries of the plaintiff, and the intense and prolonged pain he suffered and will continue to suffer, together with his permanent disability and loss of wages and expenses, we cannot say that the judgment, as reduced by the remittitur, is unreasonable or so excessive as to require us to grant a new trial or suggest a further remittitur.

For the Cab Company, however, it is urged that this verdict and judgment is "outrageously out of line, even with the largest judgments rendered in this state"; and learned counsel have reviewed and discussed the amounts in a number of our reported cases.

"Just compensation may vary widely in different cases, even when the physical injuries are the same" (*Power Packing Co. v. Borum,* supra); and there is such a wide variation in the amounts, even where the injuries are more or less the same, that no case is of much value as a precedent for another case. . . .

There are, however, a number of cases in this state in which verdicts as large, or even larger, than this verdict, as reduced, have been sustained for comparable injuries or injuries more or less similar to those here involved. . . .

All of the assignments of error are overruled, and the judgment of the Circuit Court is affirmed, and judgment will be entered here for plaintiff against defendant Yellow Cab Company for the amount of the judgment below with interest. The costs of the appeal in error are adjudged against defendant and the surety on its appeal bond.

HICKERSON and SHRIVER, JJ., *concur.*

REVIEW QUESTIONS

1. Name a crime which could not be a tort. Name a tort which could not be a crime.

2. Describe and give an example of each of the three degrees of crimes under United States law.

3. What generally must be proved in a tort action?

4. Black, an engineer, is injured while visiting the White Manufacturing Company. The injury resulted from Black being splattered in the face with hot metal from a die casting machine which he was observing at the time. What complaint and reasoning might be used by Black? What reply would be likely to be used by White?

5. Gray, an engineer, learned a manufacturing process as a trade secret from White, his employer. Later, Gray quit and went to work for Black. Upon hearing that White had sold his plant to Brown, Gray quit Black's employ and went into business for himself, using the trade secret. Brown is suing for an injunction to prevent Gray from using the trade secret, claiming that the secret process was bought with the rest of the business. Gray claims that he has respected the secret he learned from White in not using it until the business was sold by White. Would the court be likely to issue the injunction? Why or why not?

6. The Green Paper Company has responded to an invitation to set up a plant in a particular community. Several millions of dollars were spent for buildings and equipment. However, in the first few months of operation numerous complaints have been lodged and injunctions requested. It is claimed that the odors peculiar to the industry have lowered local property values; that the discharge of "black liquor" and dies in the local stream has eliminated fishing. The plant employs approximately 1,000 people. How would the court be likely to treat the problem?

7. In *Yellow Cab Co. of Nashville v. Pewitt*, show by diagram how the damage to Pewitt occurred.

6 INTRODUCTION TO CONTRACTS

Modern civilization is a world of contracts. Each one of us depends upon them. Every purchase is a contract whether it be a pair of socks or a restaurant meal or a battleship. When you turn on your television set in the evening to watch your favorite program it is done in execution of a contract. The utility company has agreed to furnish electric power and you have agreed to pay for it. You go to work as your part of a contract with your employer. On the job you do what he wants you to do and at the end of a week or a month he pays you for it. It is all part of the same contract. If he pays you by check it is because he has a contract with a bank to safeguard his money and give it out on order. If he pays you in cash, the currency represents a contract between the bearer and the United States Treasury or a Federal Reserve Bank. When you die and are buried, the security of your last resting place may depend on the terms of the contract under which the land was obtained. You can't avoid contracts, even by dying.

Even a simple thing like leaving your watch at the jeweler's for repair involves you and the jeweler in a complicated legal situation. Everything is resolved painlessly when you pick up the watch and pay him for his work a week later. Meantime the relationship between you and the jeweler involved: 1) personal property—the watch, 2) agency (quite likely a clerk represented the owner), 3) the law of bailment (personal property was left with another for repair), 4) insurance law (had the watch been lost), and 5) a contract (his agreement to repair and your agreement to pay for the service).

All contracts are agreements and, morally at least, all agreements are contracts, but moral duties are not always enforceable at law. Suppose that Black accepted Dr. White's invitation to dinner on Tuesday, then forgot the engagement and did not appear. Black broke a social contract and in doing so committed a serious breach of social ethics. But Black's contract was not an enforceable one and, no matter how much pain and suffering Black caused Dr. White, the doctor could not collect damages.

Now, suppose Dr. White is a practicing dentist and Black is a prospective patient. Black calls and makes an appointment with White for 3.00 P.M. Thursday. In breaching this appointment, Black may be breaching a contract. The commodity in which White trades is his time and ability as a dentist. Many jurisdictions would hold that unless White could otherwise gainfully use the time set aside for Black's appointment he could collect for that time. In deciding the case the court would examine business practices in the area and these practices would largely determine the outcome of the case.

If the two parties mentioned above were to enter into an agreement whereby Black agreed to purchase a car from White for $600 such agreement would be a contract, enforceable in a court of law. Each party to the contract would have an action at law available to him if the other failed to perform as agreed.

Definition

The only kind of an agreement which the law recognizes as a contract is defined in Black's Law Dictionary as "a promissory agreement between two or more parties that creates, modifies, or destroys a legal obligation."

Stated even more simply, a contract could be defined as "an agreement enforceable at law."

To be enforceable at law a contract must have certain elements.

Elements of a Valid Contract

Analysis of a valid contract shows it to be made up of five elements, each of which must exist according to law. These five elements are:

1. Agreement
    a. Offer
    b. Acceptance
2. Competent parties
3. Consideration
4. Lawful purpose
5. Form

Each element will be given only a brief introduction here, but will be treated in more detail in the next six chapters.

1. The agreement consists of an offer and an acceptance. The offeror [1] states the terms of the proposed contract. The offeree [2] must accept the terms as they are proposed to him to complete a binding contract between the parties.

2. For a contract to be thoroughly binding it must be made by at least two parties none of whom will be able to avoid his duties under the terms of the contract by pleading as a defense that he was incompetent to contract.

3. Consideration in a contract consists of the money, promises and/or rights given by each party in exchange for the money, promises and/or rights which he receives.

4. The purpose and consideration in the contract must be lawful if the contract is to be capable of enforcement in a court of law. A contract to perform an unlawful act could not be upheld by a state which imposes a penalty for committing the same act.

5. Difficulties in proving the existence, validity, and terms of contracts have brought about the requirement that certain types of contracts be in written form. Failure to comply with this requirement renders such contracts unenforceable by the court.

Stage of Completion

As soon as the offeree expresses his acceptance of the terms offered to him, a contract comes into existence. Usually the contract, at this stage, is *executory*, and as long as something remains to be done by either or both of the parties under the terms of the agreement, it remains so. Even when one of the parties has performed his obligations completely and the other party has not yet completed his performance, the contract is *partially executed*, but in a legal sense, is still executory. After all parties to the contract have performed everything according to the agreement, the contract is *executed*. A contract to purchase a refrigerator is executory when the sales agreement is made between the buyer and the seller; it is partially executed (but legally executory) when the refrigerator is delivered to the buyer, and executed when he has finished paying for it.

Parties

The common or garden variety of contract involves two parties as promisor and promisee. However, it is more difficult to determine the liabilities of the individuals where there are several parties and the individual interests of some have been merged. When there are merged

---

[1] An offeror is the person who makes an offer to someone else.
[2] An offeree is the person to whom an offer is made.

interests the relationships of the parties are treated either as *joint* or *several* or in some cases, as *joint and several.*

Individuals who merge their interests into a joint relationship to form a party to a contract may be thought of as partners in the promises made. If the individuals together agree to "bind themselves" or "covenant" to do a certain thing in the terms of an agreement, it is treated as a joint contract. The liability is much the same as it is in a partnership. That is, should they breach the contract, each is liable for complete performance of the contract until the full value has been satisfied. Black and White agree jointly to hire Gray, a contractor, to make alterations in an existing building and to pay him $1000 for the alterations. If, after completion of the alterations, payment is refused by Black and White, Gray must sue them jointly. If Black cannot pay part of the debt, White may have to pay the entire amount. If either White or Black dies, the survivor will be liable for the full amount of the debt.

Restriction of the liability of individuals merging their interests is a feature of the several contract. If, in the above contract, Black and White had agreed to "bind themselves severally," or "covenant severally" to pay $1000 for the alterations which Gray was to make (restricting themselves to, say, $500 each), the liability of Black and White, each would be limited to the amount stated. In case of default of payment, Gray could take only separate actions against Black and White.

If merging individuals agree to "bind themselves and each of them" or to "covenant for themselves and each of them" the contract is treated as a joint and several contract. If the Black and White contract, above, were joint and several, and Gray found court action necessary, such action could be taken either jointly or severally, but not both ways.

In a *third party beneficiary* contract the purpose of the contract is to benefit a third party. If the intent to benefit the third party is clear from the agreement, he has a right to a court action to enforce those benefits. If, however, the consideration under the contract benefits one of the parties to the contract and only incidentally benefits a third party, no right of court action is available to the third party. Probably the most common example of a third party beneficiary contract is life insurance.

Means of Acceptance

A *unilateral* contract is a promise of a consideration made without receiving a promise of consideration from another party. A common example of the unilateral contract is the reward notice. White publishes a promise of a reward of $100 for the return of his diamond-studded wrist watch. Black, upon finding the watch, claims the reward. To obtain the reward in a legal action, Black must have been aware of the reward promise when he returned the watch.

A bilateral (or reciprocal) contract is a mutual exchange of promises, present consideration, or both, by two or more parties.

Formation of Contracts

Express contracts involve overt agreements by the parties, the terms being expressed between them either orally or in writing, or both.

Implied contracts are based upon implications of fact. If the parties, from their acts or conduct under the circumstances of the transaction, make it a reasonable or necessary assumption that a contract exists between them, it will be held that such a contract does, in fact, exist.

Quasi contracts are contracts implied in law. They are generally based upon the theory of "unjust enrichment"; that it would, in all justice and fairness, be wrong to allow one person to be enriched by another without having to pay for it. It amounts to a legal fiction created by the courts to permit recovery in cases where, in fact, there would be no recovery otherwise. Black contracts orally to pay $20,000 for White's services for a period of eighteen months. The Statute of Frauds [3] requires such a contract to be in writing if it is to be enforceable. In ignorance of this requirement, White performs the services for Black and now sues for payment. White cannot recover on the original contract, but may recover the reasonable value of his services under a quasi contract on the theory that it would be unjust to allow Black to be enriched by White's services without having to pay for them.

Legal Status

Contracts are classified as to legal standing into valid, unenforceable, voidable, and void.

A *valid* contract is an agreement voluntarily made between competent parties, involving lawful consideration, and in whatever form may be prescribed by law for that particular kind of subject matter. It contains all the essential elements previously described.

An *unenforceable* contract is one which creates a duty of performance which may be recognized in a court of law but which, because of some defect in the contract, may not be enforced by the court. A common example of such a contract is one which is not made in accordance with the statute of frauds. An oral contract, which, because of the subject matter, should have been in writing, is an unenforceable contract.

A *voidable* contract is one in which one or both of the parties may avoid the contract if he so desires. Black, a minor, purchases a bicycle

---

[3] See Chapter 12, "Statute of Frauds."

from White, an adult. Black may return the bicycle and demand his money back. White has no similar right of avoidance.

A *void* contract is, strictly speaking, not a contract. A contract to commit a crime is an example of a void contract. The courts ordinarily treat contracts for an unlawful purpose as nullities.

Formality

Contracts may be classified as *formal* and *informal*. Most contracts are informal in nature. Contracts to perform services or surrender ownership of goods to another are usually informal contracts. There are three general types of formal contracts (so called because the contract derives its validity from its form); 1) Sealed Contracts, 2) Recognizances, and 3) Negotiable Instruments.

SEALED CONTRACTS.   Contracts under seal are required by law for certain agreements—for example, transactions involving real property Under common law and in many jurisdictions if a contract is sealed, the court will not inquire as to the presence or absence of consideration The promise of a gift, for instance, will be construed by the courts as a contract if the promise is in writing and signed and sealed by the promisor. In most jurisdiction the life of a sealed instrument is extended (frequently to twenty years). In other words the promisee has a longer time in which to bring suit after breach of the contract by the other party.

RECOGNIZANCE.   A contract which is entered into before a court of record or a magistrate to perform some particular act, such as to appear in court, to keep the peace, or to pay a debt, is a recognizance.

NEGOTIABLE INSTRUMENT.   A negotiable instrument is a contract for the payment of money. It derives its negotiable characteristics from its form. The requirements for a contract to be a negotiable instrument are set forth in the Uniform Negotiable Instruments Act, which has been adopted by the various states. Briefly, these requirements are:

1. In writing and signed.
2. Unconditional promise or order.
3. To pay, in money, an ascertainable amount.
4. On demand or at a fixed or determinable future time.
5. To order or bearer.
6. If there is a drawee, he must be identified.

1. The instrument must be in writing and signed. It is obviously impossible to have an oral negotiable instrument. The writing may be in longhand or printed; a negotiable instrument could be written on wrapping paper. The signature may be written or stamped (as is frequently

the case with payroll checks), and may appear anywhere on the instrument, although it is commonly placed in the lower right-hand corner.

2. It must be an unconditional promise or order. An acknowledgement of an existing debt is not a promise to pay it unless such a promise is made or implied in the instrument. A mere request or authorization is not considered to be a promise or order to pay. The promise or order must not be conditioned upon any future contingency other than the passage of time.

3. It must call for the payment of a definite amount of money in legal tender. The amount to be paid must be fixed or be capable of being determined from the instrument itself. Payment may actually take the form of goods or services, but the instrument must give the holder the right to call for payment in money.

4. It must provide for payment on demand or at a fixed or determinable future time. If no time of payment is stated, the instrument is assumed to be payable on demand. The instrument is also considered to be payable on demand if it is past due. "Determinable" future time may be tied to some event which is certain to take place, but about the only future event certain enough for the courts is death. Very few people have been known to live forever.

5. It must be payable to order or bearer. Certain *words of negotiability* are required in a negotiable instrument. These words are "order" or "bearer." The negotiable instrument must contain one or both of these words used in such manner as to indicate that the maker intended the instrument to be capable of being negotiated. Commonly such phrases as "pay to bearer" and "pay to the order of ——" serve this purpose.

6. It must identify the drawee. If the negotiable instrument calls for payment by a third party (as a check or other bill of exchange), the party who is to make the payment (drawee) must be indicated with reasonable clarity.

PROMISSORY NOTE. Negotiable instruments are of two general types —promissory notes and bills of exchange. A promissory note is a two-party negotiable instrument in the form of a promise by one person to pay money to another. The two parties to the instrument are the maker, who undertakes the obligation stated in the instrument, and the payee, the person to whom the promise is made. The classification of promissory notes includes conditional sales notes, chattel mortgage notes, real estate mortgage notes, and the coupons on coupon bonds.

BILL OF EXCHANGE. The bill of exchange is a three-party negotiable instrument. The drawer (corresponding to the maker of a promissory note) orders a third party (the drawee, usually a bank) to pay money to another party, the payee. Common forms of the bill of exchange include checks, bank drafts, trade acceptances, sight drafts, and time drafts.

No. 1001

Sylvania, Ohio _August 11,_ 19_-_

Pay to the order of ___Jed Black___ $ ___100.00___

One hundred and no/100----------------------------------- Dollars

For __P.O.No.10001__

Bank of Sylvania
Sylvania, Ohio   ___Sam White___

Bill of Exchange (check)

$100.00   Gainesville, Florida _August 11,_____,19_-_

Ninety days _____ after date ___I___ promise to pay to

the order of ___Jed Black___

One hundred and no/100----------------------------------- Dollars

at ___Graytown Bank,Graytown,Florida___

Value received.

No. ___1001___   Due _Nov.9,19-_   ___Sam White___

Promissory Note

NEGOTIATION. A negotiable instrument made payable to "bearer" (bearer paper) is negotiated by delivery alone. If the instrument is made payable to "order" (order paper) it is negotiated by indorsement (the signature of the holder of the instrument) on the back of it. Three general types of indorsement exist for negotiation of negotiable instruments: indorsement in blank; special indorsement; and restrictive indorsement. An indorsement in blank consists of the signature of the payee on the back of the instrument. Such an act makes the instrument, in effect, bearer paper in that it may be further negotiated by nothing more than delivery (anybody can cash it). A special indorsement names the indorsee. "Pay to the order of Jed Black, Sam White" is a special indorsement and must be indorsed by Jed Black if he wants to negotiate it. If the indorsement had read just "Sam White", it would have been an indorsement in blank. A restrictive indorsement restricts future negotiation of the instrument. "Pay to the Graytown Bank for deposit only" is an example of a restrictive indorsement.

A *holder in due course* [4] of a negotiable instrument has certain rights

---

[4] A party other than the original parties to the negotiable instrument, to whom the instrument has been negotiated in good faith and for value and without notice of defect in the instrument.

superior to those of the original parties. He is entitled to payment on the negotiable instrument in spite of certain personal defenses available to the original parties. If, for instance, the maker was induced by fraud to draw up the note, this is no defense against a subsequent holder in due course, although the maker still has his action available against the person who defrauded him. Certain so-called real defenses may, however, be used successfully against a holder in due course. The most prominent of these is forgery. If your signature has been forged, you should not be held liable.

The law of negotiable instruments is a broad and complicated field. For our purposes it is sufficient that we only touch upon that specialized field briefly.

KUENZI v. RADLOFF

34 N.W. 2d 798, 253 Wis. 575 (No. 16, 1948)

ROSENBERRY, Chief Justice.

The plaintiff is licensed under provisions of sec. 101.31 as a professional engineer. He has had 40 years experience in designing buildings, and was licensed in 1932.

In December 1945 the defendants were considering the erection of a building in the city of Waupun to be occupied by bowling alleys and a tavern. The defendant Radloff consulted the plaintiff and as a result of this consultation the plaintiff wrote the following letter:

Dec. 29, 1945

Mr. Harold Radloff
Waupun, Wisconsin
Dear Sir:

I wish to confirm our conversation of some time ago wherein I named you a fee of 3% of the estimated value of the project for services in making up plans for the construction of a proposed bowling alley to be built at Waupun, Wis. This also includes the services of securing a full approval of the Industrial Commission.

Respectfully submitted
Your truly,
Arthur Kuenzi

Accepted
O. A. Krebsbach
H. Radloff

Upon receipt of the signed proposal from the defendants the plaintiff proceeded with the design and preparation of the plans for the proposed building. The defendants from time to time during the preparation of the plans consulted with the plaintiff and his associates and changes were made in accordance with the suggestions made by the defendants. The plans were completed early in March 1946, and were presented to the Industrial Commission and duly approved by it and then promptly delivered to the defendant Radloff.

On April 11, 1946, an application for the allocation of construction materials, to which application was attached a copy of the plans, was made on behalf of Radloff and Krebsbach to the Civilian Production Administration. A second application to the Civilian Production Administration, signed by both defendants, was submitted to the Civilian Production Administration on April 25, 1946. In each of these applications the cost of the structure, including fixtures and building service, is stated to be $80,000. The following statement was made in the application.

"A site has been obtained and an architect engaged for the construction of such building and the plan submitted to a contractor who has in turn ordered various materials for the construction thereof. All of said obligations and commitments made previous to March 26, 1946." Both applications were denied on May 1, 1946.

On April 28, 1946, the plaintiff sent to the defendant Radloff an invoice for $1350 based upon the estimated value of the building of $45,000. The plaintiff also demanded payment from the defendant Krebsbach before the commencement of this action. The plaintiff received the following letter from the defendant Radloff:

Monday morning

Dear Sir:

Sorry to keep you waiting but we are still working through Washington to get started building.

We will make payment to you just as quickly as possible. Milan Nickerson one of our partners dropped out, didn't want his money laying idle so he went into the cement block business.

We are picking out another good partner and will get in touch with you or write when we have the partners lined up.

This Nickerson was undecided for some time and that's why we didn't send you any money, until we have the other party lined up.

How is the steel coming? We will have to pay you and have it on hand when it comes and wait for the permit to start to build. You said in your last letter of quite a while ago that the steel would be here within a couple of weeks.

Yours very truly,
H. Radloff

P.S. Keep this under your hat about a third party and if you should happen to know of someone who has 15 or 20 thousand and wants to put it in a good business of a bowling alley and tavern let us know.

The letter was undated; neither the plaintiff nor the defendant Radloff can fix the date on which it was sent. Evidently it was sent after the receipt of the invoice from the plaintiff because payment is promised.

Upon notice of the denial of their application by the Civilian Production Administration on May 1, 1946, the defendants abandoned the project, and the building for which the plans were prepared has never been erected.

Upon the facts it appears as a matter of law that the plaintiff had a contract with the defendants for the making of plans for the construction of the proposed building; that he proceeded to carry out his part of the contract by preparing the plans, procuring their approval by the Industrial Commission, and delivering them to the defendants; that they were accepted by the defendants and used by them in their efforts to procure a priority order from the Civilian Production Administration.

The defendants seek to defeat the plaintiffs' claim on a number of grounds. We shall first consider the contention of the defendants that there is a defect of parties plaintiff. While there was no allegation in the answer of either defendant to the effect that there was a defect in the parties plaintiff, an attempt was made upon the trial to establish the fact that the plaintiff was a member of a partnership and as such could not maintain an action upon the contract entered into between the plaintiff and the defendants. The contention of the defendants is that the other partners were necessary parties plaintiff. In his testimony the plaintiff made statements to the effect that he had partners and that the arrangement with his associates was a partnership. Other witnesses were called and from the testimony introduced it is clear that whatever arrangement the plaintiff had with other parties who performed some services in connection with the preparation of the plans, they were not partners. Sec. 123.03 (1) defines partnership as follows: "A partnership is an association of two or more persons to carry on as co-owners a business for profit."

It is said in *Montello Granite Co. v. Industrial Commission*, 227 Wis. 170, 278 N.W. 391, that what parties call themselves is not conclusive on the question of the existence of a partnership. In order to constitute an element of partnership the "profits" in which a partner is to share must be real profits, not wages. . . .

It appears from the evidence that the plaintiff makes contracts for the preparation of plans for buildings. That thereafter he is aided by some members of what might be referred to as a panel. Those who assist him are paid for their services whether the plaintiff collects on his contract or not. In this case the plaintiff had already, before the commencement of this action, made some payments. It does not appear that the associates share in the losses or that their approval is necessary for the plaintiff to enter into a contract, nor are they bound to render service to the plaintiff.

Plaintiff was asked if he had an agreement with his associates. He answered: The agreement is if they want anything I am willing to pay them for it. They generally give me a bill for it.

Q. What is the bill based on?
A. Whatever they may base it on. That is up to them.
Q. Well, you pay them whatever they ask for, is that right?
A. That's right.
Q. And that is what you will do in this case, regardless of whether you collect?
A. That's right.

He further stated: "The men that worked on these plans for me or with me have an interest in recovering this money to the extent that they may bill me for it regardless of whether I collect or not."

It is evident that what the plaintiff referred to as a partnership is some kind of a loose association which does not amount to a partnership.

Robert A. Phillips was the person who rendered the most service in the preparation of the plans. He testified: "I'm an independent operator. I don't work for Mr. Kuenzi. I go and come as I please. When I am through with a job

Mr. Kuenzi and I get our heads together and—or he has already arrived at the cost and if that is satisfactory to me I submit my bill to him."

The arrangement between plaintiff and his associates resembles more closely a fee-splitting operation than any other relation. Despite what the plaintiff said, the evidence does not establish a partnership. The necessary elements of a partnership relation are not present in this case. Under the undisputed facts in this case the plaintiff could properly maintain this action against the defendants.

It is also contended that non-licensed persons can not render service to a licensed professional engineer for which he can collect compensation. Sec. 101.31 (7) provides:

(7) Exempt persons. The following persons shall be exempt from registration under the provisions of this section, to wit: . . . (B) an employee of a person holding a certificate of registration in this state who is engaged in the practice of the profession of architecture or of professional engineering . . . provided, such practice does not include responsible charge of architecture or professional engineering practice as defined in this section.

The plaintiff testifies: "In preparing these plans I did some design work but not the actual drawing. Mr. Phillips did the drawing. Mr. Phillips is not licensed as an architect, but under the law he can work on such plans and specifications under a licensed man as an associate. I would have to assume full responsibility. I put in 42 hours actual time on these plans."

It is considered that plaintiff complied with the provisions of the statutes relating to the practice of professional engineering.

It will be observed that the contract provided that the fee should be 3% of the estimated value of the project for services in making up plans for the construction of the proposed bowling alley. The defendants place a great deal of emphasis on the term "estimated value." The defendants made the claim, and the court sustained it, that this meant the value of the building after its erection. In so holding it is considered that the trial court was in error. The basis upon which plaintiffs' fee was to be computed was the estimated value of the project, not of a building which might never be erected. In its opinion the trial court said: "The court refused to allow this testimony as to cost due to the fact that the letter which comprised the basis for the case said value of the project as the basis rather than cost of construction," and excluded all testimony as to cost except that of plaintiff, and restricted the evidence to what the building would be worth upon the site after it was constructed. Just how the value of a building which has never been constructed can be determined does not appear. "Value" in the sense in which the trial court used the term, means market value, what the property could be sold for after the building was erected. Even if that were the test, evidence of cost would be relevant and material, but it is not the test in this case.

It is considered that this case is ruled by *Burroughs v. Joint School District,* 155 Wis. 426, 144 N.W. 977. It was there held that if when the term "value" is applied to a particular contract, or conditions growing out of it, it leads to results clearly not contemplated by the contract read as a whole, and it is susceptible of another meaning which harmonizes with all the provisions of the contract, such other meaning should be given to it. In that case a building con-tract provided for payment in each month of a sum equal to 90% of the value of the work done and material furnished during the preceding month, as assessed by the architects. In that case the word "value" was construed to mean not market but contract value. It is considered that in this case the term "estimated value" of the project referred to the estimated cost of the material and services necessary to complete the building according to the plans. There is not a scintilla of evidence in this case that plaintiff was to wait for his compensation until the completion of the building and an appraisal thereof. The idea that the base upon which the fee was to be computed can be established by the sale of a mythical building owned by a mythical owner, and sold to a mythical buyer, is too elusive and indefinite a standard to apply to practical affairs. So in this case we hold that the term "estimated value of the project" means the estimated cost of completing it.

Upon this point the plaintiff testified as follows: "I made an estimate of $45,000 being the value of this building, which is the same amount as the estimated cost. My estimate was the sum of $45,000 as I recall it. I made a charge against the defendants based on $45,000 and charged 3% of that amount or $1,350."

Two witnesses were called on behalf of the defendant who testified that the value of the completed building would be fifteen to twenty thousand dollars, around twenty thousand dollars. This was on the theory that the building when completed would have to be rebuilt if used for any other purpose than a bowling alley. One witness testified: "You would have quite a job getting $20,000 for it because it would have to be torn apart and fixed over for some-thing else." This sort of evidence comes far short of establishing the estimated value of a project.

Considerable evidence was received in regard to the income tax returns of the plaintiff. So far as we are able to ascertain this evidence was immaterial. Whether the proper income tax returns were made or not is a concern of the Department of Taxation, and has no relevancy on the question raised in this case. It was introduced in an effort to establish that the real plaintiff was a co-partnership, a matter which has already been considered.

It is considered that the plaintiff having fully performed the contract be-tween the parties, including the procurement of the endorsement of the Indus-trial Commission, and defendants having accepted and acted upon the plans as delivered to them, the plaintiff is entitled to compensation on the basis of the lowest estimated cost of the project appearing in evidence, to-wit the sum of $45,000 with interest and costs.

The judgment appealed from is reversed and the cause is remanded with directions to the trial court to enter judgment for the plaintiff as indicated in the opinion.

REVIEW QUESTIONS

1. Name the essential elements of a valid contract. Identify these elements in *Kuenzi v. Radloff*.

2. Draw up a valid negotiable instrument with John Doe as payee and Richard Roe as maker or drawer.

3. Distinguish between a joint contract and a several contract. Give an example of each.

4. What is a quasi contract? Who creates it? For what purpose?

5. Distinguish between unenforceable contracts and voidable contracts. Give an example of each.

6. In reference to *Kuenzi v. Radloff,* what would be the probable effect if the court had found Kuenzi's organization to be a partnership?

7. Consider the word "value." How many ways are there to estimate the value of a project which exists only in the planning stage? How many ways are there to estimate the value of something which has been in existence for a period of time—for example a five year old hydraulic broach?

7 PARTIES

There must be at least two parties to a contract. Two minds must have met in agreement. There may be more than two; in fact the only upper limit is the number of parties it is practicable to identify.

No man may make a contract with himself. Consider Black, who is executor of White's estate and, otherwise, just an ordinary citizen. If Black, as executor of White's estate agrees with Black, as an individual, to do something, no valid contract will result.

The law protects the innocent. The law also offers its protective shield to those who, because of immaturity or for some other reason, are held to be incompetent to contract. The law will not usually, however, offer its protective shield unless it is asked to do so. A person must plead his incapacity to contract to receive the protection available.

Among those whose ability to contract is in some way limited are: infants, married women, insane persons, intoxicated persons, corporations, and professional people. To illustrate the rights and defenses of the parties, infants' contracts will be treated at greater length than the contracts of other incompetent parties.

INFANTS

Age of Infancy

It is probably best to consider first how old a person must become before he is no longer an infant or a minor. According to common law, infancy ends at 0:00 hours on the day before a person's twenty-first birthday. This rather peculiar holding appears to result from the fact that the law will not usually recognize parts of days. Reasoning from this, a person will have reached the last day of his twenty-first year and therefore must be 21 on the day before his twenty-first birthday. The reasoning is faulty, but the practice is well established at common law.

There is no legal adolescence. On one day a person is an infant according to law. On the next day he is an adult. The only status which might come close to a legal adolescence is that of "emancipated minor." Emancipation of a minor takes place when his parents or guardians surrender their rights to care, custody, and earnings of the minor. Such an emancipated minor is usually treated somewhat more sternly by the courts than a non-emancipated minor. Still, according to law, until 20 years and 363 days have passed since a person's birth, he is protected and restricted in his dealings. His ability and knowledge are considered to be less than that of an adult. A day later (at common law) he is vested with the full powers, rights, and responsibilities of an adult.

Statutes in many of the states have altered the age which ends infancy, or have provided for removal of the incapacity under other circumstances. Several states provide that legal majority is reached on a person's eighteenth birthday. In at least one state it is provided that legal majority is reached on the day of one's twenty-first birthday rather than the day before. Many statutes provide that marriage will remove the infant's incapacity. Statutes of various states provide means by which an infant may remove his incapacity by request to a court of law. This is often done when an infant undertakes a business venture.

Partnership

When an adult becomes a partner he stands to lose some or all of his personal fortune as well as his investment in the business if the partnership becomes bankrupt. However, when a minor becomes a partner in a business venture he can lose in bankruptcy only whatever values he has contributed.

Agency

Generally, an agency contract in which a minor is the principal is void (not voidable) at common law. There has been a recent trend, however, to consider such contracts as voidable, which appears to be more logical. Infancy is no bar to acting as an agent for another, however, since it is the principal who is bound rather than the agent. An adult, therefore, may enter into a binding contract with a third person through an infant agent.

Disaffirmance

In general it is true that if one party to a contract is not bound neither is the other. However, the law recognizes certain exceptions to this generality. Infant's contracts form such an exception.

An infant may avoid his obligations under almost any contract. He needs merely to notify the other party of his disaffirmance. The infant's right to disaffirm is his personal right; no one else may disaffirm for him.

If a minor elects to disaffirm a contract which is still completely executory no major problem is involved. In such a situation no formal disaffirmance is really necessary. Since no consideration has changed hands, none needs to be returned. The problems arise when consideration has been given. If a minor disaffirms a contract with an adult after having given the adult his consideration, return of the consideration to the minor is mandatory. The minor must also return whatever consideration he has received if it is possible for him to do so. It has been stated, though, that a minor's right to avoid his contract is a higher right than the adult's right to get back his consideration. If the consideration received by the minor has been demolished or depleted in value in the minor's hands he may still return it and demand his consideration back. Destruction of the subject matter in the minor's hands is only further evidence of his incapacity. Even if the minor cannot return any of the consideration received by him he may still be successful in getting back what he has given. White, a minor, buys a used car from Black Auto Sales. White pays $400 down and agrees to make a series of monthly payments for the car. Two weeks later White loses control of the car while driving it and, upon hitting a tree, the car becomes a total loss. White could return the wreck and get his $400 back. If the car were not insured for theft and White lost it to a thief, White could still disaffirm and get his down payment back.

While the above is representative of the rulings in the majority of courts, a substantial minority require that the minor return the consideration received by him or its equivalent in value in order to disaffirm. The minor still has the right to avoid the contract but the courts will not allow him to harm the other party when he disaffirms. In one such case a minor had taken his car to a garage for repairs. When the repairs were finished he refused to pay for them and demanded his car.[1] In requiring the minor to pay for the repairs the court compared the legal protection offered to minors to a shield. The judge stated, in effect, that while a defensive shield is afforded by law, it is not intended to be used as an offensive weapon. There was nothing defensive in the acts of the minor in this case. In fact, it represents a bald swindle more than it does a contract. If the repairs had amounted to replacement of rod bearings, main bearings, and piston rings, for instance, the inherent difficulty of returning the consideration to the adult would be quite apparent.

---

[1] Egnaczyk v. Rowland, 267 N.Y.S. 14 (1933).

If the infant poses as an adult to get the adult to deal with him, the court may demand that the adult be left unharmed or, at least, that the harm be minimized. It would seem unreasonable to allow an infant to harm another by his deceit and then to protect the infant.

If the subject matter of the infant's contract is something other than real property (real estate) he may disaffirm the contract at any time before he becomes an adult. In addition, the infant has a reasonable period of time after reaching adulthood to disaffirm the contract. He may disaffirm either by an express statement or by implication. If the contract is executory and the infant does nothing about it within a reasonable time it will be implied that he has disaffirmed it.

If the subject matter is real property the infant must wait until he is an adult to disaffirm the contract. There seems to be good reason in distinguishing between real and personal property in infants' contracts. Land sold by the infant will always be there. This is not necessarily true of personal property with which the infant has parted.

Ratification

It is possible for an infant's contract to be ratified as well as disaffirmed. However, to agree to be bound by the terms of his agreement, the infant must wait until he becomes an adult. This seems reasonable in that if an infant, in the eyes of the law, is incapable of making a binding contract, he could hardly be expected to ratify one which he has previously made. Contracts involving both real and personal property must wait until the infant reaches adulthood before they can be ratified. Ratification may be either express or implied. The law merely requires the infant to indicate his intent to be bound if he so elects.

Binding Contracts

Certain contracts made by an infant cannot be avoided by him. Most prominent among such contracts are agreements by which the infant obtains the necessities of life. If a minor is not provided with such things as food, clothing, or lodging by a parent or guardian he may make contracts for them himself. If the minor is already supplied with the necessaries he cannot be made to pay for an additional supply of them. Where payment is enforced by law, it is payment for the reasonable value of the goods or services, thus putting the liability on a quasi-contractual basis.

The goods and services to be considered necessaries vary according to the infant's station in life. Food, clothing, lodging, medical and dental care, vocational education and tools of a trade are necessaries for anyone. But it is conceivable that such things as a car or a university education could be considered as necessaries for an infant from a very wealthy family.

If the infant has reached the minimum age to enter the armed forces, his enlistment agreement is not avoidable at his option. Marriage, although strictly speaking not a contract, cannot be avoided by a minor who is old enough to marry according to the state law.

Parents' Liability

Ordinarily a parent (or guardian) is not liable for an infant's contract unless the parent has been made a party to it. For this reason, many who deal with infants insist that the adult responsible for the infant's welfare also agree to be bound. Only in cases where the parent (or guardian) has failed in his duty to provide the minor with necessaries will the parent be required to pay reasonable value to third parties for needs supplied.

Minor's Torts

There appears to be a rather popular misconception as to parents' and guardians' responsibility for the torts committed by infants in their charge. The usual position taken by the law is that an infant is responsible for his own torts. Unless he is either acting under the parent's direction or should have been restrained by the parent, the parent is free of liability. The law seems reasonable in this. An adult can choose not to contract with a minor and thereby avoid difficulty. However, it is often impossible to avoid tortious harm instigated by a minor (for instance from an object propelled toward one's back). Knowledge that the tort-feasor was a minor rather than an adult doesn't help much after the injury occurs. In a situation in which the occurrence of tortious injury is inevitable, knowing the age of the tort-feasor is of little value to the victim. Therefore, the minor must answer for his torts or crimes himself, even though the courts will allow him to avoid his contracts.

MARRIED WOMEN

Under common law a woman lost her right to contract independently when she married. The man and woman were one after marriage and the husband had all the contract and property rights. However, the various states have adopted statutes which alter this part of the common law. In most states a married woman's right to contract is equal to her husband's. In some states, though, there are still limitations which have not been removed. The wife may not be able to enter into a binding surety contract[2] or to make a contract with her husband once he has become her legal spouse.

Agency

A married woman's right to act as a principal depends entirely upon the state statutes. In most states she has that right. In any state she may act as an agent for another.

A wife may bind her husband through implied agency. Where a husband has previously recognized and paid obligations incurred by his wife, he will be bound to subsequent obligations created by her. The right of a wife to continue to bind her husband continues until such time as the husband gives the third party notice to the contrary. However, where necessaries have been obtained by a married woman her husband will be bound to pay for them regardless of any express or implied authority to do so. The husband's obligation to pay for necessities purchased by his wife does not arise from agency; rather it springs from duty—the husband has a duty to supply his wife with necessary items. If the wife charges the purchase of necessities to her husband, he will have to pay for them not because his wife acted as his agent, but because he owes her a duty of support.

In states where a married woman is restricted in her capacity to contract it is frequently possible to have the court remove the incapacity. When this is done the woman is then known as a "free dealer," and she has unrestricted capacity to contract.

INSANE PERSONS

Early court decisions involving contracts in which one party was insane declared such contracts to be void. The courts argued that there could not be a meeting of minds if one of the minds did not exist legally (*non compos mentis*). Court decisions today usually hold that such contracts are voidable at the option of the insane person when he recovers his sanity.

The law today recognizes that there are various forms and degrees of insanity. An insane person may have sane intervals in which he is capable of contracting. A person may be sane in one or more areas of activity and insane in others. If a contract was made during the person's rational moments providing he had not been adjudged insane, it is binding despite previous or subsequent irrational behavior. Quite obviously, there is some

---

[2] A contract, according to which one person agrees to pay another's debt if the other does not pay it.

difficulty possible in establishing proof of sane behavior of an insane person or the limits of an area of activity in which he is rational. These are questions of fact, though, and usually are left for a jury to decide on the basis of expert testimony of psychiatrists and psychologists.

Consideration

Although it is generally true that courts will not examine the value of the consideration exchanged in a contract, they appear to make an exception where an insane person's contract is involved. If it appears that the other party to the contract took advantage of the insane person's mental condition, the courts will allow the insane person to avoid the contract. If it can be shown that the other party had no knowledge of the insanity of the party with whom he was dealing and did not take advantage of him the courts will usually let the contract stand. This is especially true where the parties cannot be returned to their previous status (contract for services performed, for instance, where the work has been completed).

Necessaries

Insane persons are generally held responsible for contracts which they make for necessaries. Recovery may be obtained usually for the reasonable value of the goods on the basis of quasi contact.

Guardian Appointed

Adjudication of insanity or other improper behavior and appointment of a guardian changes the picture somewhat. When the court appoints a guardian for an insane person, an habitual drunkard, a spendthrift, or an aged person, the guardian is expected to act for his charge in all legal matters. Consequently, a contract entered into by anyone who has a legally appointed guardian is treated as void. An exception exists where the contract is one for necessaries which the guardian should have provided but did not provide.

Torts

Insane persons are liable for their torts in much the same manner as minors. Mere knowledge of impending tortious injury at the hand of an insane person does not give the intended victim much by way of self-help; one could, however, refuse to contract with another who is known to be insane.

INTOXICATED PERSONS

If a person tries to avoid a contract by pleading intoxication he must prove that he was so inebriated that he could not be expected to understand the consequences of his actions in entering into a contract. A minority of the courts take a very dim view of a suit pleading intoxication. They hold that intoxication is a voluntary state and that the person should have had foresight enough to avoid getting drunk.

In most jurisdictions, however, intoxication of a party when he entered into a contract is sufficient ground to allow him to avoid the contract. If, however, an innocent third person would be harmed by avoidance of the contract, the contract usually will be allowed to stand. Even in jurisdictions where intoxication is frowned upon by the courts as a means of avoidance of a contract, it can be used to show susceptibility to fraud. An intoxicated person is, of course, liable for his torts.

CORPORATIONS

State laws provide means whereby an organization may become incorporated. The purpose and scope of its activities are set forth in the organization's articles of incorporation or charter. The corporation is an artificial person and possesses full power to act within the limits of its charter. If a contract of the corporation goes beyond its charter limits, it is an *ultra vires* contract.

Ultra Vires Contracts

There appears to be considerable variation in court decisions in cases involving *ultra vires* contracts. They can, however, be classified in a general way and some general statements can be made about them.

It is probably best to consider ultra vires contracts from the standpoint of the stage of completion of the contract. If an ultra vires contract is entirely executory the courts will not enforce it. If it has been completely executed the courts will leave it alone. Where the contract performance has been completed by one of the parties but not by the other (partially executed), the courts will generally give a remedy. Some courts allow recovery on the contract and others place the remedy on a quasi-contractual basis, holding that the contract itself is void but allowing recovery on the basis of unjust enrichment.

Since a corporation is an artificial person it cannot personally commit a tort. But its agents can. Through the laws of agency, then, a corporation may be held liable for tortious injury to another by one of its employees.

The employee must, of course, be engaged in the corporation's business at the time of the injury. As a general rule the corporation is still liable even though the injury arose from an ultra vires act.

A corporation, as an artificial person, cannot commit crimes involving intent or violence of a personal nature. But there are many other crimes for which it may be held responsible. It is liable for criminal acts of its agents carrying out the business of the corporation, for anti-trust law violation, Bankruptcy Act violation, and numerous other crimes. Anticipated torts or crimes by a corporation may be prevented by an injunction. The penalty for a crime may be a fine or loss of the corporation's right to do business either in a particular state or in the United States.

SPRECHER v. SPRECHER

110 A 2d 509 (Maryland, Jan. 13, 1955)

HENDERSON, Judge.

This appeal is from a decree of the Circuit Court for Washington County setting aside a deed from the appellee to Martin L. Ingram, Trustee, dated July 28, 1950, and a deed of the same date from Ingram, Trustee, to Myron A. Sprecher [3] and Teresa I. Sprecher, as joint tenants,[4] with right of survivorship. The ground of the Chancellor's action was that the deeds were executed while the appellee was still an infant, and were disaffirmed by her within four months after she became of age. The appellant contends that the Chancellor erred in refusing to find that the appellee ratified and confirmed the deeds, or at least failed to seasonably disaffirm them.

The property conveyed, a six-room bungalow and a lot known as 345 S. Cleveland Avenue, in Hagerstown, was purchased as a home by the appellant and her then husband, Frank B. Sprecher, on May 16, 1939. Title was taken in their names as tenants by the entireties.[5] The price was $3750, and they executed a mortgage to the First Federal Savings and Loan Association of Hagerstown in the amount of $2700. The appellee, their daughter, had been born on July 14, 1932, and lived with her parents in the home until they separated on July 12, 1948. At that time the mortgage had been fully paid, out of the husband's wages, or perhaps out of their joint earnings since they were both employed, but on July 29, 1948, a new mortgage was obtained in the amount of $1725. The proceeds were paid to Mrs. Sprecher, who testified that she used the money in part to repay a loan of $1500 made to her by her mother, who resided in the home with them. On September 10, 1948, the par-

---

[3] The wife and mother in this case.

[4] Joint tenancy—an estate in fee-simple, fee-tail, for life, for years, or at will, arising by purchase or grant to two or more persons (Black's Law Dictionary). In this case, apparently, an estate in fee-simple in which the Sprechers joined as owners.

[5] Tenancy by the entirety—It is essentially a "joint tenancy," modified by the common-law theory that husband and wife are one person, and survivorship is the predominant and distinguishing feature of each. (Black's Law Dictionary.)

ents and the daughter, who was then sixteen years of age, met with their attorneys, and it was agreed that the property be deeded unconditionally to the daughter, subject to the mortgage. On the same day the parents executed a deed of the property to trustees, who were in fact their respective attorneys, which recited that the conveyance was "upon trust to convey the same by deed to Teresa I. Sprecher. On September 13, 1948, Frank B. Sprecher filed a bill for divorce against Mrs. Sprecher, and obtained a decree of absolute divorce on October 8, 1948. On November 13, 1948, the trustees executed a deed to the daughter.

The Chancellor found as a fact that at the time of the meeting to discuss a property settlement the father was unwilling that the mother should retain an interest in the property, but agreed that both should convey to the daughter. While the subsequent decree of divorce did not provide for custody, the daughter continued to live with her mother in the property, and the father contributed to the daughter's support until she was eighteen years of age and obtained employment. The Chancellor rejected the appellant's contention that she did not understand that she was parting with her interest in the property, in view of the plain language of the deed and the circumstances of its execution. The validity of these conveyances is not questioned on this appeal, and it is conceded that the infant was competent to take title to the property. . . .

It appears, however, that on June 4, 1949, the appellant took the appellee to the office of the appellant's attorney and had her sign an agreement whereby Myron A. Sprecher agreed to support Teresa I. Sprecher during the period of her infancy and to maintain a home for her and cause her to attend school and high school. Teresa agreed, "as soon as practical after she shall attain the age of eighteen years," to reconvey the home property to Myron and herself as joint tenants. The appellee was sixteen years old at the time. On July 28, 1950, shortly after her eighteenth birthday, there was another visit to the attorney's office, and the execution of a deed to the attorney, as trustee, and a reconveyance to her mother and herself as joint tenants.

The appellee had graduated from high school in June, 1950, secured permanent employment in August, 1950, and thereafter paid her mother $10 a week board. She testified that she also paid three or four hundred dollars on the mortgage out of her earnings, but this was denied by the mother. On January 25, 1951, the appellee married Francis A. Pheil and shortly thereafter moved to her husband's apartment. Mrs. Sprecher continued to live in the property in question, and is still there. In 1952 she obtained an improvement loan on the property in the amount of $747 and spent it on improvements. The daughter was not asked to join in the application for this loan, or to execute any papers in connection therewith. On September 23, 1953, Mrs. Sprecher married Leroy S. Hite, who moved into the property with his child. The appellee became twenty-one years of age on July 14, 1953. In August, 1953, the appellant asked the appellee to join her in placing another mortgage on the property. The appellee declined to do so and a quarrel ensued. In October she consulted an attorney and on November 10, 1953, she wrote a letter to her mother formally disaffirming the deed she had executed on July 28, 1950. Shortly thereafter she filed the present bill.

At common law the period of infancy extended to the age of twenty-one

years in the case of both sexes. . . . By statute in Maryland certain disabili-
ties were removed in the case of females at the age of eighteen. One of the
earliest of these statutes was Chapter 101, Acts of 1798, now codified as Code
1951, Art. 93, sec. 206, requiring a guardian to distribute the personal property of a female ward when she became sixteen (later changed to eighteen).
. . . But in Davis v. Jacquin & Pomerait, 5 Har. & J. 100, it was held that
although she could receive the property she could not dispose of any of it
until she attained the age of twenty-one years. . . . Likewise, in Greenwood
v. Greenwood, 28 Md. 369, 385, it was held that the right of a father to services of a female minor continued until she was twenty-one, despite a statutory
limitation to eighteen in the case of apprenticing a female child. Statutes have
been passed dealing with the right of females between the ages of eighteen and
twenty-one to release dower . . . to make a will . . . to release an executor,
administrator or guardian . . . to release a trustee . . . to execute a release
for any money paid, property delivered or obligation satisfied . . . to make a
deed of trust of her property, real, personal or mixed, provided the same is approved and sanctioned by a court of equity. . . . We do not find any statute
altering the rule stated in Davis v. Jacquin, supra. A conveyance made by an
infant under twenty-one years of age is not void, but is voidable, if disaffirmed,
within a reasonable time after he or she attains the age of twenty-one years.
. . . We think four months is a reasonable time under the circumstances. . . .

The appellant contends that the appellee ratified the deed prior to her disaffirmance. The appellant testified that in August, 1953, the appellee and her
husband, Mr. Pheil, both said they didn't want to live in the property, that the
appellee said: "I don't see why you don't let me sign the property over to you,
my share of it, then you won't have to have anyone else to sign a deed, or a
mortgage, either one." The appellant also testified that the Pheils wanted
$5,000 for their interest; she offered them $3,000, but they would not take it.
The appellant's husband, Mr. Hite, her sister and her brother-in-law testified
that Teresa, in the presence of her husband, made statements in August, 1953,
to the effect that the property belonged to her mother and she did not want it.
The appellee and her husband denied that such statements were made. We
cannot hold that the Chancellor was clearly wrong in finding these statements,
if made, did not amount to ratification under the circumstances. The offer to
convey her share for a consideration did not ripen into an agreement. At most,
it was no more than a tacit recognition of the fact that she had previously conveyed a half interest to her mother. As pointed out by the Chancellor, the
appellee had not then consulted counsel and was unaware of her rights. Indeed, it seems to have been assumed by everyone that the appellee was abso-
lutely bound by her conveyance when she was eighteen years of age. Some of
the authorities hold that ratification may be effective although made in ignorance of one's legal rights. . . . But the rule in Maryland seems to be to the
contrary. . . . In any event, mere acquiescence or inaction, if not long continued, is not enough. All of the authorities seem to recognize that there must
be some positive act or declaration of an unequivocal nature in order to establish ratification. . . . We think the general statements testified to in the instant
case fall short of this.

The appellant also contends that the appellee is barred or estopped from disaffirming her conveyance by the acceptance of benefits during her infancy which she is unable to restore. If we assume, without deciding, that the right of disaffirmance and recovery of the consideration paid may be barred under some circumstances . . . we think the principle cannot properly be invoked in the instant case. The appellee was under no legal or moral duty to reconvey a one-half interest to her mother. The prior conveyance to her had been made as a result of a property settlement between her father and mother, by which the mother was bound. The conveyance was upon a good consideration and in the nature of an advancement that would negative the implication of a resulting trust. . . . Nor did the mother undertake to perform any services for the appellee that she was not legally obligated to render. As the natural guardians of the infant child, she and the father were jointly and severally charged with its support, care, nurture, welfare and education. . . . The appellee graduated from high school before she was eighteen, and thereafter until the time of her marriage in 1951, when she left the home, was employed and paid board to her mother. Until she was eighteen her father contributed to her support. These facts distinguish the case of Wilhelm v. Hardman, 13 Md. 140, where necessaries, in the form of support and education, were supplied by a third party.

The decree appealed from set aside the deeds and declared the property to be the sole and absolute property of Teresa I. Sprecher Pheil, subject to a balance of $408.92 due on the mortgage of $1725, placed on the property July 29, 1948. The Chancellor held that the appellant was not entitled to reimbursement for mortgage payments made by her during the period from that date to March, 1953, when she discontinued making payments. The daughter did not become twenty-one until July 14, 1953. We see no occasion to disagree with the Chancellor's finding. If we assume, without deciding, that reimbursement might be allowed under some circumstances, the appellant here failed to make out a case for equitable relief. . . . The entire proceeds of the mortgage were paid to her and not to the infant, and most of the payments made by the mother were made during the period when the property stood in the name of the daughter alone. The appellee claimed to have made payments of more than $300 in 1951. The daughter is now required to assume payment of the balance due. Moreover, the mother has occupied the premises rent-free during the whole period.

The Chancellor impressed an equitable lien on the property in the amount of $897.28, representing sums expended by the appellant in improvements to the property, and to pay the balance due on her personal loan for that purpose, and required the appellee to pay the costs below. The appellee has not appealed from that part of the decree, so its propriety is not before us. Under all the circumstances, we think the decree appealed from should be affirmed.

Decree affirmed, with costs.

REVIEW QUESTIONS

1. Black, a minor, sells a piece of real estate which he inherited. He spends the money he received rather foolishly and, by the time he reaches adulthood, he is deeply in debt. His creditors force him into bank-

ruptcy. The creditors find that the land Black sold as a minor is quite valuable; in fact, the value is sufficient to pay Black's debts and give him a substantial remainder. Black refuses to disaffirm the sale. May the creditors disaffirm for him? Why or why not?

2. What is meant by an *ultra vires* contract? Give an example of such a contract.

3. How could a married woman's capacity to contract be determined?

4. Gray, a salesman, contracted with Green to sell Green a piece of equipment at a price about ten percent below the usual market price for such equipment. The contract occurred in a local restaurant during an extended lunch hour. Gray had two or three martinis before eating lunch. He now claims he was drunk at the time the contract was made and, on this basis, seeks to avoid the contract. Green has established that all of Gray's other acts (including paying both restaurant tabs) gave no indication that Gray was under alcoholic influence. Is it likely that Gray will be held to his contract? Why or why not?

5. Are contracts for professional services voidable by the recipient of the services if the professional is not licensed? (See Chapter 4.)

6. In the case of *Sprecher v. Sprecher,* what acts by the daughter would have amounted to ratification under the circumstances?

8 AGREEMENT

A contract is an agreement, although not all agreements are contracts. As stated in *Black's Law Dictionary* the agreement is "the coming together in accord of two minds on a given proposition." The agreement consists of an offer and acceptance of that offer.

Offer

An offer contemplates a future action or restraint of action. It is a proposal to make a contract. In general, an offer states two things: what is desired by the offeror, and what the offeror is willing to do in return.

The offer does not have to be a formal statement to be binding upon the offeror. When the intent to offer is conveyed from the offeror to the offeree, an offer occurs. Under certain circumstances the law will consider a series of acts by the parties to be an offer and acceptance of the offer resulting in a binding contract. A man entering a hardware store where he is well known, grasping a shovel marked $5.95, motioning to the owner who is busy with another customer and then leaving the store with the shovel has made an offer to purchase. Though no word was spoken an offer to buy the shovel at the suggested price of $5.95 was made. By allowing the man to leave with the shovel the hardware store owner accepted the offer, resulting in a contract.

Intent

The usual test in both offer and acceptance is the "reasonable man" standard. Would a reasonable man consider the statements and acts of the party to constitute a binding element of the agreement necessary in a contract? The circumstances surrounding the passage of ideas between the parties are examined to determine the existence of serious intent to contract. In the formation of a contract, the meeting of the minds is determined by the expressed intentions of the parties, not by their secret intentions. In one contract case [1] a blacksmith shop owner, enraged at the loss of a harness, stated in his irate ravings about the supposed thief, that he would pay anyone $100 for information leading to the capture of the thief, and an additional $100 for a lawyer to prosecute him. The court held that the language used, under the circumstances, would not show an intention to contract to pay a reward. In another case,[2] Justice Holmes stated "If, without the plaintiff's knowledge, Hodgdon did understand the transaction to be different from that which his words plainly expressed, it is immaterial, as his obligations must be measured by his overt acts."

It is often quite difficult to determine by the language used by the parties whether or not a valid offer and acceptance has occurred. In the haggling, "horse-trading," or bargaining which so often occurs in attempting to reach agreement words are used which, removed from context, sound very much as though the parties had formed a contract. One person may say to another: "I would like to sell my car for $500," or "Would you give me $500 for my car?" These are not offers. The courts, in recognition of business practices, view such statements as solicitations to offer and not as binding offers.

Advertisements

When a serious offer is made, the person making it must be ready for acceptance of his offer. Acceptance would complete the contract and, if the offeror could not perform his contractual obligation, the offeree would have a legal action for damages available against him. For this reason advertising, prices marked on merchandise in stores, and similar publicity are considered by the courts to be mere invitations or inducements to offer to purchase at a suggested price. Expression by a customer of willingness to buy the merchandise at the price stated does not form a contract. The customer, not the store, has made the offer. The store has the right to accept or reject the offer. It is possible that the store, having sold the last of its merchandise in that line, would find performance impossible. If an offer of the price by a customer were to be construed as acceptance and the store could not perform, it would be liable for breach of contract. To hold that the store has made a contract in all cases in which a customer tenders the price of merchandise of his choice would, therefore, be unreasonable.

It is, of course, possible to so word an advertisement that it will consti-

---

[1] Higgins v. Lessig, 49 Ill. App. 459 (1893).
[2] Mansfield v. Hodgdon, 147 Mass. 304, 17 N.E. 544 (1888).

tute an offer. Acceptance by anyone will then form a binding contract. A common example of an advertisement which constitutes an offer is an ad offering a reward. To accept, anyone with knowledge of the advertisement may perform the act required in the ad, thus completing the requirements for a valid unilateral contract.

An advertisement for bids on construction work generally will not constitute an offer. Unless the advertisement specifically states that the lowest bid will be accepted, the advertiser has the right to reject any or all bids submitted.

Continuing Offer

A proposal made to be accepted within a given time is referred to as a continuing offer. When such an offer is based upon consideration it is an "option," a contract in itself. In either case the offeror agrees to bind himself to perform or not to perform certain acts upon acceptance by the offeree, providing only that the offer be accepted within the specified time limit.

Termination of Offer

An offer may end in various ways: by acceptance, by revocation or withdrawal, by rejection, by death of a party, or through passage of time. The expiration of an option supported by consideration, however, ends only upon expiration of the time period for which it is open. It cannot be revoked, and rejection of the offer or death of one of the parties usually does not end its life.

The offeror has the right to revoke his offer at any time before acceptance. The withdrawal must be communicated to the offeree before his acceptance. If the offeree has knowledge of the sale to another of goods offered to him on a continuing offer, he has effective notice of withdrawal of the offer.

Rejection by the offeree ends the offer. The rejection of the offer often takes the form of a qualified acceptance [3] of the offer or a request for modification of the offer. Either act usually amounts to rejection. Mere inquiry as to whether or not the offeror will change his terms, though, does not constitute rejection of the offer.

Generally, the death of either party before acceptance of an offer terminates the offer. It is necessary that there be a meeting of the minds

---

[3] Such as: "I accept your offer providing you will . . . in addition." Such a statement is not acceptance, but in reality, a new offer open now to be accepted. After a statement of this nature the previous offer expires and can no longer be accepted.

for a contract to be formed. If one of the minds is no longer among the living, no contract can occur.

If a time limit is specified in a continuing offer, the offer dies with the expiration of the period of time in which the offer was to remain open. If no time was specified in the offer, the offer will be open for acceptance for a reasonable time, the reasonableness of the time depending upon the subject matter of the offer.

Acceptance

Generally, for a contract between two parties to exist there must have been an acceptance of an offer. However, an offer may be accepted and a contract thus formed only during the life of that offer. With the above-mentioned exception of an option contract, once an offer has been rejected, revoked, or its time has run out, it cannot be accepted. Similarly, once an offer has been accepted, it is impossible for the offeror to withdraw his offer. The rules sound simple, but in actual practice it is often difficult to determine whether or not an acceptance has taken place.

An offer may be accepted only by the person to whom it was made. A person other than the offeree, who obtains the offer, cannot make a valid contract by accepting. The best that he can do is to make a similar offer to the original offeror, for his acceptance.

An offer must be communicated to the offeree by the offeror or his agent to constitute an acceptable offer. Black tells Gray, a friend of both Black and White, of his intent to offer White his TV set for $100. Gray reveals this to White. White cannot at this point create a valid contract with Black by stating his acceptance. He must either wait for Black to communicate the offer to him or offer Black $100 for the TV set. At this point there is no offer to be accepted. Black could have used Gray as his agent, requesting him to give the offer to White. This, then would have constituted a valid offer.

Acceptance of an offer is held to consist of a state of mind which is evidenced by certain acts and/or statements. Mere determination to accept is not sufficient; it must be accompanied by some overt act which reveals that the offeree accepts the offer. Without such an overt act it is impossible for the offeror or the court to determine that the offer has been accepted, despite the offeree's secret intent to accept, unless previous dealings have established the offeree's inactivity as acceptance.

As previously pointed out, the means of communication used by the parties in making the offer and of acceptance of that offer is of little importance in establishing that a contract exists. When the offer and acceptance are made orally the contract is formed as soon as the acceptance is spoken by the offeree. Use, by the parties, of other means of communications may present problems, though. Under certain circumstances it may be difficult to determine when the contract took place, or whether or not there is a contract.

An acceptance must comply in every detail with the offer. Otherwise, no contract will result. The offeror makes the terms of the offer. To accept the offer the offeree must do whatever is required by those terms. If the offer contains a requirement that the acceptance be communicated in a specific manner, any other manner of acceptance used by the offeree will fail to create a contract. Acceptance by the same means as that used by the offeror in communicating his offer is effective as soon as it leaves the control of the offeree if no other means of acceptance was designated. The legal theory behind these holdings is that the offeror has either expressly or tacitly designated a particular means of communication to be used by the parties. Where no particular means of acceptance has been required by the offer, and the acceptance is communicated in a different manner than the offer, the courts are not entirely in accord. Generally, the acceptance is effective as soon as it leaves the control of the offeree. This is particularly true when the public mail is used. The main confusion appears to come from the use of a telegram as a means of acceptance when another means of communication was used for the offer. The nature of an offer made by mail would be likely to be such as to contemplate answer by either mail or telegram. If acceptance by telegram is chosen, the courts are not in accord as to the time when the contract comes into existence. Some hold that acceptance will occur when the telegram leaves control of the offeree; others hold that it is not effective until received by the offeror. It is particularly important to know when acceptance occurs if an attempt is made by the offeror to withdraw his offer.

Time of Revocation

An offer may be withdrawn by the offeror up until the time it is accepted. Withdrawal is never effective until it has been communicated to the offeree. When the negotiations are carried on by mail or telegram a question may arise as to whether or not a contract exists. To point up this difficulty, consider the following example: Black and White have been negotiating by mail as to the sale of White's land. White finally makes an offer which Black finds acceptable and Black sends a letter at 12:00 noon to White accepting the offer. Previous to this, White has sent a letter to Black revoking the offer, but the withdrawal is not received by Black until some time later than noon on the day that he mailed his acceptance. The courts would hold that there is a contract between the parties, and even loss of the letter of acceptance would not change the holding providing only that Black could prove that he had sent such a letter and that the letter constituted acceptance of the contract.

Silence as Acceptance

Unless there is some record of practice or agreement between the parties to the contrary, silence cannot be construed as acceptance. Generally, wording an offer to the effect that "If I do not hear from you, I will consider my offer accepted by you" has no legal effect upon the offeree. Mere silence will not bind him.

Conditions Precedent and Subsequent

If the parties to a contract agree that upon the happening of some future event an obligation will come into existence, the event is known as a condition precedent to the contract. The parties are not bound by the terms of the contract until the occurrence of the event or condition. A contract to build a garage on a certain piece of property providing that a building permit to build the garage can be obtained, is an example of a condition precedent. If no building permit is obtained, neither party is obligated to perform under the contract.

A frequent source of confusion to the engineer learning about contracts is the distinction between a condition precedent and a condition subsequent. A condition subsequent is a condition which, when it occurs, ends an existing contract. Assume, for example, that White's house is insured by the Black Insurance Company. The insurance policy states that if the house is ever left untenanted for a period of 30 days or more, the insurance will no longer be in effect; vacancy of the house for 30 days will terminate the insurance. Such a condition is a condition subsequent. In some jurisdictions the law has taken a more liberal view, holding that, in such a case as the example above, only for the period in which the house remained unoccupied in excess of 30 days would the insurance be terminated. According to this view, if White should resume occupancy after 45 days, the insurance would again be in effect. If the building were destroyed on the 40th day of vacancy, though, White could not recover.

MELVIN v. WEST

107 So. 2d 156 Florida (Oct. 29, 1958)

SEBRING, HAROLD L., Associate Judge.

West, a real estate broker, sued Melvin, a property owner, to recover a real estate commission allegedly earned by West for effecting the sale of certain of Melvin's lands to one Buchanan and his associates. By stipulation, the case was tried before the Circuit Judge without a jury and judgment was for the plaintiff. The defendant has appealed from the judgment assigning as grounds for reversal, that the evidence does not support the judgment and that the evidence shows that a non-licensed employee of the plaintiff actively participated in procuring the listing of the land and in procuring the purchaser and hence the plaintiff is barred by law from recovering a commission.

According to the evidence most favorable to the plaintiff, the defendant owned a piece of land which plaintiff understood contained approximately 3,000 acres and was for sale at $1,100 an acre. The defendant orally listed this property for sale with the plaintiff, and several other brokers, with the specific understanding that "the first registered real estate broker who brought in a check and a signed sales contract would be the successful negotiator of the deal."

About a month after West had been given the listing, he informed Melvin that he had a prospect who was interested in buying the 3,000-acre tract at $1,100 an acre. In reply, Melvin told West that the price was not $1,100 an acre for 3,000 acres, as understood by West, but was $3,500,000 whatever the acreage. West conveyed this information to his prospect, Buchanan, and thereafter and with full knowledge of the fact that the price of the property had been fixed at $3,500,000, West and Buchanan inspected the property. Shortly after viewing the property, West and Buchanan conferred with Melvin about the purchase of the property by Buchanan and two associates, but came to no definite agreement in regard to a sale. A few days after this conference, Buchanan informed West that he had ascertained that the tract did not contain 3,000 acres, as had been originally represented by West to him, but a lesser acreage, and hence that he and his associates were not interested in buying the property at the quoted price of $3,500,000 but might be willing to pay $2,750,000, and that if the counter offer was not acceptable they "would have no further interest in the matter."

After receiving this counter offer from Buchanan, West phoned Melvin and told him that if he was interested "in helping save the deal" he and West should "get (their) heads together and see if (they) could work out some way to work the situation out . . . (that) Mr. Buchanan was still interested in the property as such . . . and if the price and terms could be worked out to (Buchanan's) satisfaction . . . (he, West) felt the deal could still be made."

The evidence shows that a few hours after this conversation, West, Melvin, and L. V. Hart, one of West's employees, met in West's office at Ft. Lauderdale to discuss what might be done to "save the deal." The meeting ended when Melvin decided, with West's approval, that since he and Buchanan "were the two principals in the situation" he, Melvin, would negotiate directly with Buchanan, if some one would drive him to Miami Beach for the purpose. Thereupon Hart, West's employee, agreed to drive Melvin to Miami Beach where Buchanan was found and a conference was held, which began at approximately 5 o'clock in the afternoon and ended about three hours later, when Melvin finally agreed, after much discussion, to reduce the price of the property from $3,500,000 to $2,900,000, provided $600,000 was paid in cash and the remainder was paid in specifically-agreed annual installments, with interest, over a 10-year period; and also agreed that since Buchanan had no authority to commit his associates to the purchase of the property at the new price and terms agreed on at the conference he, Buchanan, might have "until two o'clock the next day (Friday, March 16, 1956) to obtain the permission of (his) associates to continue with the business on the basis of this present agreement and to authorize the contract to be drawn up on this basis"; that in the event permission was obtained "to continue with the business," Buchanan would inform West and would "deposit" with him a check in the sum of $50,000 as a "binder payment"; and that Mr. and Mrs. Melvin would meet with West and Buchanan, at Buchanan's office, on Saturday morning, March 17, 1956, to execute a contract of purchase, to be prepared by West's attorney, which would bind the parties to the sale and purchase of the property.

The evidence is to the effect that on Friday morning, March 16, Buchanan got in touch with his two associates and obtained their permission to purchase the property at the price and terms agreed to by Melvin at the Thursday afternoon conference; that Buchanan called West, at about 11:30 Friday morning, to advise him that he had had "the matter confirmed and . . . had a check available"; and that West immediately phoned the Melvin residence to inform Melvin of what Buchanan had said, but was told by the person answering the phone that Melvin was away from the premises.

West continued calling the Melvin residence at frequent intervals throughout the remainder of the day but was never able to contact Melvin. That night, at a few minutes past midnight, Melvin called West to inform him that on that day he had sold the property to two prospects produced by a real estate salesman, one Harris, who also had an open listing on the property; that a down-payment check had been offered and accepted, and that a sales contract had been executed by seller and buyers and hence that he could not sell the property to Buchanan.

The testimony of plaintiff's witness, Harris, the real estate salesman who produced the purchasers to whom the property was sold, was to the effect that on Thursday, March 15, 1956, he had interested two prospects in buying the property at the price of $3,500,000 that was being asked by Melvin; that around 6 o'clock Thursday evening his prospects had offered him a "binder" check which he had refused because "they had not stepped on the property"; that he thereupon attempted to call Melvin but could not reach him, because he was not at home; that he called Melvin between 8:45 and 9 o'clock on Friday morning to inform him that he had the property sold and to request Melvin to meet with the purchasers so that the transaction might be closed without delay; that he met with Melvin one hour and ten minutes later and introduced him to the purchasers; that Melvin then went with Harris and the purchasers to the property, where a purchase contract was executed and a check was delivered between 2:45 and 3 o'clock in the afternoon.

The evidence shows, that after receiving this information late Friday night, West went to Miami Beach early Saturday morning to inform Buchanan that Melvin had sold the property to another prospect. While there West presented a contract of purchase for Buchanan's signature, had Buchanan execute it, and received from Buchanan his personal check in the sum of $50,000 which was dated March 16, 1956 and was made payable to the order of "Wm. H. West, Realtor." According to West, he accepted the check because "Buchanan felt that there might still be a possibility that Mr. Melvin would change his mind and that the other transaction would not go through . . . (and) he wanted to be on record that he had carried out the part of the deal that he had made with Mr. Melvin."

About thirty days later, after it appeared certain that Melvin had no intention of honoring his oral promise to Buchanan, West returned the check to Buchanan and instituted the present suit to recover a commission for selling the property.

The first question on the appeal is whether the foregoing evidence, when viewed in the light most favorable to the plaintiff, is sufficient to support the judgment rendered in his favor.

Two types of brokerage contracts are generally used in the business of selling real estate. Under the first type, the seller employs a real estate broker to procure a purchaser for the property, and the broker becomes entitled to his commission, when he produces a purchaser who is ready, able and willing to purchase the property upon the terms and conditions fixed by the seller, leaving to the seller the actual closing of the sale. Under the second type, the seller employs a broker to effect a sale of the property, and the broker, to become entitled to his commission, must not only produce a purchaser who is ready, able and willing to purchase the property upon the terms and conditions fixed by the seller but must actually effect the sale, or procure from the purchaser a binding contract of purchase upon the terms and conditions fixed by the seller. . . .

Where a broker employed to effect a sale procures a purchaser who is ready, able and willing to purchase the involved property upon the terms and conditions fixed by the seller and before he can effect the sale or procure a binding contract of purchase the seller defeats the transaction, not because of any fault of the broker or purchaser but solely because he will not or cannot convey title, the broker will be entitled to his commission even though the sale has not been fully completed, if the buyer remains ready, able and willing to purchase the property upon the terms and conditions fixed; the strict terms of the contract between the seller and the broker requiring him to actually complete the sale or procure a binding contract of purchase being deemed, in such case, to have been waived by the seller. . . .

As pointed out in *Hanover Realty Corp. v. Codomo, Fla.*, 95 So. 2d 420, the rule excusing the broker from complete performance where performance has been made impossible by arbitrary acts of the seller is simply an application to brokerage contracts of the rules relating to contracts generally to the effect that "where a party contracts for another to do a certain thing, he thereby impliedly promises that he will himself do nothing to hinder or obstruct that other in doing the agreed thing" and "one who prevents or makes impossible the performance as happening of a condition precedent upon which his liability by the terms of a contract is made to depend cannot avail himself of its nonperformance."

It is vigorously contended by West that when Melvin went to Miami Beach, with West's acquiescence, and made the oral promise to Buchanan to reduce the price of the property from $3,500,000 to $2,900,000 and to allow Buchanan until 2 o'clock the following day to ascertain from his associates whether or not they would be interested in buying the property at the new price, West thereupon became entitled to his commission, because, in contemplation of law, he became "the first broker to sell, because he fully performed his contract to sell when (Melvin) took over and made the oral agreement with Buchanan." To support his contention, he relies upon what is said in *Knowles v. Henderson*, supra, to the effect that where a broker employed to sell property finds a purchaser who is ready, able and willing to buy at terms fixed by the seller, but before he can effect the sale or procure a binding contract of purchase the seller arbitrarily refuses to go through with the transaction, the broker will be entitled to his commission, if the purchaser remains ready, able and willing to buy at the terms fixed.

We fail to see how the facts of the case at bar bring the case within the exception stated in *Knowles v. Henderson*, supra.

It is perfectly plain that when Melvin went to Miami Beach to confer directly with Buchanan and thereby attempt "to save the deal," West had not become entitled to a commission, because he had not found a purchaser who was ready, able and willing to purchase the property at the price demanded by Melvin. Since Buchanan and his associates had flatly refused to buy the property at $3,500,000 and Melvin had rejected Buchanan's counter offer of $2,750,000, the most that can be said for West's legal position at the time was that he had three possible prospects, one of whom was willing to confer further about the property but had no power to bind his associates beyond the counter offer that had already been made and rejected.

It is equally plain that since West had utterly failed to perform his non-exclusive oral contract within the terms of his listing, Melvin was not legally obligated to West to negotiate with Buchanan, at the conference, in any particular manner, except to refrain from entering into an arrangement with West's prospects for the purpose of fraudulently preventing West from earning a commission.

So far as can be ascertained from the record, nothing was said or done by Melvin throughout his conference with Buchanan that could be deemed a waiver of the terms of West's original brokerage contract, or that would have, or could have, prevented West from becoming entitled to a commission if a sale had been made to his prospects at the new purchase price, prior to the time some other broker had effected a sale of the property within the terms of his listing. For, as has already been stated, when the conference ended between Melvin and Buchanan no sale had been made of the property. Melvin had orally promised to reduce the purchase price of the property from $3,500,000 to $2,900,000—which Buchanan had been unable to accept because he had no authority from his associates to do so—and had given Buchanan until 2 o'clock the following afternoon to ascertain from his associates whether or not they were interested in purchasing the property at the reduced purchase price.

Even though the oral promise made by Melvin to extend the time for Buchanan to talk with his associates was not enforceable as an option, since no consideration was given for the promise . . . it is impossible to understand how, if West had been negotiating with Buchanan, in place of Melvin, he could have accomplished as much as, or more than, was accomplished by Melvin in an effort to effectuate a sale. Manifestly, West could not have lawfully made the concession as to price that was made by Melvin, since he had no authority, in respect to price, except to offer the property for sale at $3,500,000 —a figure that had already been presented to Buchanan and rejected by him. And, assuming for the sake of argument, that West had been given authority, prior to the conference, to make concessions in regard to price and terms and thereby bind Melvin, it is plain that Buchanan could not have accepted a single concession on behalf of his associates, since at the time of the conference he had no authority to bind his associates beyond the amount of the counter offer of $2,750,000, that had already been made to, and turned down by, Melvin.

Consequently, when the conference between Melvin and Buchanan ended, West occupied no weaker position, because of anything said or done by Melvin during the conference, than he had occupied prior to that time; indeed, it appears that he was in a stronger position. Before the conference, all that West had were three prospects whom he had been unable to interest in the property at the price and terms fixed by the seller; hence he had failed to fulfill the terms of his non-exclusive contract. After the conference, West not only still had his three prospects but also had, in effect, an oral non-exclusive contract to sell that authorized him to sell the property to Buchanan and his associates for $2,900,-000 (while other brokers had to sell, under the terms of their contracts, for $3,500,000) provided, of course, he actually effected a sale of the property or procured a binding contract of purchase, prior to the time some other broker did, and provided the sale was effected prior to the time the gratuitous offer to sell the property at the reduced price terminated or was lawfully withdrawn by the seller.

As we have already stated, Harris, who also had a non-exclusive contract to sell the property on a "first come first served" basis, called Melvin not later than 9 o'clock on Friday morning March 16, 1956, to inform him that he had sold the property at the fixed price of $3,500,000; and at 10:10 on the same morning Harris introduced his purchasers to Melvin. All of this occurred more than an hour before Buchanan advised West that he and his associates were willing to buy the property and hence occurred prior to the time that West could have notified Melvin of the fact, even if the latter had chosen to remain at home throughout the whole of Friday morning. The contract of sale was executed by the seller and the purchasers produced by Harris at 2:45 or 3:00 o'clock Friday afternoon. As a matter of law, the execution of this contract terminated all non-exclusive brokerage contracts that were then outstanding. . . .

We find nothing in the oral concessions made by Melvin at the conference that could be construed as an agreement on his part to pay West a commission regardless of whether a sale was made in the meantime by some other broker; nor was there anything said or done by Melvin to indicate that Melvin intended to give West an exclusive agency to sell the property at the new price stated at the conference.

We conclude, therefore, that the trial court erred in giving judgment to the plaintiff; and consequently, that the judgment should be reversed and the cause remanded for further proceedings according to law.

The conclusions we have reached make it unnecessary for us to consider the second point urged for reversal by the appellant.

Reversed.

CITY OF HARLAN, IOWA v. DUNCAN PARKING METER CORP.

231 F. 2d 840 April 10, 1956

VAN OOSTERHOUT, Circuit Judge.

This is an appeal by the City of Harlan, hereinafter called City, defendant below, from a judgment in favor of the plaintiff, Duncan Parking Meter Corp., hereinafter called Duncan, for the unpaid balance of the purchase price of parking meters. The case was tried by the court without a jury. The facts are stipulated and undisputed.

The City on Dec. 18, 1951 entered into a written trial lease agreement with Duncan under which the City leased certain parking meters from Duncan with the agreement that when the rentals paid equalled the agreed value of the meters the meters belonged to the City. Duncan completed installing the meters on March 31, 1952. The City approved the installation on the next day. A parking meter ordinance was enacted by the City on April 29, 1952, which ordinance became effective by publication on May 6, 1952. On June 3, 1953, the City notified Duncan by registered letter of its intention to terminate the lease. The termination provision in the lease reads that the Company agrees: "To permit the City to terminate this lease after a trial period of twelve (12) months of actual operation of the meters upon written notice given by the City to the Company at 835 North Wood Street, Chicago 22, Illinois, or at such other address as may hereafter be designated in writing by the Company, during the thirty (30) day period following the expiration of said trial period. The Company will, after receipt of such notice, at its own expense, remove the meters and repair any damage caused by such removal. Time is of the essence of the provisions of this paragraph."

The City's principal defense is that it terminated the lease pursuant to the above quoted termination clause. Duncan asserts that termination was not timely, contending that the period of actual operation contemplated by the termination clause commenced on the date that the installation of the meters was completed, to wit March 31, 1952. No objection is made to the form or manner of giving the notice of termination.

The City contends that the actual operation of the meters could not commence before May 6, 1952, the effective date of the parking meter ordinance. If the City can establish this contention, it has a complete defense to Duncan's present suit as notice of termination was given on June 3, 1953, which, on the basis of the City's interpretation, would be within the thirty day period immediately following the one year trial period. Thus, the decisive question to be determined is the time of commencement of the trial period. This turns on the meaning of the words "actual operation" as used in the termination clause of the contract.

The words "actual" and "operation" are common and well understood words. We do not believe that it can fairly be said that by the use of the words "actual operation" the parties clearly manifested an intent that the trial period should begin when the installation was complete and the meters mechanically operable. If we concede that Duncan's contention as to the construction of the termination clause is a possible construction, we can not deny that the provision in question is reasonably and fairly susceptible of the construction placed on it by the City. The contract being ambiguous, resort must then be had to established rules for the construction of contracts.

The primary rule for the construction of contracts is that the court must if possible ascertain and give effect to the mutual intention of the parties. A contract must be construed as a whole, and the intention of the parties is to be collected from the entire instrument. Individual words or phrases must be considered in connection with the rest of the contract. (Case citations omitted.)

Contracts should be construed in the light of the circumstances surrounding the parties at the time of the execution of the contract. (Case citations omitted.)

What was the purpose of the trial agreement as contemplated by the parties to the contract? It seems reasonably clear that Duncan wanted the City to give the meters a fair trial for a full year before the thirty day period in which the lease could be terminated could commence. The lease required that 50 percent of the meter collection be paid to Duncan. From Duncan's standpoint this would assure it of some substantial revenue for furnishing and installing the meters. In the period of slightly over a year that the meters were in operation Duncan was paid as its 50 percent share of the collections $5,016.47, nearly one-half of the agreed value of the meters which was $10,800. From the City's standpoint the trial period would give the City a fair opportunity to determine the public reaction to the meters, their effectiveness in regulating parking, and their revenue producing possibilities.

It is obvious that no fair or proper trial could be made of the meters without the support of a valid parking meter ordinance. This circumstance was recognized by the parties in section 15 of the lease, wherein the city agrees, "Until the agreed value is paid or this lease is terminated under paragraphs seven (7) or sixteen (16), to enact, maintain and enforce appropriate ordinances relating to the installation, maintenance and operation of these meters and relating to vehicles parking next to them."

The evidence establishes that in the period from March 31 to May 12, 1952, the period between the installation of the meters and the commencement of enforcement of the parking meter ordinance, the meter collections amounted to $52.43, or less than $10 per week. During this period the meters were mechanically capable of operating. However, the public was advised by press and otherwise that the meter ordinance would not be enforced until May 12, 1952, and consequently only a relatively few of the patrons using the parking facilities placed coins in the meters. In contrast, based on the 50% of the meter collections paid to Duncan, it would appear that meter collections during the period in which the ordinance was enforced averaged nearly $200 per week. The substantial difference in results in the meter collections before and after the effective date of the ordinance clearly demonstrates the impossibility of giving the meters a fair trial without an effective ordinance.

The word "operation" is modified by the word "actual." We are convinced that the parties by their contract, construed as a whole, and in the light of the surrounding circumstances, contemplated that before "actual operation" commenced it was a prerequisite that a valid supporting ordinance be enacted.

The lease is drawn on a printed form provided by Duncan, entitled "Duncan Parking Meter Corporation Trial Lease Agreement." Most of its contents are printed. The factual situation here would warrant the application of the rule that in interpreting an ambiguous contract it will be construed most strongly against the party preparing it or employing the words concerning which doubt arises. (Case citations omitted.)

Duncan now complains about the delay by the City in enacting the ordinance and contends that the City cannot now claim advantage of its delay to the detriment of Duncan. The provision of the contract obligating the City to enact the ordinance is hereinabove quoted. The lease sets no specific time for the enactment of the ordinance. Prior to the City's efforts to terminate the lease Duncan made no complaint about the relatively short delay in passing of the ordinance. Paragraph 10 of the lease required the payment of rentals to commence thirty days after installation, and under such provision the first rental payment would have fallen due on May 1. The parties have stipulated: "That the first payment to the plaintiff by the City of Harlan, Iowa, was the sum of $400.00 mailed on June 3, 1952, and no demand for payment was made by the plaintiff prior thereto." Moreover, we feel that a complete answer to Duncan's contention is that Duncan in the present action is not seeking damages for the delay in passing the ordinance. We have serious doubt whether the delay of approximately a month in passing the ordinance was an unreasonable delay, but in any event the passing of the ordinance occurred long after the execution of the lease contract, and we cannot see how the delay in passing the ordinance can have any possible bearing upon the interpretation and construction of the lease agreement.

We conclude that the actual operation of the meters did not commence until May 6, 1952, the effective date of the parking meter ordinance, and that consequently the termination notice given by the City on June 3, 1953, was within the period of thirty days immediately following the trial period of twelve months of actual operation, and hence was timely.

The parties have stipulated that the meters have been removed by the City and placed in storage. Since the City has terminated the lease in accordance with the provisions of the termination clause, it is under no further obligation to Duncan. The meters are the property of Duncan.

The City as an additional defense asserts that it is not liable because the contract contains a provision reading, "The sole obligation of the City hereunder to pay for the meters shall be from the receipts obtained from the operation thereof." Since we have heretofore found for the City on its principal defense, we deem it unnecessary to pass upon the additional defense urged.

The judgment is reversed and this case is remanded with directions to dismiss the action on its merits.

REVIEW QUESTIONS

1. Black is in need of a turret lathe similar to one White is trying to sell. White offers Black the lathe for $2,500. Black: "I accept, providing you will deliver the lathe and have it in my shop tomorrow noon." White: "Sorry, but my truck will not be back in town before tomorrow night." Black: "Then I will pick it up myself, since I need it immediately."

White: "I believe I will wait awhile longer before selling it." Black: "You can't; we made a contract." Was there a contract? Why or why not?

2. On Jan. 3, Gray sends Brown the following offer by first class mail: "I offer you my vertical milling machine in the same condition it was when you last saw it for $4,200. This offer will remain open for your air mail acceptance until Jan. 15." On Jan. 9, at 10.00 a.m., Brown sent the following telegram to Gray: "I accept the offer of your vertical milling machine for $4,200. Am sending truck for it immediately." Is there a contract? Why or why not?

3. In question No. 2, assume that Brown received a withdrawal from Gray at 9:00 a.m., Jan. 9, but, since the original letter stated that the offer was open until Jan. 15, Brown sent an air mail acceptance an hour later. Was there a contract? Why or why not?

4. In question No. 2, assume that Brown's air mail acceptance on Jan. 9 was lost in the mail and not delivered until Jan. 16. Was there a contract? Why or why not?

5. Green required parts for an appliance which he intended to manufacture. He sent out blueprints and specifications to several manufacturers, including the White Manufacturing Company, requesting bids on 100,000 of such parts. White Manufacturing Company submitted what turned out to be the lowest bid. However, the bid was refused. Can White Manufacturing Company demand and get the job on the basis of its bid? Why or why not?

6. Brown lost an expensive watch which had his name engraved on it. He placed an advertisement in a local paper offering a $100 reward for its return. Black found the watch, noticed Brown's name on it, found Brown's address in a telephone book and returned the watch to him. Later, he read the reward notice and demanded the reward. Is he entitled to the $100? Why or why not?

7. Use examples to distinguish between condition precedent and condition subsequent as they apply to contracts.

9 REALITY OF AGREEMENT

In Chapter 8 it was stated that there must be an agreement or meeting of the minds between the contracting parties. The meeting of minds must be voluntary and intentional. It is implied that neither of the parties has been prevented from learning the facts of the proposed contract. In short, the assumption is made that each contracting party has entered into the agreement "with his eyes wide open."

If this is not true about a particular agreement, the contract can be avoided. Although the law will uphold a person's right to contract as part of his freedom, and will hold him, as well as the party with whom he bargains, to the agreement they have made, it would be unjust to do so in the absence of free and voluntary action on his part. Where one person knowingly attempts to take advantage of another, it would not seem right to enforce the attempt.

The rules and principles of contracts are very practical and logical as, of course, they should be when they govern practical events. Probably there is no place where this is better demonstrated than in the handling of cases where agreement by one of the parties is not voluntary and intentional.

Contracts in which the reality of agreement is questionable fall into five general categories: 1) mistake, 2) fraud, 3) innocent misrepresentation, 4) duress, and 5) undue influence. These will be treated separately.

Mistake

Mistake may be either unilateral or mutual. A unilateral mistake is a mistake by one party to a contract as to material circumstances surrounding the transaction. Usually the law will not allow relief for unilateral mistakes. A mutual or bilateral mistake occurs in circumstances in which both of the parties were mistaken as to some material fact. When both are mistaken the law will not bind either of them.

UNILATERAL MISTAKE.   Where the mistake involved results from poor judgment of values or negligence by the injured party, the law will hold the party to his bad bargain. Black sells White a used automatic screw machine for $5,000 and White finds later that a similar machine could have been purchased for $3,500. White can not avoid the contract because of the difference in value.

An agreement in writing binds the parties to the agreement according to the wording on the paper. When a person has signed such an agreement he is held to have understood the terms set forth. If he did not understand it, he should not have signed; or else he should have insisted that any questionable parts be rewritten. If one wishes to enter into a written agreement with another, but disagrees with some of the terms, he has the right to eliminate these terms, get the other party to the contract to agree to the change, and obtain his signature to the change before signing. Most written contracts are either typed or printed. If, in reaching an agreement, one of the parties changes the contract in long hand with knowledge of the other party, this writing will stand in lieu of the printed part with which it is in conflict. Where the terms of a written agreement are capable of two different interpretations, they will be construed most strongly against the person who drew up the contract.

There are certain instances of unilateral mistake in which a party may rescind his contract. If the other party to the contract, in full knowledge of the mistake, took advantage of the situation, the courts will not hold the injured party to his bargain. Such a situation might easily fit into the picture of fraud given below. Certain types of clerical or calculation errors will also allow rescission. If a contractor in preparing a bid on a job, makes a clerical error or a mathematical miscalculation, courts may, in some instances, allow the contract to be avoided. Such judgments have occurred. This is particularly likely if the error is an obvious one and the other party must have known or reasonably suspected an error in the quotation.

MUTUAL MISTAKE.   If both parties to a contract are mistaken as to a material fact regarding the subject matter involved, the courts generally hold the contract to be voidable. There are two possible situations: mistakes as to identity and mistakes as to existence. Black agrees to purchase White's horse for $500. The two parties have two different horses in mind. The courts would say that the minds of the two parties have not met; therefore, no enforceable contract resulted. In the foregoing example, the two parties may have contracted for the sale of the horse at some location away from the place where the horse is kept. If the horse is found to be dead, the contract is not enforceable. The subject matter has ceased to exist (at least in the manner assumed by the parties). The situation would be the same if the parties had agreed to the sale of a house which was discovered to be burned down. The assumed existence of the subject matter was a mutual mistake.

Where the value is something different from that assumed by both of the parties, though, a different view is taken by the law. For instance, Black purchases farmland from White at a reasonable value for farmland. Later, a valuable mineral deposit is discovered in the land. If Black had no prior knowledge of such deposits, the sale stands and it is Black's gain. There are, of course, many instances of purchases of valuable paintings and antiques where the parties involved knew nothing of the true value of the subject matter. Such sales are generally quite valid.

Where the mistake concerns legal rights and duties involved, it is not ground for rescission of the contract. Every person is supposed to be familiar with the law and is charged with that knowledge.

Fraud

There are six basic elements which must be proved to sustain a charge of fraud. There must have been:

1) A false representation
2) of a material fact
3) knowingly made
4) with intent to deceive
5) which was relied upon by the injured party
6) to his detriment.

Let us examine what is meant in the law by each of these elements. The first element may be an outright misstatement, but it does not have to be put into words. It may, instead, take the form of an omission of information which should have been passed along to the injured party. Or it may result from an artful concealment as, for instance, using S.A.E. 90 oil in the crankcase of a car to conceal the need of an overhaul. In certain instances, particularly where a previous relationship of trust has existed between the parties, there may be a duty to speak and reveal all information concerning the subject matter. The courts have been quite general in describing how fraud may arise, preferring not to set up a fixed blockade for the sharp operator to attempt to avoid.

The false representation must be of a material fact which is *not obviously untrue*: For instance, if you are told that a car which you are thinking of buying is in perfect condition when, in truth, it has a broken rear window which anyone could see, the statement would not support an action for fraud. It must be a *material* thing which is falsely represented.

If the seller represented the car mentioned above as having brand-X spark plugs when the spark plugs were really another brand of equivalent make, the statement would hardly be considered material. The representation must falsely represent a *fact*. When you stop to think of it, it may be a little difficult to define what is "fact." Certainly, what you did yesterday and what you are doing today at the present time may be stated as facts. But, aside from a few accepted certainties, it is impossible to state something about the future as fact. In attempting to get Black to buy land from him, White tells Black, "I intend to start a housing development in a section very near this land." If Black buys in reliance upon the statement and no housing development is begun, there might be some question as to whether or not White ever intended to build. Was the statement a statement of fact? It could very well be, since it is a statement of a present intention. If a statement is made in such a way as to express an opinion it is not held to be a statement of fact. Sales talk, puffing, statements that a certain thing is the "best," or is "unsurpassed," or "a good buy" are not fraudulent statements. The only exception to this occurs where a person holds himself out as qualified to give an expert opinion on the subject matter. If a party is injured in reasonable reliance on this opinion, he may be able to recover for fraud. Generally, then, the misrepresentation of material fact must be a false representation, other than opinion, having to do with something past or present. It is not necessary for the statement to be the sole inducement to action by the injured party. It is only necessary that, if he had known the truth, he would not have taken the action which he did take.

Knowledge of the truth or falsity of a statement made does not necessarily determine the existence of fraudulent representation. If the person making the representation knows it to be false, it is fraudulent. However, if the person does not know whether it is true or not, but makes the representation in reckless disregard of the truth to persuade the other party, he may be charged with having made a false representation.

A misrepresentation for the purpose of fraud is normally made with the intent that the party to whom it is made will act upon it. If the other party does not act upon it there is no fraud. If a third party (for whom the representation was not intended) overhears it and acts upon it to his detriment, it is still not fraud. Action must be taken by the person for whom the false representation was intended.

The injured party must have acted in reliance upon the representations made to him. People are assumed by the courts to be reasonable and the courts assume that they will take ordinary precautions when dealing with others. One is charged with the knowledge or experience which anyone in his trade or profession would normally possess. For instance, an auto mechanic should be far less gullible than a lingerie salesman when purchasing a used car. If a person has conducted his own investigation before the agreement, rather than relying upon another's representations, it is far more difficult to sustain a charge of fraud.

The false representations of material fact for the purpose of fraud may be proved; they may have been made with full knowledge of their falsity and with intent to deceive; action may have been taken in reliance upon the misrepresentations, but if no injury resulted there cannot be recovery for fraud. Black is induced by White, as a result of various fraudulent misstatements, to purchase 1000 shares of "Ye Olde Wilde Catte" oil stock at $1.00 per share. Upon discovery that he has been taken, Black sues, but before the case comes up on the court docket the oil company strikes oil and the stock price increases to $2.00 per share. Black quite obviously would not continue the action, but even if he wanted to he couldn't recover damages because he has not been injured.

Several remedies are available to a person who has been defrauded. He may, first of all, wish to continue the contract with full knowledge of the fraud. If the contract has been completed he may wish to retain what he has received and institute a damage action for whatever damage he has suffered. He may rescind the contract, return his consideration, and get back what he has given. If the contract is still executory the defrauded party may merely ignore his obligations under it, relying on his proof of fraud if the other party brings an action against him. In any event, if the defrauded party wishes to bring a court action after he discovers that he has become a victim, he must do so in a reasonable time. If he does not take action within a reasonable length of time, his right to take action will be lost by laches or the statute of limitations.

Innocent Misrepresentation

To point up the distinction between fraud and misrepresentation, consider the following example: Black contracts to buy a hunting dog from White for $200. During the negotiations White tells Black that the dog is three years old. A few months later the dog becomes ill and Black takes him to a veterinarian. After treatment the vet tells Black that he has a fine *ten*-year-old dog. Black has been a victim. He has been defrauded or has been victimized by an innocent misrepresentation. The distinction depends upon the presence or absence of the third and fourth elements of fraud (knowledge and intent). If White was present ten years ago when the dog was born, then he can certainly be charged with knowledge of the dog's age. If White knew the dog's age, the statement to Black indicating that the dog's age was three could have been made only with an intent to deceive Black. If, however, the dog was acquired by White six months ago from Gray who stated the dog's age to be two and a half years, the statement made by White was an innocent misrepresentation (or mistake, in some courts).

Although no fraud results from an innocent misrepresentation, the injured party has the right to rescind his contract, giving up the consideration which he has received. However, in innocent misrepresentation there is no right of tort action for damages as there is in fraud or deceit.

Duress

Duress consists of forcing a person to consent to an agreement through active or threatened violence or injury. The threat must also be accompanied by the apparent means of carrying it out. It places the victim in a state of mind such that he no longer has the ability to exercise his will freely. In the early court decisions, a holding of duress was limited to cases in which the victim's life or freedom was endangered or in which he was threatened with bodily harm. Modern courts take the view that duress is the deprivation of a person's free will; the means of accomplishing this is immaterial as long as unlawful violence is involved. Threat of injury to other persons, even to property, could conceivably be the means employed to gain the desired end. White is an art lover and has a collection of paintings. Black, to obtain White's signature on a promissory note, threatens to cut up one of White's paintings with a pocket knife. This could be duress.

Some courage is inferred by the courts. It must be shown not only that threats or unlawful violence occurred, but that they were sufficient to overcome the person's will. When duress has been used the victim has the right to rescind the contract formed.

Undue Influence

Duress and undue influence are quite alike in at least one respect. When either has been successfully exercised, the free will of the victim has been overcome. The means of accomplishing the objectives are somewhat different. Duress requires violence or a threat of violence. Undue influence results from the use of moral or social coercion, usually arising where a relationship of trust or confidence has been established between two people. Common relationships of this nature where undue influence may arise are those between: husband and wife, parent and child, guardian and ward, doctor and patient, and attorney and client. It also may be suspected where a person is in dire need, or in some physical or mental distress which would put him at the mercy of the other party.

Three things must be proved in undue influence. First, it must be shown that there was a person who, because of a trust relationship, was in position to be influenced. Second, there must be the fact of improper pressure being exerted by the person in the dominant position. Last, there must be roof that the pressure, being sufficient, did influence the victim; that he cted upon it and was injured as a result.

PUGET SOUND NATIONAL BANK v. McMAHON

330 P. 2d 559 Wash. (Oct. 17, 1958)

WEAVER, Justice.

Plaintiff appeals from a judgment dismissing with prejudice her action for escission of an exchange contract of real properties.

In October, 1955, plaintiff conveyed the Liberty Bell Motel, in King County, to the defendants, A. J. and Bernice McMahon, in exchange for the Broadway Cut-off apartments, in Snohomish county. Plaintiff alleged that defendants misrepresented certain observable physical facts; namely, that there was new plumbing throughout the Broadway Cut-off apartments, and that the equipment and furniture were new and in good condition. Plaintiff also alleged that defendants represented that the property produced gross annual earnings of twelve to fourteen thousand dollars, from which a net profit of five to seven hundred dollars a month was realized. These allegations were controverted in the answer and the evidence. The court made no finding of fact as to whether or not the misrepresentations were actually made.

The trial court found, however, that plaintiff, eighty-one years of age, had ". . . many, many years experience in the ownership, management and control of a considerable number of apartment houses, motels, and other rental units"; and that ". . . plaintiff inspected the Broadway Cut-off Apartments on an undetermined number of occasions in the company of the defendant Taylor and also of others. She consulted with counsel and was advised against the proposed exchange. If the plaintiff believed that she was to receive from the operation of the Broadway Cut-off a net income of $500.00 per month, that the plaintiff was a woman of such vast business experience that upon her extensively viewing and examining the premises, it was impossible for her to have any reasonable belief that the net income from the property would be $500.00 per month, and that her viewing and inspecting of these premises and her personal experience in handling large properties would not permit her to say that she believed the property would afford her a net income of $500.00 per month. Further, her experience in handling properties for a number of years and her inspection of these premises were such that she could not close her eyes to the condition of the plumbing or of the furniture in the furnished units of the Broadway Cut-off Apartments. In other words, the court finds that she exchanged these properties with full knowledge of the conditions surrounding and after full and complete inspection of an experienced person. That if any representations were made, the plaintiff had no right to rely thereon, due to her multitude of years of experience in owning and managing rental units and operating properties of similar character."

Plaintiff died pending appeal. Although the Puget Sound National Bank, as

executor of her estate, has been substituted as appellant, we will refer t
plaintiff as the appellant.

It appears from her proposed findings of fact that appellant has no particula
quarrel with the court's findings that she had no right to believe any misrep
resentations that may have been made as to the observable condition of th
plumbing, furniture, and equipment in the apartments.

The gravamen of the appeal is appellant's contention that past net profit
from operation of the apartments is not an observable physical fact; hence, th
finding that she had no right to rely upon defendants' alleged representation o
net earnings is a bare conclusion of law, without any supporting finding of fac
or evidence upon which it can be based.

From these facts, appellant asks us to assume that a representation as to ne
earnings was made, that it was false, that she believed it, and had a right to d
so. Upon this theory, appellant seeks a reversal of the judgment.

This court said in *Marr v. Cook*, 1957, 51 Wash. 2d 338, 340, 318 P. 2d 613
614: "It is unnecessary to discuss again all of the elements which a purchase
must prove to be entitled to recover in an action for fraud in connection with a
sale. They have been set out in almost identical form in a long line of case
beginning with *Webster v. L. Romano Engineering Corp.*, 1934, 178 Wash
118, 34 P. 2d 428, and repeated as recently as *Swanson v. Solomon*, 1957, 5(
Wash. 2d 825, 314 P. 2d 655."

In an action for fraud, the burden is upon plaintiff to prove the existence o
all the essential and necessary elements "that enter into its composition" . .
one of which is that the representee had a right to rely upon the representation
All of the ingredients must be found to exist. The absence of any one of then
is fatal to recovery. To be remedial, a representation must have been of such a
nature and have been made in such circumstances that the injured party had a
right to rely on it. It is this element that the trial court found was missing i*
the instant case.

"The right to rely on representations is inseparably connected with the cor
relative problem of the duty of a representee to use diligence in respect o*
representations made to him". . . .

The trier of the fact is justified in finding that the representee did not have
the right to rely on a representation, if made, if the representee had exper*
knowledge of the general subject matter and was peculiarly fitted and qualified
by knowledge and experience, to evaluate that which he sees and appreciate
the obvious falsity of the claimed representation. . . . A finding that the representation was actually made is not a necessary condition precedent to a
determination that the representee did not have the right to rely upon it; such a
determination assumes, for the purpose of argument, that the representation
was made.

The past net profits from operation of the Broadway Cut-off apartments is
as appellant contends, not an observable physical fact; but the evidence supports the trial court's finding that the combination of the condition and extent
of the apartments, as disclosed by appellant's investigations, with her vast business experience in the ownership and management of such projects, could lead
only to one conclusion: She was not entitled to rely upon representations as to
net profits.

The evidence has failed to establish one of the essential and necessary elements that enters into the composition of fraud, and the judgment must be affirmed.

It is so ordered.

HILL, C. J., and OTT and HUNTER, JJ., concur.

MALLERY, Justice (concurring). The trial court predicated its conclusion that the appellant had no right to rely upon representations, if made, relating to income from the Broadway Cut-off apartments upon the ground that they were in a bad physical condition, which was open to the inspection. It is the condition of the Broadway Cut-off apartments that is the crux of the appeal. Appellant aptly points out that there is no *testimony* on the question. However, the trial court *knew* their condition from its own inspection of the premises. Its conclusion was therefore not speculation.

REVIEW QUESTIONS

1. Black is a representative of a company making data processing machines. He tells the White Manufacturing Company that installation of a punched card system of cost control and rental of his machines to process them will save the company $2,000 per month. As a result, the White Manufacturing Company rents the machines and installs the system. After six months of operation, it is determined that the system is losing money for the company at the rate of $1,000 per month. The White Manufacturing Co. sues Black's employer for the $6,000 so far lost by use of the system and the $12,000 which would have been saved if Black's claim had been correct. White Manufacturing Co. charges fraud. How much can White Manufacturing Co. recover? On what basis?

2. List the six elements required for fraud. Which four of these elements are required for misrepresentation?

3. Gray, an engineer for a manufacturer of die cast parts, inadvertently used the weight of the parts rather than the labor cost in calculating the bid price. As a result the price bid per part was about 25% above the cost of the raw die cast material rather than about 80% above the raw material cost (which would have resulted from proper bid calculation). The manufacturer to whom the bid was submitted immediately accepted. Gray's employer claims that he should be allowed to avoid the contract since an error was made in the calculation. Will the court be likely to uphold the contract or dissolve it?

4. Distinguish between duress and undue influence.

5. Brown, a machine operator in Green's plant, lost his left hand in the course of his employment. Because of the character of the work, the state workmen's compensation laws do not apply. Brown threatens to sue Green for $80,000 for damage to his ability to earn a living for the remainder of his working life. Brown claims, with apparent good reason, that the machine should have been guarded at the point where the injury occurred. Green offers to pay $20,000 to Brown if Brown will drop the court action. Brown agrees and Green pays him $5,000

on account. It soon becomes apparent that this is all Green intends to pay. Brown starts a court action for the remaining $15,000. Green sets up as a defense that the contract resulted from duress. Who would win the court action? Why?

6. In *Puget Sound National Bank v. McMahon,* assume the plaintiff to be an electrical engineer whose only other delving into the real estate field involved the purchase of his home. Purchase of the apartments was to be merely a sideline investment venture in real estate. Would this be likely to change the outcome of the case?

10
CONSIDERATION

Consideration is the price (in terms of money, goods, or services) paid for the thing that the promisor wishes to have. It is required in all contracts. It may take the form of a benefit to one of the parties or a detriment to him or a forbearance by him. Whatever form it takes, if the price is freely bargained by the parties, it is construed by the courts as their consideration.

Essentials of Consideration

There are four general requirements which the consideration given by each party to a contract must meet:

1. The consideration *must have value*. With the lone exception of money given in satisfaction of a debt, the amount of which has been acknowledged by both parties, it is not required that the values exchanged by the parties be equal. Usually it is assumed that in the free play of bargaining, the parties have arrived at what each believes to be a reasonable consideration. If the consideration appears grossly insufficient, this insufficiency may be used to establish a case of fraud or other unreality of agreement, but inequality of value usually is not sufficient proof by itself. Black promises his uncle, White, that he will not smoke until he has attained the age of 22. White, in turn, promises to pay his nephew Black, $5,000 for not smoking until he, Black, is 22. Each consideration has value. Black's consideration is a forbearance of a legal right to smoke before age 22. White's consideration is the $5,000. It may seem to an outsider that $5,000 is a high price to pay for the value received. Or it might seem to others that no price would be sufficient to pay for giving up the use of tobacco. However, in this contract, Black and White set the price—the value of the forbearance *to them* was $5,000. A court would not question their determination of values.

139

2. The consideration *must be legal.* The courts usually will not enforce a contract in which the consideration given by one of the parties to the contract is contrary to an established rule of law. If, in the above example, a statute pronounced the act of smoking before age 22 a crime, Black's forbearance of smoking would not have been valid consideration; legally, he couldn't smoke, anyway. To be valid consideration, Black's forbearance would have to be forbearance of something which he was lawfully entitled to do. Similarly, if it is a positive act which is promised as consideration, the act must be lawful. If Black's consideration had been a promise to use narcotics or, for that matter, not to use them, the contract would not be enforced.

3. The consideration *must be possible* at the time the contract is made. If the impossibility of performance was known to either or both of the parties at the time of the offer and acceptance, the courts ordinarily will not grant damages for non-performance. The situation is a little more difficult, though, if the contract calls for performance which later becomes an impossibility. The subsequent destruction of an item essential to the contract, through no fault of either party, renders performance of the contract impossible and ends the obligations of both parties to the contract. For instance, destruction by fire of a building onto which a builder has contracted to add a room would discharge the contract for the work. It would no longer be possible to add something to the original structure. Impossibility of performance is discussed further in Chapter 14, on Discharge of Contracts.

4. The consideration *must be either present or future.* A present contract cannot be supported by a past consideration. An exception to this may exist in certain instances resembling gifts. For the past consideration to be sufficient to support a contract it must not have been intended as a gift when it was given to the other party. If the past act or forbearance was not intended as a gift, then an unliquidated (undetermined) obligation was created by it. A present promise to pay for such past act or forbearance is binding upon the promisor. The unliquidated obligation has become liquidated. Past relationships between the parties concerning similar acts or forbearance will often be determinative of their intent either to make a gift or to create an unliquidated obligation. But valid past considerations form a rather minor exception to the rule.

Contracts generally look to the future. Exchange of valuable, lawful, and possible present or future consideration for similar consideration has virtually unquestioned standing at law. If Green orders 10,000 die castings of a particular design, to be delivered by August 31, and agrees to pay for them, both considerations are to take place in the future. Either this or present payment for future delivery sets up an obligation which the other party must carry out or risk action for breach of contract.

Seal as Consideration

In ancient times an impression was made on a piece of clay or (later) a blob of wax attached to a document. The seal took the place of the signature. Later certain documents of exceptional importance or high security were required to be sealed. Under the common law the seal came to have such significance that the courts would not inquire as to whether or not any consideration existed for a contract if the contract bore a seal. The formality of the act of sealing the document made it legal and binding. Today in the United States a great deal depends upon the jurisdiction in which the contract is brought into court. In some states the effect of the seal is similar to that under common law. Generally, in those states where the seal is recognized, the effect is to lengthen the time of obligation for performance under a contract and remove any question of consideration. In many states documents concerning transactions in real property must be sealed by the parties to the transaction. Black promises in a letter to White to make White a gift of $1,000. At this point White has nothing since the present promise of a future gift either orally or in writing is worthless if it is unsupported by consideration from the other party. However, if the promise of the $1,000 had been sealed, it would be supported as a contract in many states.

In private transactions the seal is no longer an impression made on wax. Now it is comprised of the word "seal" or the letters L.S. (locus sigilli, or location of the seal), or any other notation intended by the parties as a seal, following the signature.

Theories of Consideration

Certain theories of consideration form the basis of court opinions in contract cases. A primary one is the bargain theory which, in effect, holds that the parties have bargained in good faith for the consideration to be received. Each of the parties has determined the value of the consideration to him. If the agreement to exchange consideration was voluntary and intentional the values involved, regardless of how dissimilar they may appear, are not subject to question.

Another theory is the "injurious reliance" theory which is based on the principle of estoppel. Where one of two innocent parties must suffer, he whose act occasioned the loss must bear that loss. Gray promises to contribute $10,000 to a charitable organization's building fund. In reliance upon Gray's promise, the charitable organization contracts with others for a structure to be built. Gray's promise to contribute will be enforced in the courts if this is necessary to pay for the building.

A third theory is that of moral consideration. The moral consideration theory is generally confined to those cases in which a pre-existing debt has been discharged by law and the debtor, subsequent to the termination of his obligation to pay the debt, agrees to pay it anyway. The basis of the argument here is that though the *obligation to pay* the original debt has been relieved by law, the debt still exists. The debtor, in reaffirming this obligation to pay his debt has created for himself a moral obligation to pay. This moral obligation is sufficient consideration to sustain court action to recover on the debt. Cases of this nature often arise from bankruptcy proceedings and creditor's compositions.[1]

Mutuality

Generally, both parties must be bound to a valid bilateral contract or neither is bound. The promises constituting consideration in a contract must be irrevocable. If either party to a contract can escape his duty under it as he so desires, there is no contract between the parties. The contract must fail for lack of consideration and mutuality. In one case,[2] a contract was made to sell and deliver 10,000 barrels of oil. The price per barrel was stipulated in the contract. Delivery, though, was to take place in such quantities per week as the buyer might desire. Payment was to be made upon delivery. No minimum quantity per week was agreed upon; the buyer apparently could, if he so chose, refuse delivery of any oil each week during the life of the contract. The buyer, in other words, really had not agreed to do anything as his part of the agreement. A contract may be sustained, however, if the quantities are ascertainable with reasonable certainty. If, in the above case, the purchases had been tied to the buyer's needs, the contract probably would have been upheld. In a case similar to the one above,[3] the contract was to furnish coal for the steamers of a certain line. Although, in one sense, the quantity was indefinite, it was limited to the requirements of the steamers. Since the quantity was ascertainable at the end of any period of time, the contract was sustained.

Forbearance

Forbearance or a promise to forbear or give up a legal right is sufficient consideration to support a contract. One instance of forbearance occurs when one party gives up his right to sue another. A person has a legal right to resort to the courts to have his claim adjusted. For such forbearance to sue to constitute consideration, the claim upon which the

---

[1] See Chapt. 14, "Discharge," for bankruptcy and creditor's compositions.
[2] American Co. v. Kirk, 68 F. 791, 15 C.C.A. 540.
[3] Wells v. Alexander, 130 N.Y. 642.

uit would be based must be a valid one. The party who forbears must have at least reasonable grounds upon which to bring court action. If the claim is reasonably doubtful, or would be a virtual certainty in favor of the plaintiff, the promise to forbear is sufficient consideration. In a small minority of cases, some courts have extended this reasoning even further allowing as sufficient consideration forbearance to sue when only the party who would be plaintiff thinks, in good faith, that he has a valid claim. However, if a person brings court action maliciously (e.g. only as a nuisance to the defendant), he renders himself liable for tort action. Forbearance of court action in such a circumstance does not constitute consideration upon which a contract may be based.

One type of case in which forbearance of court action often occurs is that in which the amount of a debt is in dispute. If, in a compromise, the disputing parties agree upon the amount to be paid, this agreement is binding upon them. Each has given up his right to have the court decide as to the correct amount of the debt. It would be a different situation if the amount of debt were certain and due or past due. When such is the case, the acceptance by the creditor of a lesser sum does not discharge the complete debt. The creditor may bring an action at law later for the remainder of the debt.

Time has value. Pre-payment of a lesser sum may, by agreement, discharge a fixed debt. Also, payment by means other than money may discharge a liquidated debt. The court ordinarily will not examine the value of goods or services tendered and accepted in payment of a fixed debt.

Legal Detriment

Consideration for a contract may consist of a legal detriment. Legal detriment means that the promisor agrees, in return for the consideration given by the other party, either to give up some right which is lawfully his or to do something which he might otherwise lawfully avoid doing. Agreeing, for consideration in the form of a discount in price, to restrict this year's purchases of raw material requirements to a particular source, is an example of legal detriment. A company agreeing to so restrict its purchases would be giving up its legal right to choose to purchase its raw materials from any other source for the years' time.

Existing Duty

The law allows you to collect only once for what you do. If a person already has a duty to perform in a certain way, he cannot use that same performance as consideration in another contract. For example—the house next door is on fire. The city firemen are attempting to extinguish the blaze. An offer by you to pay a fireman $500 extra to spray water on your roof to keep the fire from spreading to your house would not create a valid contract upon acceptance. The fireman is already paid for doing everything in his power to keep the fire from spreading. He can give nothing that he is not already paid to do in exchange for the $500.

An exception exists to the rule that consideration must not be something which one already is bound to do. Assumptions are usually made before entering into a contract. The actual conditions may not exist in the manner assumed by the parties. Where this is found to be true and the performance of the resulting contract is thereby made more difficult, the added difficulty may be treated as consideration to support an addition to the contract price. If, under these conditions, the parties agree to added compensation, the courts will often enforce the added payment. The additional difficulty, though, to be enforceable, must be something which could not be anticipated by normal foresight. Black, a contractor, agrees to build a structure for White for a fixed price. Test borings have shown the soil to be mainly clay. However, upon excavation for the foundation and basement it is discovered that the test borings somehow missed a substantial rock layer. If White agrees to pay extra because of the necessity of excavating through the rock, he will be held to his agreement. This is true even though the original contract did not require White to make such payment if unusual conditions were met. White might successfully refuse to pay extra, but once he has agreed to pay, he will be bound. If the price increase agreement had been based upon something normally considered foreseeable there would have been no lawful consideration. Such contingencies could be anticipated and covered in the original price agreement; these would not support added consideration.

MEADOWS v. RADIO INDUSTRIES

222 F. 2d 347, U.S.C.A., May 6, 1955 (Ill.)

LINDLEY, C.J.

Plaintiff sued in the District Court to recover damages occasioned, as he averred, by defendant's wrongful termination of his contract of employment. At the conclusion of his evidence, the court directed the jury to return a verdict for defendant and entered judgment against plaintiff. On appeal plaintiff contends that the court erred in directing a verdict.

On the 30th day of April, 1950, plaintiff was, and for some years prior thereto had been a mechanical engineer residing in Wisconsin. In response to defendant's advertisement, he contacted defendant's officials and, as averred by plaintiff, the parties entered into a parol contract whereby he was to under ake production of resistors for defendant in its plant in Chicago. The agreement rests entirely upon the parol discussion between the parties, as related by the plaintiff. He testified that the parties made "an agreement and I (the plaintiff) was supposed to go with them," first, to make cold molding resistors, and then, to develop hot molding devices, for which defendant agreed to pay him $10,000 a year, and one-half of 1% of the gross sales; that he was supposed to be plant manager in exclusive charge of operating that part of the enterprise relating to resistors; that he went to work with this understanding without any further contract, was paid $190 per week and stayed with the company for almost a year, when he was discharged. In the meantime he had twice threatened to quit, but on each occasion had been prevailed upon to stay. He admitted that nothing was said about whether his employment was to be for a year, two years, or for life. He "supposed" it was permanent. There is nothing in his testimony to indicate that he ever promised to remain in employment for any certain period of time, or that there was any definite term of employment. He expressly denied that he was hired for a year and said that he did not at any time before he began working for defendant, offer to work for one year, two years, three years, or "whatever the time was."

His work during this period was largely the designing and building of machinery for the purpose of making hot mold resistors. At the time of his discharge, defendant told him the company was no longer going to continue the process that he claimed to have designed, and, upon his inquiry as to what that meant with regard to him, he was told "you're through." The evidence discloses that the defendant engaged in the resistor business for a few months after terminating plaintiff's employment and then dropped out of it entirely. On appeal plaintiff insists that his employment was to run until the resistor campaign had been fully launched and as long as it continued in operation.

It is apparent, therefore, that, if there was a contract of any character, it was of nebulous substance only, with absolute uncertainty as to duration and with lack of mutuality of promises upon the parts of the respective parties. In that situation, it seems clear (first), that the contract was void for lack of mutuality, and (second), that if any agreement existed it was one wholly at will, which either party had the right to terminate at any time.

It is well settled in Illinois that whenever a contract is incapable of being enforced against one party, that party is equally incapable of enforcing it against the other. . . . As the Appellate Court has said, in *Farmers' Educational & Cooperative Union v. Langlois*, 258 Ill. App. 522 at page 534: "Mutuality of obligation means that both parties are bound or neither (is) bound. In other words there must be a valid consideration. Without a valid consideration, a contract cannot be enforced in law or in equity." In various Illinois cases contracts have been held void for lack of mutuality. . . .

In the present case, a careful examination of the record discloses that there was not the slightest bit of evidence that plaintiff ever agreed that he would continue in the employment of defendant for any specified time. In other words, he had a right to terminate his employment at any time and did not promise to perform for any definite length of time. Therefore, the contract could not have been enforced against him and was lacking in mutuality. Consequently, he cannot enforce it against defendant.

Plaintiff is in no better position if we consider his alleged agreement from th point of view of its term of existence, for the period of its continuance is in definite. It is a contract at will, which may be terminated at the option of eithe party at any time. See *Davis v. Fidelity Fire Insurance Co.*, 208 Ill. 375 at pag 385, 70 NE 359 and *Joliet Bottling Co. v. Brewing Co.*, 254 Ill. 215 at pag 219, 98 NE 263, where the court held that, no time being fixed during whic the agreement shall remain in force, it may be terminated at the will of eithe party. . . .

Nor can it avail plaintiff that his contract was, in his own words, permanen *Davis v. Fidelity Fire Insurance Co.*, 208 Ill. 375, at page 385 70 NE 359, 36: In that case, the court approved of the decision in *W. L. Milnert Co. v. Hil* 19 Ohio Cir. Ct., R. 663, where the document recited that the employmen "(would) be a permanent one." The court held that either party might termi nate it at any time; even though the business was permanent rather tha temporary. In other words, the Supreme Court of Illinois has expressly held tha a contract for "permanent employment" is one at will. This is in accord wit' the decisions of other jurisdictions that contracts not expressly made for fixe periods may be terminated at the will of either party. . . .

Plaintiff's complaint also charged that two certain notes, aggregating $2,30(given by him to defendant were void and that collection thereof should b enjoined; he also claimed that $380.00 is still due him for unpaid accumulate salary at the time of his discharge. However, it appears undisputed that th balance due on the notes had been reduced to judgment which stands unin peached. The court could grant him no relief in a collateral action against a unreversed judgment. Inasmuch as the amount of the judgment exceeds th amount he claims due him for unpaid wages, he had no right to recover ther for: Consequently, there was no basis for relief. The judgment is affirmed.

REVIEW QUESTION

1. Does a conditional promise, such as a promise to resell a piece
   property if you are able to buy it, constitute a legal consideration
   Why or why not?

2. Black agreed to pay White, a member of the state house of represent
   tives, $1,000 to do everything "reasonable and lawful" to defeat a bi
   which was to be presented to the legislature. Can White collect th
   $1,000 whether the bill passes or not? Why or why not?

3. What is the effect of sealing a contract in your state?

4. Black hires White Automation to build a piece of automatic machine
   for him for $150,000. During the construction of the machinery, unic
   pressures result in a wage increase for the electrical suppliers. As
   result, electrical equipment costs more than anticipated. White deman
   $8,000 more for the automation and Black agrees to pay. After insta
   lation, Black refuses to pay more than $150,000 for the machine. Whi
   sues. What will be the result? Why?

5. Gray owed Brown $600 on an old debt. Gray refused to pay the del
   several times, claiming lack of funds each time. Brown finally attempte

to collect the debt at a time when he knew Gray had sufficient money. Gray offered to pay $400 and give Brown a wrist watch worth about $30 if Brown would consider the debt paid in full. Brown accepted. Later Brown brought an action for the remainder of the debt. Can he get it? Why or why not?

6. In *Meadows v. Radio Industries,* would the outcome of the case have been different if the employment contract had been made for 10 months and Meadows was then fired after 8 months?

7. In the usual employment contract between an engineer and his employer, how much notice is required for termination of the employment by either party?

11

LAWFUL SUBJECT MATTER

Freedom to deal or to refuse to deal with others is
one of our guaranteed rights. Just as limitations must be placed upon
freedom of speech and the right to bear arms to protect the public,
limitations also must be placed upon the right to contract. The necessity
that any contract have a lawful purpose is fundamental in the law.
Generally, a contract based upon illegal subject matter is considered by
the courts as void.

Subject matter considered by the courts to be illegal may be classified
in three categories: contrary to statutes (federal, state, local); contrary
to common law; or contrary to public policy. More generally, illegal consideration consists of any act or forbearance, or promise to act or forbear
which is contrary to law, or morality, or public policy. Ignorance by the
parties as to what constitutes illegality cannot make valid a contract which
is void because of illegality.

Intent

The intent of the parties at the time the contract was made often
determines its legality. If both parties intended the contract to be performed illegally it usually will not be enforceable in the courts. This is
true even though actual performance was lawful. If only one of the parties
intends to perform illegally, the courts will usually uphold the contract.

A very large number of contracts are capable of being performed either
legally or illegally. A contract to drive a truck, for instance, may be performed either according to the law or in violation of it. If there is no
evidence of intent by both parties to perform the contract illegally, the
truck driving contract would be valid. Generally, the contract must be

incapable of being performed in a legal manner for the courts to declare it void on the basis of illegality.

Knowledge that the subject matter of a contract is intended for later unlawful use by one of the parties usually will not void the contract. However, where the subsequent unlawful use involves a heinous crime (treason or murder, for instance), an exception is made to this rule. An action to collect for the sale of a gun where the seller knows of the intent of the buyer to commit murder with the gun would not be successful. If the seller had no knowledge of the intended use of the gun and complied with the law in all other respects in the sale, the contract of sale would be valid.

CONTRARY TO STATUTE OR COMMON LAW

If the subject matter of a contract is contrary to an existing statute, the contract is usually void. The statute concerned may be a federal or state statute or a local ordinance. It is not necessary that the contract be in violation of the wording of the statute; the contract may be legally void if it is in conflict with the implied meaning of the statute or the intent of the legislature when the law was passed.

Law Passage Following Contract Formation

If a continuing contract [1] is formed and later a law is passed making performance unlawful, the entire contract is not voided. Performance of the contract subsequent to the passage of the statute cannot be recovered for in the courts, but the contract is enforceable as to performance prior to passage of the statute. Shortly after the U.S. entry into World War II, several regulations were passed by Congress outlawing the sale of various items and restricting the sale of others. In a case resulting from these restrictions where a new car sales agency had leased premises for the sole purpose of display and sale of new cars (so stipulated in the lease), it was held that because of the U.S. Government restriction on the sale of new cars, the lease contract was terminated. If the lease had been so written that the use of the premises had not been restricted to the sale of new cars, the governmental restrictions would have had no effect.

Type of Statute

In considering the legality of subject matter the courts attempt to draw a distinction between laws passed for the protection of the public

---

[1] A contract, the performance of which will take place over a considerable length of time.

and statutes, the primary purpose of which is to raise revenue. If a contract violates a statute passed for the protection of the public, it is treated as void and completely unenforceable in the courts. If the contract violates a revenue statute, though, it is usually enforceable, subject to court penalties for avoidance of the statute. An excellent example of this is to be found in the state licensing laws (e.g. for business establishments and professional people). If the purpose of the law is to protect the public and safeguard the lives, health, property, and welfare of citizens (for instance, licensing of professional engineers), a contract for professional services made by one who is not licensed in the state will not be enforced in the courts. If the primary purpose of the law is to collect revenue only (for instance, state gasoline taxes), the courts will usually enforce the contract and impose a penalty upon the violator.

Harm to Third Person

If a third person would be harmed by a crime or tort in the performance of a contract, the subject matter of the contract is unlawful. It is, of course, quite evident that a court could not punish for the commission of a crime or tort on one hand and support a contract to commit such a crime or tort on the other. Where the contract is an inducement to commit a crime or a tort, but the commission of such crime or tort is not a necessity in performance of the contract, the courts will examine the strength of the inducement and the general nature of the contract. Life insurance may be an inducement to murder; fire insurance an inducement to arson. For this reason an insurable interest often must be shown before insurance can be obtained. A contract, in the performance of which a party to the contract must breach a contract with another, is usually unenforceable in the courts.[2]

Contracts Which Restrain Trade

Our economy is based on the principles of free enterprise and freedom of competition. Under the Sherman Anti-Trust Act, the Clayton Act, and amendments to them, contracts which tend to create a monopoly or maintain price levels or in other ways restrain trade are unlawful. The penalty for violation of these acts is up to triple the amount of damages shown plus payment of the court costs and reasonable attorney's fees for plaintiff's attorney.

Despite the seeming restraint of trade present in such agreements, the court will protect the purchaser of a business and the "good will" that

---

[2] See Reiner v. North American Newspaper Alliance, 181 N.E. 561 (1930), in which a contract to breach the contract of passage on the Graf Zeppelin was held illegal.

goes with it. The "good will" portion of the sale of a business is often protected in a radius agreement between buyer and seller. By such an agreement the seller states that he will not compete with the buyer of his business. Typically, the agreement will state that the seller agrees not to enter into the same type of business in the same market area for a given period of time. If the restrictions as to type of business, market area, and time are all reasonable, they will be upheld in court. It is only when these restrictions are unreasonable that a court will hold them to be in violation of the law.

Usury

Most states have passed laws limiting the rate of interest which may be charged for the use of money. Considerable variation exists in the attitudes of the various states when these laws are violated. In some states, when usurious interest is charged, the courts will not aid in collection of principal or interest; in other states, all interest may be forfeited as a result of usury; and in still other states collection of principal and maximum allowable interest results. Borrowing by corporations is listed as an exception in most state laws.

Wagering Contracts

In most states wagering contracts are illegal. It is often difficult for the courts to determine whether a particular contract is a legitimate business transaction or a wager. The test used by the courts in making their determination is centered about the creation of the risk involved. Is a risk created for the purpose of bearing that risk? If so, then the contract is deemed a wager. In a dice game, on the first throw, a total of seven or eleven on the two dice pays off for the holder of the dice. The two bettors have created a risk of loss by placing their bets before the dice are thrown, with the score on the dice determining who shall lose his money. In a business contract calling for future delivery of a commodity for the payment of a present price, risk of loss resulting from a change in price of the commodity between the present and the delivery date is assumed by the parties. Has a risk been created for the purpose of assuming it? The courts answer no, providing future delivery is actually intended. Manipulations in the stock and grain markets are often open to this criticism in that the final result in the contract is, and was originally intended by the parties to be a transfer of money rather than commodity.

Others

A contract to withhold evidence in a court case is unlawful; so are contracts which tend to promote litigation. This is one reason why contingency fees for attorneys or others connected with a trial are frowned upon. If a would-be plaintiff stands to lose nothing in a court case, this is an actual incentive for him to undertake the litigation.

A large category of unlawful contracts is included in those which either restrain marriage or promote a divorce action. The courts do everything within their power to promote matrimony and to restrain its dissolution.

Contracts which are immoral in subject matter or which tend to promote immorality are declared by the courts to be unlawful and against public policy.

CONTRARY TO PUBLIC POLICY

Contracts must conform to the common law and statutory regulation to be lawful and enforceable. However, these are not the only limitations imposed by the courts on contract subject matter. In addition to the requirement that contracts conform to the written and unwritten laws of the community, the courts require conformity to public policy. Public policy is rather difficult to define because it is continuously changing. It must change to conform to changing ideas and changing technology, just as city planning has had to change to include cloverleafs and jet transportation. Generally, those contracts which would be held contrary to public policy are those which, if allowed, would be injurious to society in some way. It is not necessary that someone, or the public in general, be injured by the performance of the contract. Courts frequently have held that a contract may be unenforceable because of an "evil tendency" found to be present in it. Unenforceability because of the "evil tendency" of the contract is particularly characteristic of contracts in which the judgment or decision of a public official might be (or has been) altered by the contract. In fact, any contract which tends to cause corruption of a public official may be subject to censure in the courts. All of which brings up a rather tender problem with which the courts often are faced—What acts of lobbying are to be condoned? First, the end sought to be accomplished must be a lawful objective—one which, if accomplished, would improve the public welfare, or at least would do it no harm. Second, the means used must be above reproach. Generally, a lobbyist must be registered as such; his lobbying practices must not involve threats or bribery or secret deals.

Courts generally treat contingent fees as being against public policy. Assume Green to be hired as consultant for an engineering design job, with payment to depend on his achieving acceptance of the design by political officials. Green, being human, might be tempted to go beyond what is considered right and ethical to obtain his fee. In the court's eyes contingent fees are an inducement to the use of sinister and corrupt means of gaining the desired objective. Although the court may, in certain cases, overlook the presence of contingent fees, it nearly always detracts from the case presented by the proposed recipient of the fee.

Fraud or Deception

A contract which has the effect of practicing fraud or deception on a third person is against public policy. Black agrees to pay White $200 if White (a prominent nuclear engineer) will recommend Black to Gray for a job as a nuclear engineer. White knows nothing of Black's qualifications for the job. Even though White wrote the recommendation and Black succeeded in getting the job, it is likely that White could not get the $200 by court action. The contract would be void as against public policy. In contrast, payment for a recommendation from an employment agency would be quite enforceable. The employment agency is in the business of recommending people for jobs for a fee. Thus, those who hire employees through an employment agency have knowledge of the usual arrangement; those who hire based upon individual recommendations have a right to assume that such recommendations are given freely and without prejudice.

Breach of Trust or Confidence

Contracts which breach a trust or a confidential relationship are against public policy and will not be supported in a court. Agency is one such fiduciary relationship—the agent acts for his principal in dealing with others. White, as Black's agent, contracts with Green for the purchase of steel. Unknown to Black, White is to receive a five percent kickback from Green for placing the order with him. Even though the steel purchase occurred, the five percent kickback agreement could not be enforced in court.

Contracts having the effect of compounding a crime are against public policy; tax evasion agreements are unlawful. In general, almost any contract which is intended to be hidden from the public for reason other than national security is questionable. The agreements mentioned here represent only a few areas in which public policy sharply restricts the right to contract.

Sources of Public Policy

Our public policy is to be found in the federal and state constitutions, in statutes, in judicial decisions, and in the decisions and practices of our government agencies. Lacking these, the court must depend upon its own sense of moral duty and justice for its decision.

EFFECT OF ILLEGALITY

The general principle followed by the court in dealing with the subject matter of contract is that no action will be allowed in law or in equity if it is based upon an illegal agreement. That is, court actions based upon agreements which are illegal, immoral, against public policy, have as their purpose the commission of a crime, or are forbidden by statute, will not be enforced. In the interest of justice and fairness this principle has been slightly tempered in certain cases.

The reason for the court's dismissing unlawful contracts as void is that the defense of illegality is allowed, not as a protective device for the defendant but as a disability to the plaintiff. The public is better protected against dishonest transactions if the court places this stumbling block in the path of those attempting to avoid the law. Suppose a member of a gang of thieves, upon being cheated out of his share of the loot, went into court to try to force a split. What should the court do as to the division of the spoils? The court would contend that the agreement to split is void, being based on a crime. The public interest is best served if the court does everything in its power to discourage the crime. Thus, as far as the loot-splitting is concerned, the case would be dismissed.

The public interest, then, is the determining factor in such cases. The court's decision is based upon its opinion of what would be the greatest aid to the public. If the public interest would be promoted better by a decision for the plaintiff, the court will so decide. Consider a confidence game in which the victim is placed somewhat afoul the law by his agreement with the confidence men (as is usually the case). Swallowing pride and guilt alike, the victim asks the court to order the return of his money. The court may decide to do just that as a discouragement to continued practice of such con games on the public.

Disaffirmance of an illegal contract while the illegal portion of the agreement is still executory will allow the person disaffirming to recover lawful consideration given by him. A person paying money to another to have him commit a crime ordinarily may disaffirm the contract so that the crime may be stopped and thus obtain restoration of his money. Here again, the public interest is the determining factor, with the court acting as the representative of the public.

WECHSLER v. NOVAK

26 So. 2d 884, 157 Fla. 703, (July 12, 1946)

Chapman, Chief Justice.

The plaintiff below (Wechsler) in his declaration alleged, in part, that on or about June 15, 1943 the defendants were engaged in operating the Atlantis

Hotel at Miami Beach, Florida, and the hotel at the time was leased to the United States Army and the defendants were desirous of having the hotel returned to civilian use, that on the 20th day of June, 1943, the defendants employed the plaintiff to assist in securing the return of the hotel to civilian use; the defendants promised and agreed in consideration of the services to be performed and money spent and subsequent services to be performed in the event the Atlantis Hotel was returned to civilian use that they would pay the plaintiff the sum of $10,000.

The sum of $5,000 would be paid on December 15, 1943, provided said hotel was returned for civilian use on or before December 15, 1943, and the remaining $5,000 was to be paid on or before January 15, 1944, plus a bonus equal to 10% of all the gross profits resulting from the operation of the hotel from the date the hotel would be opened and returned for business until January 1, 1945, or in the event the hotel was sold prior to January 1, 1945, the plaintiff was to receive 10% of the gross profits of the sale in addition to 10% of the gross profits accruing prior to the sale of the Atlantis Hotel.

The plaintiff rendered certain services to the defendants at their request. He appeared before the United States Army Real Estate Board in Washington, D.C., on dates viz: June 27, 1943; July 11, 1943; September 5, 1943, and October 4, 1943; and assisted the defendants in securing information as to the possibilities of having the hotel released from the army; the plaintiff reported to the defendants what had transpired at the respective hearings before the United States Army Real Estate Board and the total amount of his expenditures incident to the return of the hotel to the defendants approximated $3,500, and this expenditure was made in accordance with the terms of his contract of employment with the defendants. On November 12, 1943, plaintiff notified defendants that the hotel would be returned to civilian use and they would receive within a few days an official notice thereof through the proper authorities of the United States Army.

The plaintiff had performed and complied with all the terms and conditions of employment existing between them and as a result of plaintiff's efforts the Atlantis Hotel on or about December 12, 1943, was returned to the defendants, yet the defendants refused and failed to pay plaintiff the sum of $50,000 cash. The common counts were viz: for work done and materials furnished at defendants' request; and for money found to be due on accounts stated between them in the sum of $50,000. A bill of particulars in the total sum of $50,000 by appropriate words was made a part of the declaration.

The several defendants by their respective attorneys filed separate demurrers to the declaration and some of the grounds are common to each demurrer, viz: (1) the declaration fails to state a cause of action; (2) the original contract sued upon is so vague, indefinite and uncertain that it is incapable of enforcement; (3) the original contract sued upon is contrary to public policy, illegal and void in that the plaintiff was therein seeking compensation for exerting influence upon public officials of the United States Government; (4) it is not shown that the plaintiff performed any services for which he was entitled to be paid; (5) it is impossible to determine the exact services rendered by the plaintiff for which he seeks compensation; (6) it appears from the allegations of the declaration that the compensation plaintiff was to receive for services rendered was and is contrary to public policy. Final judgment on demurrers for the defendants below was entered and plaintiff appealed.

Counsel for appellant pose for adjudication here the question, viz: Where it appears that the plaintiff was employed to assist in the procurement of the release from Army occupation of a hotel and the plaintiff rendered services and had expended money in his efforts therefor and the defendants orally agreed, in consideration of the services rendered and to be rendered in the event the hotel was returned, that they would pay to the plaintiff the sum of $10,000 in cash, for the services therefor, is such a contract contrary to public policy and void?

Counsel for appellees contend that the question presented here is viz: Is an alleged contract entered into in June, 1943, (during the middle of World War II) to procure for a contingent compensation the release from the United States Army and the return to the owner of a hotel at Miami Beach occupied by soldiers, illegal and void as a contract contrary to public policy?

The early case of *Providence Tool Co. v. Norris* . . . involved a contract entered into between the Secretary of War and the tool company providing for the delivery of 25,000 muskets of a specified pattern for $20 each, and the muskets were to be delivered by a certain date. The contract was obtained through the exertions of Norris with an agent of the tool company and it was agreed that if Norris would obtain the contract from the War Department then he (Norris) would receive stipulated compensation to be paid to him by the tool company. Norris brought suit and the court held that he could not recover because his contract was against public policy and therefore invalid. It was said, "agreements for compensation contingent upon success, suggest the use of sinister and corrupt means for the accomplishment of the ends desired. The law meets the suggested evil and strikes down the contract from its inception. There is no difference in principle between agreements to procure favors from legislative bodies and agreements to procure favors in the shape of contracts from heads of departments."

The case of *Trist (Burke) v. Child* . . . involved a claim of Trist against the Federal Government for services rendered touching the treaty of Guadelupe Hidalgo and he entered into an agreement with Child to the effect that Child would take over the claim and prosecute it before Congress and the compensation for his services would be 25% of such sum as Congress might allow in payment of the claim. Congress appropriated the sum of $14,559 to pay the claim. Trist died and Child brought suit to collect the 25% of the sum appropriated. The court, in holding that the contract was contrary to public policy and therefore void, in part, said: ". . . The theory of our government is, that all public stations are trusts, and that those clothed with them are to be animated in the discharge of their duties solely by consideration of right, justice, and the public good. They are never to descend to a lower plane. But there is a correlative duty resting upon the citizen. In his intercourse with those in authority, whether executive or legislative, touching the performance of their functions, he is bound to exhibit truth, frankness, and integrity. Any departure from the line of rectitude in such cases is not only bad in morals, but involves a public wrong. No people can have any higher public interest, except the preservation of their liberties, than integrity in the administration of their government in all its departments."

The case of *Oscanyan v. Winchester Repeating Arms Co.* . . . was an action to recover money alleged to be due to the plaintiff on a contract with the defendant as commissions on sales to the Turkish Government effected through the efforts of the plaintiff. The sales were made while the plaintiff was an officer of the Turkish Government and through plaintiff's personal contacts with the Turkish agent. At the trial the plaintiff made an opening statement, and at the close of this opening statement the defendant moved for a directed verdict, which motion was granted by the trial court. The Supreme Court upheld the trial court. Although the question of illegality was not raised by demurrer, a directed verdict was granted after the plaintiff's opening statement without the taking of any testimony. The Court, in part, said: "It is legitimate to lay before the officers authorized to contract, all such information and may apprise them of the character and value of the articles offered, and enable them to act for the best interests of the country. But where, instead of placing before the officers of the governments the information which should properly guide their judgments, personal influence is the means used to secure the sales and is allowed to prevail, the public good is lost sight of. . . ."

McMullen v. Hoffman . . . involved a contract held to be contrary to public policy and invalid. The contract recited that whereas Hoffman and Bates have with the assistance of McMullen at a recent bidding submitted the lowest bid for said work and expect to enter into a contract with the Water Committee of the City of Portland for doing such work the said Hoffman and McMullen shall and will share said contract equally, inclusive of the profits and losses. Pursuant to the agreement Hoffman put in a bid for the work at the sum of $465,720, while McMullen's bid was for the sum of $514,664, and Hoffman was the lowest bidder and got the contract. McMullen sued on his contract with Hoffman for one-half the profits. The Court held the contract invalid because it was obtained through fraud and contrary to the public policy.

The inherent and inalienable right of every man to enter into contracts or refuse so to contract is not only recognized but well established. Competent persons have the utmost liberty of contracting and when these agreements are shown to be voluntary and freely made and entered into, then the courts usually will uphold and enforce them. The general right to contract is subject to the limitation that the agreement must not violate the Federal or State Constitutions or state statutes or ordinances of a city or town or some rule of common law. Individuals have never been allowed to stipulate for iniquity. The doctrine relating to illegal agreements is founded on a regard for the public welfare and therefore each contract must have a lawful purpose. . . .

Agreements entered into against the public interest or contrary to the public policy of a State or Nation usually are by the courts held illegal and void. The legality of agreements to influence administrative or executive officers or departments is to be determined in each case by weighing all the elements involved and then deciding whether the agreement promotes corrupt means to accomplish an end or to bring influence to bear on public officials of a nature other than the advancement of the best interest of government. Agreements employing one to secure government contracts or concessions, etc., may be without taint on the face and yet illegal or unenforceable. . . .

A contract involving the use of personal influence with public executives or administrative officers or the heads of departments in order to induce them to grant favors or privileges, as a general rule, is regarded as against public policy. Many courts hold such agreements invalid on the theory of their tendency to introduce corrupt means in the influencing of public officials and especially is it true in those cases where compensation is contingent on success. . . .

The case of *Atlantic Coast Line v. Beasley* . . . involved a contract between a railroad and one of its employees, by the terms of which the employee released a claim, in advance, for personal injuries. We held that the contract offended the rule against public policy. The case of City of Leesburg v. Ware . . . involved certain transactions for the purchase of bonds of a bank by the bond trustees of the City of Leesburg and we held the transaction void as against public policy. . . .

The case of *Edwards v. Miami Transit Co.* . . . involved a written agreement whereby Edwards was to render services in an effort to secure a franchise over the streets of the City of Miami. The plaintiff obtained the bus franchise for the defendant and the latter declined to pay the stipulated compensation when Edwards sued. Edwards submitted to the official facts, figures and information sufficient to convince the authorities that the general public interest would be served by granting the bus franchise. These facts are distinguishable from the facts presented in the case at bar.

It must be admitted by the parties here that at the time (June 20, 1943) the agreement was entered into that the United States Government was engaged in a bitter and desperate war with powerful enemies; that many points in Florida had by the Federal Government been fortified and otherwise prepared against possible invasion by the public enemy; cautious measures were continuously exercised for protection of the American people; our troops were housed in tourist hotels at Miami Beach. It was a time when all citizens were expected to sustain every effort to conquer or overcome the enemy. The opportunities of self-aggrandizement and personal gain were secondary objectives. The agreement sued upon here not only violates the rule against public policy and is therefore void, but it is reasonable to conclude that the shifting of our troops from the Atlantis Hotel could have given an invading enemy an advantage not anticipated. If the plaintiff had the power or influence to obtain a return of the Atlantis Hotel—then by analogy other hotels on the Miami Beach likewise could be returned. Thus the prosecution of the war indirectly could be adversely affected. We fail to find error in the record.

BROWN, Justice (concurring specially): The large amount of this allegedly agreed compensation, and the fact that it was conditioned upon success in getting favorable action by the board in Washington inclines me to agree to the foregoing opinion. The mere employment by a person, or corporation, or a city, of some competent person to represent them and to present legitimate arguments before any one of the many boards and commissions in Washington, in order, if possible, to get favorable action by such a board on any matter vitally important to the protection of their legitimate interests, would seem to be not only lawful, but, frequently, vitally necessary.

STONE v. FREEMAN

298 N.Y. 268, 82 N.E. 2d 571, 8 ALR 2d 304 (Nov. 24, 1948)

DESMOND, J.

The suit is by a broker or agent for his commissions earned in arranging a sale by defendant, who is a jobber of clothing, to the French Purchasing Mission, in New York City, in 1946. However, the sole question here is as to the sufficiency of the two counterclaims. For present purposes, those counterclaims may be treated as one, since each alleges the same things: That defendant (vendor) agreed to pay, and did pay to the plaintiff (broker) certain sums, on plaintiff's agreement that he would divide those sums with an employee or representative of the French Supply Council (vendee), but that plaintiff paid to that French representative part only of the latter's agreed share, wherefore defendant, in these counterclaims, sues for return of the part so assigned to the French representative but not paid to him. The question of law is aptly stated in the appellant's brief thus (p. 2): "May a seller of goods, who has agreed with his broker that the broker shall divide his commissions with the buyer's purchasing agent and has paid the broker moneys intended to be so divided, recover back from the broker a portion of such moneys intended to be paid to the buyer's purchasing agent but not yet so paid?" Both courts below answered that question in the affirmative. We answer it in the negative.

These counterclaims plainly allege a conspiracy . . . to violate section 439 of the Penal Law, which makes it a misdemeanor to give or offer such a commission or bonus to a purchasing agent. The contract or arrangement between plaintiff and defendant was thus illegal, criminal and unenforceable. . . . It is the settled law of this state (and probably of every other state) that a party to an illegal contract cannot ask a court of law to help him carry out his illegal object, nor can such a person plead or prove in any court a case in which he, as a basis for his claim, must show forth his illegal purpose. . . . For no court should be required to serve as paymaster of the wages of crime, or referee between thieves. Therefore, the law "will not extend its aid to either of the parties" or "listen to their complaints against each other, but will leave them where their own acts have placed them". . . . Conforming to that settled rule, this court and its predecessor have several times held that when an agent receives money to be spent for illegal purposes, his principal may not recover back so much of that money as the agent has failed so to spend, particularly when the illegal purpose has been partly or wholly attained and a part of the money expended therefor. . . . Both *Staples v. Gould,* supra, and *Leonard v. Pool,* supra, say that a broker or agent who knowingly participates in a criminal scheme is a principal, and in pari delicto with the one who employs him, so that neither may sue the other. Such is the New York law and it disposes of this case. Insofar as the Restatement of the Law of Agency (para. 412) is to the contrary, we do not concur in it.

We point out that we are passing on the precise question here involved, and no other. This is not a case where a mere agent or depository, receiving money for his principal, refuses to pay it over, on the ground that it was the fruit of an illegal contract between his principal and another. . . . Nor are we deciding what the result would be had this defendant repented of his wrong, and demanded back his money, before any attempt had been made by plaintiff to bribe the purchasing agent. . . .

The orders should be reversed, with costs in all courts, each certified question answered in the negative, and the motion to dismiss granted as to both the first and the second counterclaims in the amended answer.

REVIEW QUESTIONS

1. Black, an engineer, agrees to act as an expert witness for White in a court case. In return, Black is to receive $500 plus expenses for his services. Is the contract lawful? Why or why not?

2. In the above example, assume that Black agrees to accept $1200 if White wins, or payment for expenses only if White loses. Is the contract lawful? Why or why not?

3. Gray is a process engineer for Brown. Green has made the low bid on equipment for a manufacturing operation which Gray had started to set up. The equipment meets the specifications as well as equipment proposed by other bidders. To improve the chance for acceptance of his bid, Green has offered to give Gray two per cent of the bid price if Green's equipment is used. If the equipment is bought, can Gray get the two per cent? After receiving the two per cent offer, what, if anything, should Gray have done about it?

4. Explain why an insurance contract is not a wagering contract.

5. What is public policy?

6. Give two reasons why contingency fees are looked upon with disfavor by courts.

7. According to *Wechsler v. Novak,* what is the limit to which one may go in attempting to obtain desired legislation or to get a favorable ruling from an administrative board?

12 STATUTE OF FRAUDS

An oral contract generally is just as enforceable as a written contract, but a written one has at least one major advantage—its terms are easier to ascertain. The relationships of the parties are set forth for interpretation by the individuals concerned and by a court of law if need for the court should arise. Although it is true that in most circumstances an oral contract is as good as a written one, it is sound common sense to put in writing any contract of more than a trivial nature.

In England during the reign of Charles II, the courts were faced with many cases concerning oral agreements. Instances of perjured testimony were frequent as the contending parties attempted to prove or disprove the existence or terms of contracts. In 1677, the English Statute of Frauds was passed as "An Act for the Prevention of Frauds and Perjuries" to relieve the courts of the necessity of considering certain types of contracts unless their terms were set forth in writing and signed. The statute does not require a formally drawn instrument. The only writing required is the minimum needed to establish the material provisions of the agreement. The writing need not be all on one instrument, but if it is not, a connection between them must be apparent from the documents themselves. The statute does not require a signature from both parties. Only the defendant must have signed. The signature itself may consist of initials, rubber stamp, in ink or pencil, or apparently anything intended by the party to constitute identification and assent; it may appear anywhere on the document.

The English Statute of Frauds consisted of several sections but only the sections numbered four and seventeen are of major importance to us today. These two sections have become law in all of the states in the U.S.A. with only minor modifications of the original statute. The principles are the same.

Fourth and Seventeenth Sections

According to the fourth section, "no action shall be brought" on certain types of contracts unless the agreement which is the basis for such action is in writing and signed by the defendant or his agent. The following types of contracts are specified in the fourth section:

1. Promises of executors or administrators of an estate to pay the debts of the deceased from the executor's or administrator's own estate.

2. Promises to act as surety for the debt of another.

3. Promises based upon marriage as a consideration.

4. Promises involving real property.

5. Promises which cannot be performed within a year.

The seventeenth section states the requirements for an enforceable contract having to do with the sale of goods, wares, or merchandise. It says that unless one of three things is done to secure such a transaction where the consideration is at least 10 pounds sterling, the contract will be unenforceable at law. Either:

1. Part of the goods, wares, or merchandise must be accepted by the buyer, or

2. The buyer must pay something in earnest toward the cost of the goods, or

3. Some note or memorandum of the agreement must be made and signed.

The £ sterling minimum has been changed by the states to dollar minimums. In two states, Florida and Iowa, the minimum is nothing— in other words one of the three requirements must be present in *any* contract for it to be enforceable, regardless of the price involved. Ohio has the highest minimum ($2500). In a few states any size contract is enforceable if made orally. In most of the states, the minimum is between $50 and $500.

Promises of Executors or Administrators

In law an executor is a person appointed in a will by the testator [1] to execute, or put in force, the terms of the instrument. An administrator serves a somewhat similar function where the deceased died without a

---

[1] Person making the will.

will (intestate). He is appointed by a court to collect the assets of the estate of the deceased, pay its debts, and distribute the remaining estate to those entitled to it by law.

If the executor or administrator of an estate agrees to pay the debts of the deceased out of the executor's or administrator's own estate, he is acting as surety for the debt of another. In effect, he is saying: "If the estate of the deceased is insufficient to pay you, I will pay the debt." This situation is covered under surety contracts, below.

Promises to Act as Surety

The requirement that a contract to answer for the debt, default or miscarriage of another person must be in writing covers all types of guaranty and surety contracts. Lending institutions frequently require either collateral or a responsible co-signer as security for a loan. If White wishes to borrow $1000 from Black Loan Company a co-signer may be required for the loan. If Gray is to act as surety, agreeing to pay if White does not pay, such a contract must be in writing to be enforceable against Gray.

It is appropriate here to distinguish between primary and secondary promises. An oral primary promise is enforceable but an oral secondary promise is not. Wording of the promise can be quite important, but the apparent intent of the promisor when the promise is made is even more important. If the wording and other facts make clear an intent such that "If White does not pay, I will" it is a secondary promise. However, if the circumstances show the intent to be that "I will pay White's loan" the promise is a primary one. The primary promise is enforceable against the promisor if it is made either orally or in writing. Similarly, where the defendant had agreed to make good any loss sustained by the plaintiff if the plaintiff would act as surety for a third party, the defendant's promise was held to be primary in nature and enforceable against him even though the promise was oral.[2] This comes closer to an undertaking of indemnity or insurance than surety.

Indemnity (insurance) contracts need not be in writing. Under such contracts no liability is held to exist until obligation arises between the insured and some third party.

Promises in Consideration of Marriage

Marriage is the highest consideration known to law. This provision of the statute of frauds applies particularly to situations in which the agreement to marry is based upon consideration such as a marriage settlement.

---

[2] Gilinsky v. Klionsky, 251 N.Y.S. 570.

If Mr. White agreed to pay Black $10,000 in consideration of marriage to White's daughter, the contract would have to be in writing to be enforceable. The statement that contracts in which marriage is to be a consideration must be in writing does not mean that when a man and woman simply agree to get married, with neither giving up anything but his unmarried status, such an agreement would have to be in writing. Under common law oral mutual promises to marry are quite actionable at law if one of the parties attempts to breach his promise.

Real Property Transactions

Transactions involving "lands, tenements, and hereditaments" (i.e. real property) must be in writing to be enforceable at law.

Real property law is treated more thoroughly in Chapter 18, "Property." It is necessary here, however, to make some distinction between real and personal property. Real property is anciently defined as consisting of land and those things permanently attached to it, or *immovables*. Personal property, then, includes the *movables*, or things not firmly attached to the land. These definitions comprise only a part of the distinction currently applied by the courts.

The courts also distinguish between *fructus naturales* and *fructus industriales*. Fructus naturales is usually held to consist of things present on or in the land, which are not the product of human attention or cultivation. Minerals in the soil, trees on the land, and natural grass, for instance, are fructus naturales, and are considered by the courts as real property requiring a writing for their sale. An exception exists, though, in dealing with these natural fruits of the land. When the contract contemplates immediate severance or removal of these things, an oral contract to such effect will be enforceable. Black orally sells White a stand of timber to be cut and sold by White with Black to receive payment as cutting proceeds. If cutting is to begin immediately the oral contract is enforceable; if it is to begin ten months from now, it is unenforceable under current interpretations of the statute. Fructus industriales are those things, such as cultivated crops, which result from human effort. An oral contract in which such things are to be a consideration is enforceable. For instance, a contract to sell the fruit in an orchard as it ripens would be enforceable under the fourth section of the statute of frauds, even though made orally.

Lease contracts involve an interest in land but, for most purposes, are considered as personal property. An oral lease for a period of time of a year or less is valid, but must be in writing if it is to run longer than a year.

Part performance of an oral contract for the purchase of real property can influence the court to disregard the statute of frauds. It is only in an unusual case, however, that the courts will enforce such an oral contract. It must be a case in which the extent of improvements by the buyer has been so vast and material as to make it unjust to hold the oral agreement unenforceable. In such circumstances an equity court may decree for specific performance by the seller.

Promises Requiring More Than a Year to Perform

The legal interpretation of a year is important here. Generally, the time starts to run from the time of making the agreement, not from the time when performance is begun. An oral contract, then, to work for another for a year, starting two days from now, would be unenforceable under the statute of frauds. In most jurisdictions it is held that parts of days do not count in the running of time. If a contract is made today, time will start to run on that contract tomorrow.

The statute refers to contracts "not to be performed within one year of the making thereof." The court interpretation of this statement is that it means contracts which, by their terms, *cannot be* performed within one year. White promises orally to pay Black $20,000 if he (Black) will build a certain house for him. No time limit is set on the construction. The fact that actual construction took place over a two-year period would not bring the contract under the statute of frauds. If the contract could be completed within one year an oral contract for its performance is binding. By this reasoning, a contract to work for someone "for life" or to support someone "for life" is capable of being performed in one year and need not be in writing to be binding.

If an oral contract, performance of which is to take place in less than a year, is extended from time to time by increments of less than a year, but in such a way that performance continues for more than a year such a contract is valid. For instance an oral lease contract for nine months might be continued orally at the end of the period to run to eighteen months.

Sale of Goods

A large majority of the states have adopted the Uniform Sales Act, which governs the transfer of goods, wares, and merchandise within those states. It incorporates the seventeenth section of the statute of frauds in slightly altered wording.

If the transaction undertaken involves goods of a value great enough to be governed by the statute of frauds in the particular state, an oral agreement will be valid only if (1) part of the goods are accepted by the buyer, or (2) if he pays part of the purchase price in earnest, or (3) signs some note or memorandum as to the terms of the sale. Payment of part of the purchase price may be made in money or in anything of value to the parties.

What actually constitutes goods, wares, and merchandise under the statute has led the courts into some difficulty on occasion. It is apparent that if the goods exist, a contract for their sale will involve merely passage of title to those goods. However, if the contract is for the purchase of goods not now in existence, but to be made by the seller, there is a question as to whether this is not a contract for services to be performed. A contract for services would not involve the seventeenth section of the statute of frauds. Generally, the courts have settled upon what is known as the *Massachusetts Rule* for the answer to that question. According to the *Massachusetts Rule,* if a contract is made for the purchase of goods not in existence at that time, coverage by the seventeenth section will depend upon the nature of those goods. If the goods are the usual product of the seller and are made by him for an established market, the seventeenth section will apply. If the goods are specially made for the particular buyer under an oral contract with him he will be obligated to take them. Black wishes to purchase a gate to match a very old wrought iron fence around his house. Black contracts orally with White to have such a gate specially made for him. The contract will be enforced. This, of course, is a logical rule since the gate probably would be unsaleable to anyone else.

Effect of the Statute

The words "no action shall be brought" on oral contracts which should have been in writing according to the statute of frauds does not render such a contract either voidable or void. It may still be valid for some purposes. Where one party has performed his obligations under such an oral contract he has probably enriched the other party. A court of equity may recognize the obligation created by such a performance and enforce payment by the other party under a quasi-contract. Generally, when the result would be inequitable or grossly unfair the courts will not allow the statute of frauds to stand as a defense.

Where the oral contract which should have been written is either completely executory or completely executed, the courts will not consider it. The parties, generally, are left where they are found.

MAZZOTTA v. GORA

110 A. 2d 295, 19 Conn. Sup. 96 (Connecticut, July 7, 1954)

FITZGERALD, Judge.

In this action the plaintiff is seeking to recover of the defendants, husband and wife, the sum of $684 for the plastering of their home on Barbara Road, Middletown, while under construction by a general contractor. Since the decision turns on technical aspects, the essential facts require a general statement.

On September 24, 1951, the defendants entered into a written contract with one Fred Dean, a building contractor, for the construction of a dwelling house and incidentals connected therewith. The total cost was to be $12,500, payable in specified instalments as the work progressed. The plaintiff is also a contractor and specializes in masonry work. On February 26, 1952, he entered into a written subcontract with Dean in which he agreed to build the fireplace in the defendants' house and plaster certain rooms therein. The agreed total price to be paid the plaintiff by Dean was $1134. This latter contract did not provide for instalment payments as the work thereunder progressed.

The plaintiff built the fireplace in the following month over a four-day period. Dean found fault with the plaintiff's work, taking the position that the placement of the fireplace was several inches at variance with its proper location. As a result the plaintiff quit the job without commencing the plastering work. It does not appear that the defendants had any altercation with Dean or the plaintiff regarding the variance in the placement of the fireplace. Neither up to that time nor at any later time did the plaintiff ever receive any money from Dean. Nor did the plaintiff ever file a mechanic's lien against the property to protect his interest.

Sometime in the middle of May, 1952, the defendant wife urged the plaintiff to complete the plastering work under his sub-contract with Dean. She told the plaintiff that she would shortly be making a $2000 instalment payment to Dean through her attorney, and added: "I'll see that you will get your money." She further testified, and the court finds it to be a fact, that she told the plaintiff that she would let him know the day that her check would be turned over to her attorney for transmission to Dean. Such a check, dated June 2, 1952, and cashed by Dean a few days later, was issued by the defendant wife pursuant to the foregoing stipulation. Thereafter Dean defaulted in the balance of his contract with the defendants.

The plaintiff did complete the plastering work after the request of the defendant wife and before the June payment to Dean. In resisting the plaintiff's claim that they are owing money to him for the plastering work, the defendants take the following stand: (1) The plastering work done by the plaintiff is reasonably worth $684 but, contrary to the plaintiff's complaint, there was not in law and in fact an express promise by them to pay for the undertaking; (2) the statement of the defendant wife—"I'll see that you will get your money" —being oral, is unenforceable under the statute, General Statutes, sec. 8293, as an agreement upon which they can be charged.

It is found that the statement by the defendant wife to the plaintiff—"I'll see that you will get your money"—was never intended by her to signify, or understood by the plaintiff as meaning, that the defendants would become primarily liable for the plastering work to be performed by the plaintiff. Hence the plaintiff must fail in this action. . . .

The short answer to the plaintiff's suggestion that he should be entitled to a recovery in any event under the doctrine of unjust enrichment is that the case as pleaded and tried does not warrant the invoking of that doctrine.

For all that appears, the general contractor in the person of Dean has imposed in a rather vicious manner upon both the plaintiff and the defendants.

He has cost the parties hereto money and heartaches. That he has dealt dishonorably with the parties by running out on his contractual obligations with them does not advantage the unfortunate plaintiff in this action against the equally unfortunate defendants.

Judgment is required to be entered for the defendants.

REVIEW QUESTIONS

1. Why is a written contract better than an oral one?

2. Name three ways in which the seventeenth section of the English Statute of Frauds differs from the fourth section.

3. What is the difference between surety and insurance or indemnity?

4. Are the following things real property or personal property?
    a. A gas operated water heater.
    b. A bird bath.
    c. Flowers and shrubs in a flower bed.
    d. A television aerial mounted on a roof.
    e. A window mounted air conditioner.

5. Black orally contracts with White to build a brick garage for Black for $1,800. When the garage is finished Black refuses to pay the price claiming that the garage is an addition to real property and, therefore, should have been in writing to be enforceable. Can White collect? Why or why not?

6. Green orally contracts with the Gray Die Shop to build a punch press die for $2,000. The production for which Green was going to use the die is cancelled and Green refuses to accept and pay for the die. Gray claims that the contract was for a service and, thus, he is entitled to payment. Green points out that dies are the usual product of the shop and, therefore, that the contract had to be in writing to be enforceable. Who is right? Why?

7. In *Mazzotta v. Gora* the defendant stated, "I'll see that you will get your money." This sounds like a primary promise. Why did the court hold it to be a secondary promise?

13

THIRD PARTY
RIGHTS

A contract is a voluntary, intentional, and personal relationship. The parties involved determine the rights and obligations exchanged. Ordinarily, only those who are directly involved have rights stemming from the contract. In law, the relationship between parties to a contract is known as *privity of contract;* generally, only a person who is *in privity* with another may enforce his rights in the contract.

Strict interpretation of the privity of contract principle would prevent common transactions of considerable value and convenience in our economy. Therefore, the courts recognize two exceptions:

1. Rights assigned by a party to a contract to a third party are enforceable by the third party.
2. Rights arising from third party beneficiary contracts are enforceable by the beneficiary.

Assignment

Probably the most common form of assignment occurs when an indebtedness which is not yet due is assigned to another for value. In payment for a machinery installation, the White Company holds a $10,000 note to be paid by Black six months from now. If the White Company finds itself in need of funds, it may be able to sell this right to payment from Black to someone else (possibly a local bank). The bank would pay something less than face value (known as discounting) and then take over Black's note with the same rights White had.

Assignment involves at least three parties. The obligor (or debtor) is the party to the original contract who now finds that because of the assignment he owes his obligation to someone not in privity of contract with him. The obligee (or creditor, or assignor) is the person to whom the obligor originally owed the duty to perform. Now, because of the assignment, the right to that performance has been delegated to another. The assignee is the one to whom the obligor now owes the duty of performance.

Most contract rights are assignable if there is no stipulation to the contrary in the contract. Generally, an assignment in violation of a contract provision renders the contract voidable at the option of the obligor.

Contract rights to personal services and services based on the skill of an individual are treated exceptionally; and it seems right that they should be. If Black contracts to perform personal services for White, it should not be possible to force him into a choice of either performing those services for a third person or breaching his contract. The same reasoning applies where the rights involved are in the nature of a trust or confidence (services of a lawyer, for example).

RIGHTS AND DUTIES. Rights can be effectively assigned, but not duties. At least, one cannot relieve himself of liability for nonperformance or poor performance by delegating his duties to someone else. The duties may be delegated to another, but the person delegating the duties is still responsible for their performance. He is essentially a guarantor of the performance. Black hires White to build a structure. White subcontracts the plumbing to Gray. White's subcontract with Gray does not relieve White of his responsibility for Black's structure, including plumbing. But White is only responsible as guarantor if he was the one to deal with Gray. His responsibility is relieved if Black makes the plumbing arrangements with Gray.

Assignment differs from novation. In a novation both rights and duties are effectively assigned. The distinction depends upon the number of parties involved. If all three parties agree to the substitution of one party for another, the effect is a new agreement by means of a novation. Assignment of rights requires only an agreement between assignor and assignee. The obligor or debtor must, of course, be informed of the assignment if it is to be binding on him. Also, the obligation must be made no greater as a result of the assignment—the obligor may not be forced to do more than he originally agreed to do.

ASSIGNEE'S RIGHTS. The assignee (the third party) acquires no better right than the assignor had. His right to performance is subject to any fault which the obligor could have found with the right in the hands of the original obligee. In other words, if there is a defense available to him (fraud or misrepresentation, for instance) the obligor may use this defense against the assignee's claim just as he could have against the original obligee. If the obligor exercises such a claim, the assignee is left with only his action against the assignor for whatever consideration he has given up.

There are three implied warranties in an assignment. The assignor warrants (guarantees, according to common parlance) that there is a valid claim, that he has a right to assign it, and that there are no defenses available against it except as noted in the assignment. If any of these are not as warranted, the assignee has a right of action against the assignor. However, the assignor does not warrant that the obligor will be able to perform. If the obligor becomes bankrupt, for instance, the assignee may have to settle for considerably less than he bargained for. He takes the same risk here as he does in any claim where he is obligee.

If the obligor has made part payment to the assignor, or if he has a counterclaim against the assignor, the right obtained by the assignee may be subject to these claims. Black has a $6000 claim against White for installation of a machine. He assigns this claim to Gray in return for operating cash. If the installation proves to be substantially less than a proper performance, requiring White to spend $1000 more to put it in operating condition, this amount might be used as a set-off against the $6000 claim. As a result, Gray would get only $5000.

A gratuitous assignment creates no rights. If an assignment is made gratuitously (the assignor getting nothing back for it), the assignee gets nothing but a promise of a future gift. Such a promise is unenforceable. Until the assignee actually gets something, the gratuitous assignment may be recalled and avoided at will by the assignor.

NOTICE. A debtor cannot be charged with non-payment of his debt if he innocently pays a creditor who has assigned the obligation. To make the assignment legally effective, there must be notification. When an assignment of rights is made, the assignee obtains, along with his rights, a practical duty to notify the obligor of the assignment. If such notice is not given and the obligor pays his debt to his original creditor, the obligor's debt is discharged. The assignee is then left with his action for recovery against the assignor. If notice has been given to the obligor and he still pays the assignor, such payment does not discharge the obligor's debt.

It is possible, though unlawful, to make subsequent assignments of the same right. The results as to the respective assignees are somewhat controversial. Some court holdings are based on the argument that after the first assignment the assignor had nothing more to assign; consequently, subsequent assignments are null and void. Another view is taken by other courts. According to them, the first assignee to notify the obligor has priority in his claim. The argument here is that only proper notification completes the assignment. The losers, in either instance, have only their actions against the assignor.

WAGES. The assignment of future earnings for a present debt is governed by statute in most of the states. These statutes vary considerably, some making such assignments void. Many set a maximum amount (e.g., 25 per cent) which may be assigned from expected wages. In states where wage assignments are upheld, the right to lawfully assign future wages usually depends upon present employment. One must be presently employed to make an effective assignment of expected wages. Generally, if a person is employed, he can assign his wages even though it might be argued that the employment may be terminated at the option of his employer. However, an unemployed person cannot assign expected wages from hoped-for employment, even though his hopes may be well founded.

Third Party Beneficiary Contracts

If Black and White make a contract which will benefit Gray, what right does Gray have? The nature of the contract, the intent of the parties, and prior indebtedness existing between them all have a bearing on Gray's rights. Courts are not in complete agreement in their holdings in such cases. Given the same set of facts a case may be decided quite differently in two different jurisdictions. Only in insurance contracts is the law regarding third party beneficiaries likely to be applied uniformly.

INSURANCE. Probably the most common type of third party beneficiary contract is the life insurance contract. There are two possibilities relating to the beneficiary's right to recover following death of the insured. First, if the insured has purchased insurance from an insurer, he has the right to name anyone as beneficiary. When the insured dies, the beneficiary has a right of action to enforce his claim against the insurer. White contracts with the Black Insurance Co. to insure his own life, agreeing to pay the stipulated annual premiums, and naming Gray as beneficiary. When White dies, Gray can collect.

The second situation differs from the first in that it is the beneficiary who purchases the insurance. Gray contracts with the Black Insurance Co. to insure White's life. Gray agrees to pay the annual premiums and is to be beneficiary. For Gray's right as beneficiary to exist, he must be able to show an *insurable interest* in White's life; he must risk a loss which would occur upon White's death. In other words, there must be some anticipated benefit to result from White's continued existence. Insurable interest is present where the insured is a member of the beneficiary's immediate family. It does not extend to outsiders unless there is an economic tie involved, as between creditor and debtor or partners in an enterprise.

Insurable interest in property extends to those who have an owner or lien interest in the property or merely possession of it with the attendant risk of loss. Both mortgagor and mortgagee, for instance, have an insurable interest in real estate being purchased under a mortgage contract. There is a limit to the insurable interest created by an economic tie, though; usually the courts will not see justification for insurance very much in excess of the amount of economic benefit expected or the risk of loss involved.

The time when insurable interest must exist differs in the two types of insurance. In life insurance it must be shown to have existed at the time when the insurance contract was made. A later change in the relationship does not serve to terminate the insurance. In property insurance the insurable interest must exist when the loss is suffered.

DONEE BENEFICIARY.   An unsealed promise of a future gift is worthless as far as enforceability is concerned. That is, it is worthless if the donee tries to enforce it against the donor—as a contract it is unenforceable for lack of consideration. A donee beneficiary and an assignee in a gratuitous assignment are in about the same legal position. The difference between the two types of contracts essentially depends upon the time of the intent to benefit the third party. A contract *created* to benefit a third party is a beneficiary type contract; assignment of a right occurs after formation of a contract. Black is creditor and White is debtor to the extent of $500. If Black gratuitously assigns to Gray his right to collect the $500 from White, Black can renege on his promise at any time before Gray gets the money; Gray has nothing enforceable from Black until he receives payment. However, he does have an enforceable claim against White. In fact, either Black or Gray may undertake enforcement of the claim against White. In the above example Gray would have been third party beneficiary if the original contract between Black and White had given him the right to collect the $500. However, his rights would be the same in either case. In neither instance would he have a right of action against his benefactor.

CREDITOR BENEFICIARY.   Assume that Gray is to receive $500 in payment of an obligation which Black owes him. If Black and White make a contract whereby Black's consideration is to be paid for by White's paying $500 to Gray, Gray is a creditor beneficiary. As such he may enforce his claim against either Black or White. As a creditor beneficiary Gray is in a stronger position than he is as a donee beneficiary. He may collect from either the promisor or the promisee. He can sue the promisee on the previous debt or he can elect to force the promisor to perform.

INCIDENTAL BENEFICIARY.   There are innumerable situations in which contracts may be made which will indirectly benefit third parties. Failure of the promisor to perform properly does not necessarily give an incidental beneficiary the right to take legal action. Generally, if there was no intent by the contracting parties to benefit the third party, he has no legally enforceable interest in the contract. Brown hires White (a landscape architect) to landscape his estate. Gray, who lives next door, will incidentally benefit as a result of the landscaping. However, Gray has no legally enforceable interest in the completion of the landscaping.

Gray was not a party to the contract and whatever benefit he might have received was merely incidental to the primary purpose. Brown is a manufacturer and supplier of parts for the automotive industry. Brown contracts with Green, a builder of automation equipment, for Green to build and install an automatic machine. Gray supplies most of Green's steel. Although Gray would be likely to benefit from the automation contract, the agreement is not for his benefit and he could not enforce it.

Contracts in which the government is a party are sometimes considered to be third party beneficiary contracts. The logic is that citizens are to benefit from contracts made by the governing body, and that they have an interest in these contracts since they pay taxes and thereby acquire rights to benefits. If a small segment of a community is to receive benefits and, possibly, pay a special assessment toward them, the argument for enforcement by a citizen is even stronger. However, the right of a citizen to take action as a third party beneficiary to enforce a government-made contract is largely a matter of local statute.

R. B. TYLER CO. v. LAUREL EQUIPMENT CO

192 So. 573, 187 Miss. 590, 1940

GRIFFITH, Justice.

Appellant at the times mentioned herein was a general road contractor, and appellee was a dealer in motor trucks. Appellant had a contract with the State Highway Commission to do certain road work at McLain, in Greene County, among which was the hauling of what was estimated to be about 52,000 yards of sand. Appellant had made an arrangement with one J. J. Broome to perform this particular work, but Broome had no motor trucks with which to do it, nor any money with which to buy them, although he had arranged to borrow from a friend $800 with which to make the first or down payment on the necessary trucks and equipment.

In order to aid Broome in obtaining the trucks, appellant gave him the following letter:

McLain, Miss. June 19, 1937

To Whom It May Concern:

We, R. B. Tyler Co. have approximately fifty two thousand yards of sand to put on our project in McLain, Miss. We figure this between sixty and ninety days work for approximately ten trucks. Furthermore, we are willing to pay fifty per cent of the amount due the party furnishing, to the party selling the trucks, and the other fifty per cent to the party furnishing the trucks.

R. B. Tyler Co.
Per: J. B. Carrington.

With this letter in his hands Broome went to appellee, who, relying on the letter, made a contract with Broome, dated June 24, 1937, by which contract appellee agreed to sell to Broome, with delivery on or about June 26, 1937, ight used motor trucks, together with some additional motor truck equipment, he purchase price aggregating $3875, on which Broome paid the $800 already nentioned, and gave a series of weekly installment notes due from and including July 3, 1937, down to and including October 16, 1937.

After the delivery date of the trucks, as mentioned in the sales contract, Broome gave to appellee the following formal assignment:

Laurel, Mississippi, June 29, 1937

R. B. Tyler Company,
McLain, Mississippi.
Gentlemen:

I hereby assign to Laurel Equipment Company 50% of my weekly gross earnings until my indebtedness to them and to the Mississippi Truck Equipment Company or 8 used trucks and new hydraulic dump bodies has been entirely discharged.
This is in accordance with your letter of June 19th signed by Mr. Carrington.
Yours truly,

J. J. Broome

This assignment was sent down to McLain, after seven of the trucks had been delivered to Broome, and had been put to work, the testimony of appellee's general manager being that the assignment went down about the time the last truck was taken down there. When the assignment reached the office of appellant at McLain, it was endorsed at the bottom: "Accepted, J. B. Carrington."

No person was introduced as a witness who testified as to the terms of the contract between appellant and Broome. Apparently, it was not in writing. What was actually done by them, however, was that appellant at the end of each week paid all the payrolls of Broome for his truck drivers and other help; paid for the gasoline and oil used in operating the trucks; paid for repairs thereon, and deducted this from the total truck time for the week, and thereupon paid the entire balance to appellee, the Laurel Equipment Company. We must assume that the terms of the contract between appellant and Broome provided for this course of procedure; for what the parties to a contract consistently do thereunder throughout is evidence, indeed is often the best evidence, of what the contract between them required that they should do. And besides this, the proof discloses that appellee knew, or had knowledge sufficient to put it on notice, that Broome was without means to pay these necessary operation expenses except out of the current proceeds of the contract, and that without its being handled in the manner stated Broome could not have done the work at all.

The gross amount of the so-called truck time earned under the contract was $5,126.27. The total amount due Broome, after deducting the amounts paid for labor, oil, gasoline, repairs, etc., was $1,638.13, which latter amount, as already stated, was paid over in full to appellee. But appellee insisted that it should receive one half of the gross amount, or $2,578.13, it being the contention of appellee that the quoted letter of June 19th meant this, or if mistaken in that contention, then the quoted assignment of June 29th did expressly so state. Broome failed to pay the balance due on the trucks, appellee repossessed them under its retention of title contract, sold them at public sale, credited Broome with the proceeds; and the remainder of the debt being in excess of the difference between $2,578.13 and $1,638.13, appellee sued appellant for that differ ence and recovered in the trial court.

We do not agree that the letter of June 19th is properly to be interpreted a promising to pay to the seller of the trucks one half the gross proceeds of the work. The letter stated that appellant would pay to the party selling fifty per cent of the amount due the party furnishing them. Broome was the party who was furnishing the trucks; appellee was the party who was selling them to him And we have already shown that the amount due Broome under the contrac was subject to the deduction, before being due at all, of what was paid out by appellant for labor, gasoline, oil, repairs, etc.

This leaves to be considered what were the rights of appellee under the as signment of June 29th.

We think the rule must be accepted as well settled under the authorities that, so far as the assignment itself is concerned, one to whom a contractua right is assigned, takes such right subject to the burden of the provisions o the contract by which, and under which only, the assigned right would accrue to the assignor, or as otherwise sometimes expressed, the assignee is bound by the terms of the contract to the same extent as the assignor. 4 Am. Jur. pp. 234 235, 311, 312. The assignment of a contractual right confers only the righ which the assignor has therein, and no more. 6 C. J. 5, p. 1156. All this is upor the obvious proposition that a party may not transfer to another something which the transferrer does not own or to which he has himself no ultimate right

In fact, a right under a contract may not be assigned at all if the substitution of a right of the assignee for the right of the assignor would (1) vary materially the duty of the obligor, or (2) increase materially the burden or risk imposed upon him by his contract, or (3) impair materially his chance of obtaining re turn performance. Section 151, A.L.I. Rest. Contracts. From which it follow that to uphold an assignment as valid it must be construed so as not to do any of the three things next above mentioned.

The above statements of the rule may have simple illustrations. Thus where the contract between a railway company and its employee provided that the company might deduct from the wages of the employee any sums paid out by the company for board, meals and lodging of the employee, the right of the company to deduct such payments is upheld as against an assignee of the em ployee's wages. . . . Or we may take an every-day illustration. An owner con tracts with a builder for what is commonly called a lock and key job in the building of a residence, the gross contract price to be $3,000 on completion but the contract provides also that the owner shall pay or advance the weekly payroll of the carpenters and laborers employed in the work during its progress There the owner would be entitled to deduct the payments so made by him, as against an assignee of the contractor, although the latter had attempted to assign the entire gross contract sum of $3,000.

Nor does the acceptance of the assignment aid appellee under the facts here presented. The acceptance of the assignment by the obligor in the simple terms used in this case does not of itself create a new debt between him and the as signee, . . . ; and with no more in the facts than a formal acceptance, the rights of the assignee in the proceeds of a contract are still limited to the right which the assignor had in those proceeds. 6 C.J.S., Assignments, sec. 100

pages 1156, 1157. If, however, in the case before us, the assignee, first before making the sale and delivering the trucks to the assignor, had obtained the acceptance of the obligor to pay the assignee one half the gross proceeds of the contract—had the assignee in making the sale and deliveries acted in reliance upon the acceptance of the assignment rather than upon the assignment itself—a different question would be presented; but the evidence shows that the sale and deliveries were made to the assignor before the acceptance, appellee's chief witness having testified, as already stated, that the last of the several trucks went down about the time the assignment was sent down. Reliance not having been placed on the acceptance and delivery having been made before the acceptance, the legal effect of the acceptance was but an acknowledgement of the assignment, and created no new or independent obligation.

In fact, appellee expressly averred in its bill, and the proof shows that it relied on the letter of appellant, dated June 19th, in making its sale of the trucks and equipment to Broome and on its insistence that the letter implied by its terms that the payments made by appellant to the seller of the trucks would be fifty per cent of the gross proceeds of the work, an interpretation which we have rejected. Appellee does not mention in its bill that in making the sale and delivery of the trucks and equipment to Broome, it relied on appellant's formal acceptance of the assignment; and if it had so averred the proof would not sustain that averment.

Applying the pertinent rules of law to the facts disclosed by the record, we are of the opinion that appellee was not entitled to recover anything of appellant, and that the bill should have been dismissed.

Reversed, and decree here for appellant.

REVIEW QUESTIONS

1. What is meant by *privity of contract?*

2. Black is purchasing a house under a real estate mortgage held by the White Mortgage Company. Under the terms of the mortgage Black is obligated to make a payment to White Mortgage Company each month. Part of the payment is for interest, another part reduces the mortgage balance, and a third part is deposited in an escrow account to pay for taxes and insurance. Black sells his house to Gray, with Gray agreeing to take over the mortgage payments. If Gray defaults can White Mortgage Co. take action to recover from Black?

3. Why must the obligor be notified of an assignment?

4. What is meant by insurable interest?

5. Distinguish between assignment and a third party beneficiary contract.

6. According to the case of *R. B. Tyler Co. v. Laurel Equipment Co.*, how much is assigned in an assignment of "gross earnings"? If Laurel Equipment Company had waited for receipt of the June 29th assignment before starting delivery of the trucks, how would the outcome of the case have been changed?

14 DISCHARGE

Contracts, as you have observed, are made every day. They are quite ordinary things. Agreements are made and the terms of the agreements are usually carried out in a reasonable manner. This chapter deals with the exceptions, where a party has bargained away more than he intended, or where performance became more difficult than was expected. Public attention is called to exceptions; they are publicized in court cases and newspaper articles. It must be kept in mind, however, that these cases are exceptions, and that the vast majority of contracts are carried out satisfactorily and with benefit to both parties.

In this chapter we shall see how the court interprets contracts. We shall see how well the parties are held to their bargain, what constitutes performance, or a real offer to perform. We shall see when the law will discharge a person's obligations for him. Then, in Chapter 15, we shall examine the remedies available if a contract is breached by one of the parties to it.

Before the court can rule in a contracts case it must know what the parties have agreed to do. This is the first job and sometimes actually the only job with which the court is faced. Determining what the parties have obligated themselves to do is known legally as "construction." Essentially, this means interpretation. The court attempts to interpret from the wording of the contract the legal relationships of the parties. To do this the law has settled upon certain rules and guides, only the more prominent of which will be reviewed here.

RULES ON CONSTRUCTION

Which Law Governs

Contract law varies somewhat from state to state. Parties to a contract may be residents of different states when the contract is made. For example, after a series of offers and counter-offers, Black, in Detroit, Michigan makes an offer which appeals to White in Chicago, Illinois and White accepts. If a question concerning the contract arises, according to which law will the question be settled? The courts are not entirely in accord in the answer to this. However, as a general rule, questions involving the validity, reality, and construction of a contract are answered according to the laws of the state in which the last act necessary to bring the contract into existence was performed. In the example above, the Illinois law would determine the outcome of a case of fraud or duress on the contract.

As to performance of a contract, generally the law of the state in which performance is to take place governs. If the contract between Black and White were to be performed in Indianapolis, the laws of Indiana would govern the performance.

Intent

The court attempts to interpret the contract according to the apparent intent of the parties when the contract was formed. To do this, the court looks at the circumstances surrounding the formation, and at the parties' conduct since then. Looking at the entire picture, what must have been their intentions? What the parties say about their intentions is not, of course, very good evidence. The intentions may well have changed since the contract was made. Black agrees to build a special machine for White for $120,000. Before he begins work Black is offered an opportunity to completely automate a production line for Gray for $500,000 and at a much greater profit. Black cannot complete both jobs satisfactorily within the time limit set so he decides to break his contract with White. If taken to court, Black might well attempt to argue that his agreement with White was merely a tentative arrangement rather than a contract. For this reason the court would look into the circumstances surrounding the transaction—such as letters and testimony of disinterested parties—rather than take Black's testimony as controlling the case.

Parol-evidence Rule

One frequently hears of people entering into insurance contracts, chattel mortgages, conditional sales contracts, and other long-term agreements on the basis of what salesmen have told them, without having read the agreements themselves. Mildly speaking, this is foolishness. Read before you sign! The written agreement sets forth the obligations of the parties as far as the court is concerned. No testimony about the preliminary negotiations of the parties is allowed to alter the terms of a written contract or add to them. The rule is not absolute or all-inclusive; it is used reasonably. There are circumstances in which oral testimony concerning a written contract is admissible. Briefly, these exceptions to the parol-evidence rule are:

1. Where there is a question of reality of the agreement (for instance, fraud or duress).

2. Where one of the parties may not have had capacity to contract (for instance, a minor).

3. Where there may have been lack or failure of consideration.

4. Where the language of the writing is not clear to the court, possibly from the use of terms common to a particular trade or profession.

5. Where a new agreement over the same subject matter may have been made.

Black purchases a machine from White for $5000. In the negotiations White stated that he would repair the machine free of charge until 6 months after its purchase. When reduced to writing the contract says nothing about this warranty. Black would not be allowed to give oral testimony to establish and enforce the warranty in a court action. If the contract had not been reduced to writing the warranty could have been enforced, once it was established that such a warranty had been given. Even though the warranty could not be enforced, testimony might be allowed as proof that White used the promise to repair fraudulently to persuade Black to enter into the contract.

Wording Used

It is quite apparent that words may be used either to explain or to confuse a meaning. If insurance policies written by various companies are examined, examples can easily be found to confuse almost anyone who might read them. Other policies may be found which say just about the same thing in such clear language that almost anyone who can read can understand them. The court construes a written contract most strongly against the writer. Therefore it is advisable, at least for those of us who are not lawyers, to write in clear, simple language which is capable of only one interpretation.

Words are generally given their usual, unspecialized meanings in a court of law. If the words used have a particular meaning in the geographical area involved, or in a certain trade or profession involved in the case, this meaning will be given to the words. If the wording is inconsistent in various parts of the contract, the contract as a whole will be interpreted according to the intentions of the parties, and the wording construed to follow those intentions. If two different interpretations are possible, one lawful and the other unlawful, the lawful interpretation will be assumed by the court. If words and figures or words and abbreviations are in conflict, the words will govern.

PERFORMANCE

Theoretically, a party to whom a contractual obligation is owed has a right to precise performance of that obligation. Anything short of the performance to which he is entitled would be cause for a damage action against the other party to the agreement. However, performance or nonperformance is not always as self-evident as it might appear. The nature of the obligation undertaken determines the performance. As noted earlier in Chapter 10, on consideration, where a liquidated amount of money is owed, payment of a lesser amount will not satisfy the obligation. Where the contract requires building something, though, exact performance may not always occur and cannot seriously be expected. This is particularly true where research and development is to be part of the performance of the contract. Such is the case in many engineering contracts.

Conditions

Frequently contracts are so written that the apparent intent of the parties is that performance by one party will precede performance by the other. For instance, one might contract to have a machine built and installed in his plant with payment to be made when the installation is complete. A condition such as this would constitute a condition precedent in a contract.

Commonly, the obtaining of an architect's certificate is made a condition precedent. So, also, is the passage of time until the completion date.

Architects' Approval

Where an architect's approval is required by a contract clause, the courts will usually enforce it. However, it must be recognized that architects are human, too, and capable of human failings. The architect may have died or may be insane when his certificate is required. Or he may unreasonably or fraudulently refuse to issue his certificate. Under such circumstances the court will ordinarily dispense with the requirement of the architect's certificate. If there is any sound reason for the architect's objections though, the court will enforce the requirement.

Satisfactory Performance

Where the purchaser of a certain performance must be satisfied, two possibilities exist. The nature of the contract may be such that the only test of satisfaction is the personal taste of the buyer. Black, an artist, agrees to paint White's portrait to White's satisfaction for $5000. White may never be satisfied even though to a third person the portrait appears to be a perfect likeness. White could conceivably state, after each submission of the portrait for his approval, that "it just isn't me" and require Black to continue. If the court determined the contract to be binding (the consideration of Black's performance might be termed illusory), Black would have to continue to paint or breach his contract.

If the nature of the contract is such that, even though satisfaction of the buyer is specified, it provides for mechanical or operational suitability, it is a different story. In this case, if performance is such that it would satisfy a reasonable person, the court will deem the condition satisfied. Black agrees to install an air-conditioning system for White, to White's satisfaction. After the installation, if White says he is not satisfied, Black may still collect by proving that the air-conditioning system will do all that a reasonable person could expect it to do.

Completion Date

Time limits are frequently stated in contracts. Where performance is to take place by a certain date and it actually extends beyond that date, any of several situations may result. In many contracts there are provisions for liquidated damages (so-called penalty clauses) which set forth an amount to be paid for each day's delay beyond the date specified in the contract. If the amount specified reasonably covers the damage which would be caused by delay, it will be enforced. If the amount of the liquidated damages is excessive, the court will hold that it is really a penalty clause and will refuse to enforce it. It is the prerogative of the court and not of the private citizen to assess penalties. If there is no liquidated damage clause, and performance runs beyond the time agreed upon, the court may be called upon to estimate damages. Usually, either court-estimated damages or liquidated damages merely serve to reduce the price paid for the work accomplished. Ordinarily, nothing but very unreasonable lateness of performance would give the buyer of the performance sufficient grounds to rescind the contract. Where performance is not unreasonable, the buyer must accept the performance, but at a price reduced by the damage which he has suffered.

In certain circumstances time of performance is critical in a contract. In this event, a clause to the effect that "time is of the essence of the contract" usually is included. In instances such as this where such a clause is included the courts generally will allow rescission of the contract for late performance.

Substantial Performance

Nearly all building contracts or contracts in which machinery or equipment is to be built and installed are performed in a manner which deviates from that specified. Some flaw in such a project can be found by looking long enough and thoroughly enough. If variations from specifications were not to be condoned at all, few projects would ever be undertaken and fewer yet would be paid for. Those completed would cost so dearly that very few could afford them. As it is, if a building contract calls for a concrete floor of a uniform five-inch thickness, it is not likely that the resulting floor will be precisely five inches thick throughout. However, if the result accomplished approximates closely the result specified, the contractor can still recover his price. His performance has been *substantially* the same as that specified. If gross inaccuracies occur, or if substitutions are found to have been made which do not reasonably satisfy the specifications, it is no longer substantial performance. Just where the line will be drawn between substantial performance and outright contract breach is a question of fact, and is properly submitted to a jury. Substantial-performance cases frequently result in the performer receiving the amount for which he has contracted, less damages. The extent of damages is determined by the value of the performance rendered compared with the value of the performance specified, or the cost of additional work to complete the performance properly.

Substantial performance assumes that the performer has pursued his contract in good faith and with the intent that his performance would agree with the standards specified. If this is not the case—if the performer wilfully abandons the performance or the work is unreasonably poor—he may not be able to recover anything as a result of his breach of the contract.

Impossibility of Performance

The law, as it deals with impossibility of performance, is not entirely clear or settled. In certain cases involving death or illness of the promisor, definite statements can be made. In other cases, particularly where performance has turned out to be much more difficult than was anticipated, general conclusions can be drawn from the majority of decisions, but numerous exceptions may also be cited.

Generally, when a person undertakes a contractual obligation he assumes certain risks. He can hedge against such risks in various ways. He can insert contract clauses which state that if certain things occur he will be excused from performance. He can add enough money in the price to cover "contingencies." Or he can purchase insurance against the risks he assumes. In fact, almost the only hazard which he can't cover in some way when he makes the contract is liability for his performance if the public is injured by it. For example injuries resulting from the collapse of a public building built by the contractor, which collapse was caused by his negligence, would allow recovery against him by either the injured person or the insurance company.

DEATH OR ILLNESS.   Ordinarily, death or illness of a party to a contract does not discharge that contract. If a person dies or becomes incapacitated by illness, his estate or those appointed to act for him, must take over and complete his obligations. Only where a contract is such that personal services are involved, will death or incapacity because of illness serve as a lawful excuse for nonperformance. For instance, death or illness of a free-lance consulting engineer would discharge his remaining obligations to his clients.

DESTRUCTION OF AN ESSENTIAL TO THE CONTRACT.   By destruction of an essential to a contract is meant destruction of something without which the contract cannot be performed. Black hires the White Construction Company to build an addition to his plant. Before the work is begun the plant is destroyed by fire without fault of either party. White Construction Company's obligation is terminated. If the White Construction Company had begun work and were, say, half done, White's obligation to complete the structure would be ended, but White could collect for the work which his company had completed in addition to any materials which had been accepted by Black. If, as a third possibility, the contract had been for the building of a structure by itself (not an addition to an existing structure), and if the work again were half done by the time the building was destroyed, White Construction Co.'s obligation would not be ended and the contractor would have to rebuild. One cannot make an addition to a structure which no longer exists, but he can build a separate structure even though his first attempt to do so was destroyed.

UNEXPECTED HARDSHIP.   As previously indicated, one who contracts to perform in some way runs a risk that conditions may not remain as they are when he enters into the contract, or that conditions may not be as they seem. It is not an uncommon experience to have a materials price increase or a wage increase cut deeply into the profit margin. If the cause of hardship is anything that the contractor reasonably could have anticipated, the courts will not relieve him of his duties. It is only where the difficulties which have arisen are of a nature such that no one reasonably could have anticipated them that the court may, in some way, either relieve the burden or lighten the load on the contractor. Under such circumstances a subsequent contract with the owner, whereby the contractor is to receive more money for his performance, may be enforceable in court. Or the court may enforce a subsequent contract to give the contractor more time in which to perform. It should be remembered though that these rulings are exceptions and that if the difficulty were forseeable the law would give no relief. A subsequent contract based upon a forseeable difficulty which did arise (e.g., a materials price rise) is void for lack of consideration as to the increase in the contract price.

COMMERCIAL FRUSTRATION. The doctrine of commercial frustration is often treated in the same manner as the destruction of an essential to a contract. In the United States courts the result is the same. Commercial frustration commonly results from a contract which was made to take advantage of some future event not controlled by either party. The event is then called off and, as a result, the contract has no purpose. Black leases a concession stand from White for a certain week during which an athletic event is to be held. The athletic event is called off (or moved to a different location). The courts would allow Black to avoid his lease contract. Similarly, if a law were passed preventing such an event, Black would not be held to his contract.

Prevention of Performance

In every contract it is implied that each party will allow the other to perform his obligation. If one of the parties prevents performance by the other, he thereby discharges the other party's obligation, and he subjects himself to the possibility of a severe damage action should the other party be inclined to sue. Black sells White some standing timber, giving White a license to use a private road to the timber. Black prevents White from using the road. White's obligation is terminated and he may sue Black for damages.

Waiver

A waiver consists of voluntarily giving up a right to which one is legally entitled. To waive a right a party must first know that he is entitled to it. He must also intend to give up the right. If Black purchases a machine from White according to a description, specification or sample he can expect to receive the described machine. If the actual machine received varies significantly from the description, Black has a right to refuse to accept it. If, with knowledge of the difference involved, Black keeps the machine and uses it as his own, he has waived his right to return the machine to White and get one more closely resembling the description. Black's failure to do anything about the discrepancy would be an *implied* waiver. If after receipt and examination of the machine

Black had told White that he intended to keep it despite its variation from the description, this would amount to an *express* waiver.

Agreement

RENUNCIATION.   If two parties have a right to make a contract by an agreement between them, it is only reasonable that they could also agree to disagree. If no rights of a third person are involved the parties may discharge their contract by mutual agreement without performance in several ways. The parties may agree merely not to be bound by the terms of the original agreement or they may make a new contract involving the same subject matter, thus discharging the old contract. The original agreement, itself, may specify some event, the occurrence of which will end the contractual relation. Both of the parties may ignore their rights under the contract, each going about his business in such a manner that a waiver of performance may be implied from his actions. When a contract is discharged by these methods, the release of one party constitutes the consideration for the release of the other.

ACCORD AND SATISFACTION.   Accord and satisfaction occurs when a party agrees to accept a substitute performance for the one to which he was entitled. Ordinarily this occurs when there has been a breach of performance by one party, giving the other party cause to sue. In common terminology it is the "settlement out of court" which one frequently hears about in connection with both contract and tort cases.

To be effective as a discharge, both accord and satisfaction must have occurred. Accord refers to a separate agreement, substituted for the original one. Satisfaction occurs when the conditions of the accord have been met.

NOVATION.   A novation replaces one of the parties to a contract. For a novation to be legally effective, all the parties to a contract must agree to it. For a simple illustration, assume that Black owes White $100. White owes Gray $100. If the three parties agree that Gray will collect his $100 from Black, a novation has occurred which completely relieves White of his obligation to Gray. Black no longer owes White $100, but has a legally enforceable obligation to pay Gray. Common examples of novation occur when a person buys a house or a car from another, substituting himself as a mortgagor and agreeing to make the loan payments to the lending institution.

ARBITRATION.   A court action for damages is sometimes impractical because of the time required for it or the cost involved or for some other reason. In many states it is possible to substitute a procedure known as arbitration for a court action. Arbitration is a procedure in which a dispute is submitted to an impartial umpire or board of umpires whose decision on the matter is final and binding. The legality of the procedure depends upon the statutes of the state in which the controversy arises. At common law, arbitration has no standing; even though a decision had been rendered by an arbitrator, the cause might still be taken to court and the arbitration would have no effect. Many of the states have seen in arbitration a means of relieving crowded court dockets and have passed laws setting up the procedure and giving an arbitration decision almost the same force as a court judgment. In these states, almost any controversy in which damages are requested can be submitted to arbitration—not just contract cases, but tort cases and even property settlements following divorces.

Arbitration has several inherent advantages when it is compared to court proceedings. Probably the main advantage is found in specialization —the disputing parties decide among themselves what person is to act as judge and jury. This allows them to select someone who has a specialized knowledge of the field involved—someone who would not have to be educated on the general technical principles before deciding the case. Often this results in a more equitable decision than a judge and jury might render in court.

A second advantage of arbitration is found in the speed of the procedure. Court dockets are quite crowded—it is not unusual for a year to pass before a particular case comes up, and delays as long as five years occur in some jurisdictions. In the intervening period witnesses may have died or moved away, and, certainly, memories have dimmed. Arbitration affords an immediate solution. Today's dispute may be settled yet today or tomorrow if the parties so desire. It is only necessary to select a disinterested person and submit the dispute to him for decision. A minimum of formality is involved.

Cost saving is a third advantage which may result from arbitration. In addition to the saving of whatever monetary value may be attached to waiting time, the cost of the procedure itself is often less than court costs.

Arbitration is not bound by the evidence rules encountered in a court of law. Whether this is an advantage or a disadvantage is questionable and would depend largely on the case. However, if the arbitrator considers hearsay testimony, for instance, as desirable in determining an issue, such testimony can be taken.

In states where arbitration is used, the proceeding is conducted as an extrajudicial action of a court. Questions of law may be submitted to the court for determination and the final arbitration award is enforced by the court.

There are three main legal requirements for arbitration. 1) The parties must agree to arbitrate—when the agreement to arbitrate took place is of

little matter as long as the parties did agree at some time prior to th
arbitration. 2) A formal document known as a *submission* must be pre
pared by the parties and given to the court. The submission is roughly
combination of the complaint and reply required in a court case;
presents the issue to be decided. 3) The arbitrator(s) must be imparti
and disinterested parties. If these requirements are met, the arbitrator
award will bind the parties.

The popularity of arbitration as a means of settling disputes has in
creased considerably in recent years. Probably the main reason for th
is the efficiency of the procedure. It is conceivable that laws *requirin*
arbitration in certain types of civil cases may be passed to further reliev
the courts of burdensome cases in civil disputes.

Tender of Performance

Tender of performance, if refused, may discharge the obligation c
a party to a contract. There are three conditions, however, which mus
prevail in a lawful tender of performance:

1. The party offering to perform must be ready, willing, and able to per
   form the obligation called for.
2. The offer to perform must be made in a reasonable manner at th
   proper time and place according to the contract.
3. It must be unconditional.

Not only is the obligation discharged if such a tender is refused, but th
party who refused has breached the contract and may be sued fc
damages or specific performance, as the case may dictate.

There is one notable exception to the general rule of tender of per
formance discharging an obligation. If it is an offer to pay a debt whic
is due and payable in money, the debt is not discharged by refusal c
the payment. However, there are three rather important effects:

1. The accrual of interest is stopped.
2. Any liens used to secure the debt are discharged.
3. Any surety for the debt is no longer obligated.

If the debt is payable in money, an offer to pay with anything other tha
legal tender may be refused by the creditor; he is under no duty to ac
cept a check, for instance. If the offer to pay is made before maturit
of the debt, the creditor need not accept. In such cases, if the credito

rejects the offer to pay, for the reasons indicated, there has been no tender of performance.

Anticipatory Breach

Breach of contract ordinarily results from someone's failing to perform his obligation as agreed and at the proper time. However, a contract may be breached before the time of performance has arrived. If the party who is to perform notifies the other party that he cannot or will not perform when the time comes for him to do so, an anticipatory breach has occurred. Such anticipatory breach gives the would-be recipient of the performance two possibilities if he still desires performance:

1. He may sue the nonperforming party for whatever damage may have been caused by the breach.

2. He may obtain performance from someone else if it is possible to do so.

Black Construction Company agrees, as general contractor, to build a structure for White. Gray is hired as subcontractor to do the electrical work. A month before the electrical work is to be undertaken Gray informs Black that he cannot do it because of other commitments. At this point, if there were no rule as to anticipatory breach, Black would be in quite a dilemma. If he obtained the electrical work from someone else and Gray subsequently had a change of heart, Gray could demand to be allowed to perform and sue if he were to be denied the opportunity to do so. If Black hired a second subcontractor and then Gray returned and performed the work, the second subcontractor could sue. If he waited until he was certain that the contract was breached, thus causing him to be late with his contract, White could sue him. Anticipatory breach gives him a way out. Black can hire another electrical contractor to do the work without any fear that Gray will be able to take successful action against him. Of course, Gray has the right to change his mind at any time before Black takes such a step, thus resuming his obligation. Generally, information of anticipatory breach must come directly to the innocent party to give him a right to act on it. And the source of the information must be sound enough to justify the action—vague rumors are not enough.

Anticipatory breach cannot occur in regard to payment of a debt. Although a debtor may notify his creditor that he cannot or will not pay his debt when due, the creditor must wait until the duty to pay has actually been breached before he may take action. The creditor, of course, is not likely to be placed in a dilemma similar to that in which Black, in the foregoing example, would find himself in the absence of anticipatory breach.

BY OPERATION OF LAW

Certain laws have been passed and rules developed to provide for contract discharge as a matter of law. In Chapter 11, "Lawful Subject Matter," the result of a change in legislation was discussed, showing the effect of legislation in discharge of contracts. Here we will consider alteration of the contract, the statute of limitations, bankruptcy, and creditor's compositions.

Alteration of the Contract

If a contract is intentionally altered by some of the parties to it, without the remaining parties taking part in or having knowledge of the alteration, the obligations of the remaining parties under the contract are discharged. A party cannot be held to changes in contract terms if he had no hand in making the changes. Black uses White as surety to secure a $500 loan from Gray, dated July 1, and due Sept. 1. During August it appears to Black that he will not be able to meet his obligation on schedule. Black asks Gray for a loan extension to Oct. 1, to which Gray agrees. On Oct. 1, Gray, discovering that Black has gone and has left no forwarding address, turns to White as surety. White's surety agreement would not be enforceable against him under these circumstances unless he had been made a party to the extension.

Statute of Limitations

Each of the states has adopted a statute which limits the suable life of a contract. Most of the states specify a certain length of time for oral contracts, a longer time for written contracts, and a still longer time for contracts under seal. The state of Florida, for instance, specifies 3 years for oral contracts, 5 years for written contracts, and 20 years for contracts under seal. A party who has a right of action on a contract must take such action within the time limits stated in the statute or he loses his right to take such action. The time is figured from the date that the contract was breached, but with the possibility of renewal whenever the debt is acknowledged in any way, e.g. by part payment. Under most statutes time does not continue to run while the person who has breached is outside the state. Black orally hires White to add a roof to a structure. The contract is made March 1, 1955. White finishes his performance on March 31, 1955, but is never paid. If the statute of limitations states five years for this type of contract, White has until March 31, 1960 to commence his court action for recovery. In most states, if Black made a part payment or in some other way acknowledged the debt on, say, April 15, 1957, the time for White to take action would not expire until April 15, 1962. Similarly, if Black left the state for a year, White would have until March 31, 1961 to begin his suit. If suit is not begun by the dates mentioned, White loses his right to take action for recovery.

Although the legal duty to perform a contract is ended by the statute of limitations, it may be reinstated by the debtor. Any act or promise by the debtor by which he could be said to resume the obligation will revive it and give the contract new life under the statute. If Black made part payment for the roof in 1963, the statute of limitations would start to run again. Much the same is true of bankruptcy, discussed below. Reacknowledgement by the debtor of a debt discharged in bankruptcy serves to reinstate its legal life despite the discharge.

Bankruptcy

When a person owes more than he can pay, should the law help him or leave him where it finds him? Should one creditor be allowed to receive payment for his entire debt at the expense of other creditors? These and similar questions have been debated by legislatures since the problem of bankruptcy was first recognized.

It is not surprising that our Constitution gives Congress the power to establish "uniform laws on the subject of bankruptcies throughout the United States." Debt was the greatest single cause of imprisonment at the time of the American Revolution. Inability to pay a debt was a prison offense. In fact, forgiving a debtor's obligations and allowing him to begin again with a clean slate is somewhat of an innovation in the law. Bankruptcy proceedings for the purpose of paying off creditors are not new, but it is only recently that the debtor could receive discharge of his obligations in such an action.

Three federal bankruptcy laws were passed and repealed after very short lives before our present act was passed in 1898. Our Bankruptcy Act has two main purposes: 1) to obtain an equitable distribution among the creditors of whatever assets the debtor may have, and 2) to discharge an honest debtor from future liability on the obligations. To accomplish these purposes the Bankruptcy Act provides for:

1. Full disclosure and surrender of the debtor's assets.
2. Appointment of a referee to supervise the creditor's meetings.
3. Creditor's meetings in which claims are allowed and a trustee elected to take over the debtor's estate.
4. Discharge of the debtor.

The legal machinery enacted to carry out these steps is quite lengthy and complicated. Our purposes will be adequately served if we consider only a simplified version of these steps here.

The Bankruptcy Act is a federal law. Bankruptcy petitions are filed in a U. S. District Court, which normally appoints a referee to conduct the proceedings. Appeal of a bankruptcy case may be made to a U. S. Circuit Court of Appeals and, finally, to the U. S. Supreme Court.

TO WHOM THE LAW APPLIES. A distinction is made between voluntary bankruptcy and involuntary bankruptcy in the law. Almost anyone who has the capacity to make a contract may become bankrupt voluntarily. The only requirement is possession of debts. The prospective voluntary bankrupt is not even required to be insolvent although, as a practical matter, bankruptcy would be pointless otherwise.

There are five types of public and quasi-public organizations which cannot go bankrupt under the Bankruptcy Act—there are special statutes for them. These five are: 1) banks, 2) building and loan associations, 3) railroads, 4) insurance companies, and 5) municipalities. Neither voluntary nor involuntary bankruptcy is available to them under the act.

Involuntary bankruptcy may be forced upon anyone except the five organizations mentioned above and farmers and wage earners. The two added exclusions sound large but, nowadays, it essentially boils down to an exclusion of farmers. Since a wage earner is anyone who works for wages not exceeding $1500 per year according to the law, few people are to be found in this category.

CREDITOR. For bankruptcy purposes, a creditor is a person to whom the debtor owes an *unsecured* obligation. A person who holds title to or an equitable interest in a particular thing which the debtor has is not a creditor. Black has bought a car from White under a conditional sales agreement and a house from Gray on a real estate mortgage. Neither White nor Gray would be a creditor in a bankruptcy action. Each would be entitled to exercise his interest in a particular part of Black's property. Only if sale of the property returned an insufficient amount to pay Black's obligation to, say, White would he then be considered a creditor and be allowed to share in Black's remaining estate.

PETITION. To go bankrupt voluntarily a debtor need only petition a U. S. District Court for bankruptcy action. However, to be driven bankrupt, the procedure is a little more complicated. Involuntary bankruptcy requires that the debtor owe at least $1,000 in unsecured obligations. The obligations owing to those creditors who bring the action must total at least $500. If the debtor has more than 12 creditors, at least three must join in the action; if there are 12 or fewer creditors, the action requires only one.

In addition to the necessity for the creditors to meet the above requirements, the debtor must have committed an *act of bankruptcy* if a petition for involuntary bankruptcy is to be lodged successfully. There are six acts of bankruptcy: 1) fraudulent conveyance. If the debtor conveys, conceals, or removes his property in an effort to hinder, delay, or defraud his creditors he has committed an act of bankruptcy. The debtor transferring title to property to his wife's name, or removing it from his state would give his creditors cause to act; 2) preference. If the debtor is insolvent—has more liabilities than assets—he must exercise care in payment of his creditors or risk committing the second act of bankruptcy. If it appears from payment to some of his creditors that he intended to prefer them over the others, the others may bring a bankruptcy action; 3) judicial liens. It is to the obvious advantage of an individual creditor to have security for his debt. If, to obtain such security, the creditor establishes a lien against the insolvent debtor's property and the debtor allows it to remain, the debtor has committed the third act of bankruptcy; 4) general assignment. If the insolvent debtor transfers his property into the hands of a third party, to be liquidated and divided among his creditors, he has given his creditors reason to act; 5) receiver. Allowing a receiver to be appointed (e.g. by a state court) is an act of bankruptcy; 6) written admission. Admission by the debtor in writing of his inability to pay his debts and his willingness to become bankrupt is an act of bankruptcy.

DEBTOR'S PROPERTY.   Not all of the debtor's property may be taken from him—bankruptcy is not allowed to "take the shirt off the debtor's back," so to speak. Statutes in the various states, commonly known as "homestead laws," specify a minimum of property with which the debtor must be left. Then, too, that property which is being used to secure a loan is not available for division among the unsecured creditors until it has been sold and the loan satisfied. Anything left over after the sale of such security property and payment of the secured loan balance goes into the general pot.

PROCEDURE.   The first step in bankruptcy following the appointment of a referee is the calling of creditor's meetings. In these meetings three orders of business are undertaken. First, creditor's claims are allowed or disallowed. Second, a trustee is elected and, after qualification, takes over as owner of the debtor's estate, with the duty to turn the estate into money in the best interests of all parties. Third, the debtor is examined by the referee (and the creditors, if they wish) to determine the facts of the bankruptcy and the truth of the debtor's disclosures.

DEBTS.   If a creditor is to share in the bankrupt's estate, his claim must be proved and allowed. Nearly all claims arising from contract are provable. Certain claims have priority and must be paid before distribution of the estate among the creditors. Costs of preserving the assets and administration of the bankruptcy are paid in full. Claims of employees (wage earners) earned with three months prior to filing bankruptcy are paid up to $600 for each employee. Taxes assessed by the United States or any political subdivision must be paid. Whatever is left is shared by the general creditors.

Certain debts are not capable of being discharged by bankruptcy even though the debtor receives discharge. His discharge has no effect upon:

1. Any remainder of taxes.
2. Alimony or child support.
3. Liability for fraud or tort if no action was taken prior to bankruptcy.
4. Any remaining unpaid employee's wages earned in the three months prior to bankruptcy.
5. Money held to secure faithful performance.
6. Money due a creditor who had no knowledge of the proceedings, a so-called "nonprovable" claim.

DISCHARGE.   As far as the debtor is concerned, the objective of bankruptcy proceedings is discharge of his obligations. Such a discharge will generally be forthcoming if the debtor has dealt honestly and fairly with his creditors and the court during the action. Most of the reasons for denying discharge are based upon actual or reasonably suspected deceit by the debtor. Discharge is denied for the following reasons:

1. The debtor has received a discharge in bankruptcy within the past six years.
2. Debtor made a fraudulent transfer within one year before the petition for bankruptcy was filed.
3. Debtor failed to keep or preserve accounts of transactions.
4. Debtor refused to explain or failed to explain satisfactorily any losses of assets.
5. Debtor refused to obey a lawful court order during the proceedings.
6. Debtor committed an offense punishable by imprisonment under the act.
7. Debtor obtained property or credit by a fraudulent financial statement.

Once the debtor has been through the bankruptcy mill and has received his discharge, his contractual obligations are ended. New property acquired by him belongs to him, free from claims of his previous creditors. One exception to this generality exists—if he gains new property by means of inheritance within six months after bankruptcy, it can be taken from him by the trustee to satisfy the creditors. Aside from this, though, he is given a new lease on life in a debt-free world.

Creditors' Compositions

It is often to the advantage of both the creditors and the debtor to avoid bankruptcy proceedings. There are many costs of bankruptcy and each cost reduces the assets to be divided. It is costly, for instance, to pay the receiver and the trustee to maintain and then dispose of the property involved. There is a much less expensive procedure available. The creditors' composition does almost the same thing as bankruptcy. It discharges the debtor's obligations. Each participating creditor gets some return on his account receivable. The procedure is informal but binding. It is not necessary that all the creditors join in the composition; two or more are sufficient—if only one creditor is involved it is not a creditor's composition and the remainder of the debtor's obligation is not discharged, as pointed out in Chapter 10, "Consideration." Black owes White $1000, Gray $2000, and Brown $3000. Black has $3000 cash available plus various other assets, but finds that he cannot pay all his debts and remain solvent. Black meets with White, Gray, and Brown, telling them of the situation. The creditors are faced with the possibility of bankruptcy proceedings where, after the costs are paid and Black's assets sold for whatever price they may bring, the creditors may get $.25 for each dollar of debt. As an alternative the creditors may choose to divide Black's cash assets in any way they see fit, $.50 for each dollar being one such possibility. The creditors may agree, instead of taking a straight percentage, to divide the assets in some other way which is satisfactory to each. They might agree, for instance, that White will receive $600, Gray $1000, and Brown $1400.

There are several explanations of the consideration involved in a creditor's composition. Perhaps the most common one holds that the consideration received by each creditor for giving up his right to sue for the remainder of his debt is found in the forbearance of the same right by the other creditors. Several states have statutes which specifically state the conditions and procedures for creditors' compositions. Where such statutes exist, examination of the consideration involved is, of course, unnecessary.

MINELLA v. PHILLIPS

345 F. 2d 687, 65 ALR 2d 994 Texas (June 20, 1957)

JONES, Circuit Judge.

Angelo Minella, the appellant, was in the plumbing supply business in Houston, Texas. He was adjudicated a bankrupt on August 23, 1955. He filed a petition for discharge which was opposed by the trustee in bankruptcy and by several creditors. During the eighteen months prior to bankruptcy, the appellant drew out of his business over $75,000. His books showed these withdrawals charged to him, but did not show what disposition he made of the funds withdrawn. During this period the appellant deposited in his bank account nearly $30,000 and claimed he had gambling losses of about $15,000. No explanation was made as to what became of the difference of $30,000, more or less. In the bankruptcy schedules which the appellant made and filed, a question was asked as to losses from fire, theft or gambling within the year prior to the filing of the petition. The appellant gave the question this answer, "Gambling, about $15,-000 in various places in Galveston." At the first meeting of creditors the appellant testified that over a period of a year he gambled "sometimes twice a week, maybe once, maybe not for two or three weeks." He was asked the places where he gambled. At first he answered, "Well, I really don't know". On being reminded that he was under oath he explained and amplified: "Well, what I meant by that was this: I made it a practice not to know anybody or to ask the names of where I was. All I can tell you is a place in Richmond, a couple of places in Kemah and maybe a few places in Galveston, or something like that." He reiterated that he did not know the name of any of the places. Nobody went with him, as a general rule, when he gambled. Several months later he could remember or had since learned the approximate location of three or four places where he had gambled, the name of one of them and the name of the operator of another.

The appellant acquired a piece of property in Boston from his mother and stepfather. This property was sold in late March of 1955 for about $7,500. Early in the next month the appellant gave $5,000 of the sale proceeds to his son-in-law and two daughters. No entries with respect to the Boston property nor as to the proceeds of the sale of it were made on appellant's books. The appellant testified that his mother had told him that if the property was ever sold, she wanted the proceeds to go to his children and his son-in-law. This he thought, so he claimed, made him a trustee of the property for his children and son-in-law although the title was in his name prior to its being conveyed. The daughters and son-in-law of the appellant used that $5,000 to form and furnish capital to a corporation of the name of A. Minella Plumbing Supplies. Minella conveyed to the corporation the property in which he had conducted his business. This property was encumbered by a mortgage. For the appellant's equity in the property he received $10.00 in cash and an unsecured note for about $10,000 payable in monthly installments of $100. Appellant transferred the major part of his merchandise and fixtures to the corporation. Part of the merchandise was sold on consignment with payment to be made by the corporation as it made sales. The rest of the merchandise was sold on open account. A down payment of $10.00 was made by the corporation. It gave no security. The appellant agreed to rent from the corporation a part of the premises conveyed, for $400 per month which was to be deducted from the payments to be made to the appellant.

The referee in bankruptcy determined that the appellant failed to explain satisfactorily the losses of assets, that the Boston property was not charged legally with any trust which would excuse the appellant from accounting for it to his creditors, that the sales of the real estate and improvements, and the fixtures and merchandise, were made for the purpose of hindering, delaying and defrauding his creditors, and that by reason of these matters and things the appellant should be denied a discharge in bankruptcy. The referee entered an order denying the appellant a discharge from his debts. The district court held that the referee's findings of fact were well supported by the evidence. The referee's findings of fact and conclusions of law were approved. A judgment of the district court was entered affirming and approving the referee's order. On appeal from that judgment, the matter is now before this Court. The appellant urges three propositions: first, that where a bankrupt has kept good business records which show personal withdrawals, a discharge should not be denied because the records do not itemize specifically who received the money; second, that if a bankrupt is not in the business of gambling he need not keep a record of gambling losses; and third, a discharge should not be denied when a debtor, prior to bankruptcy received moneys in trust which he did not believe belonged to him and therefore did not show the receipt or disbursement of such fund on his books. These propositions, which the appellant vigorously champions, are not, we think, those which were presented to and passed upon by the referee and the district court.

Section 4 of the Bankruptcy Act provides that the court shall grant the bankrupt a discharge unless satisfied that, among other things, he "has failed to explain satisfactorily any losses of assets or deficiency of assets to meet his liabilities". . . . The referee found, and the finding is not challenged, that the bankrupt withdrew from his business over $75,000, returned about $30,000 to the business, claimed gambling losses of $15,000, leaving unexplained $30,000 of withdrawals. The bankrupt, by showing that the books of his business were complete and accurate, asserts that his discharge should not be denied because the records do not show what became of the money withdrawn. The bankrupt is not charged with having failed to keep books of account or record. . . . He is charged with failure to explain what became of a substantial portion of the funds after the withdrawals and book entries were made. The bankrupt sought to explain disposition of $15,000 withdrawn by saying it was lost in gambling. Such an explanation may suffice if proved but is looked upon with disfavor. . . . Minella's equivocal and uncorroborated testimony might well have been disbelieved. However, the referee made no finding, and needed to make none, with respect to the gambling losses. The admitted lack of any explanation of what became of $30,000, exclusive of the claimed gambling losses, forms a sufficient justification for denial of a discharge. . . .

The referee held that the property in Boston and its proceeds were not charged with any valid trust which permitted the diversion of the amount received from the sale of such property from his creditors to his daughters and son-in-law. Where land is conveyed under an oral agreement that it shall be sold and the proceeds held and disbursed to designated third persons, the courts are not in accord as to whether the third party may enforce such agreement. Massachusetts has adopted the rule that an oral agreement to hold land in trust, or its proceeds, when sold, in trust for another, while not enforceable by reason of the statute of frauds so long as the real estate is unsold, becomes enforceable when the land is converted into money. . . . If the referee intended to hold otherwise the ruling would, we think, be erroneous as the property was in Massachusetts. But we think the referee's holding is sound for another reason. All the evidence indicative of an intent to create a trust is the bankrupt's testimony that his mother told him "that if the property was ever sold she wanted it to go" to the bankrupt's children and son-in-law. Expressions of hope or desire do not manifest an intention to create a trust. . . . It would not follow, however, that because there was no valid trust and the bankrupt was entitled in his own right to proceeds of the sale, the failure to make entries on his records as to the receipt and disbursements of the funds should result in the denial of a discharge. If the court deems the failure to keep the required records "to have been justified under all the circumstances of the case" such failure will not bar a discharge. The referee might have discredited the bankrupt's testimony about the desires of his mother, particularly in view of the fact that he retained for himself one-third of the sale proceeds which he believed, so he said, was received in trust for others. There was no finding with respect to this question. If the bankrupt in good faith believed, though erroneously, that he was acting as trustee and the sale proceeds belonged to others, it might well be that the failure to make the entries was justified under the circumstances. But this was not decided by the district court and, as other grounds require an affirmance, the question need not be here decided. Nor, since the sole question presented is the correctness of the order denying the bankrupt a discharge, do we need to consider whether a trust created by parol would be valid against creditors or against the trustee in bankruptcy. . . .

The bankrupt urges that the transfer of assets to the corporation was for a sufficient consideration, was intended to be and in fact was for the benefit of creditors and was not in any sense made with any intent to hinder, delay, or defraud creditors within the statute. . . . The referee found otherwise and the district court approved and affirmed the finding. It is difficult to see how a creditor of the bankrupt could be helped by the putting of his assets into a corporation that had little other assets and which gave no security for payment. The finding that the transfer was such as to justify refusing the bankrupt a discharge was amply sustained by the evidence. . . .

The referee in bankruptcy has reasonably broad discretion in granting or refusing a discharge to a bankrupt. When the referee's determination has been approved by the district court, it should not be disturbed on appeal except for the most cogent reasons. . . .

We do not find error in the order of the referee or in the judgment of the district court. The judgment is

Affirmed.

REVIEW QUESTIONS

1. Black Tool and Die Company agreed to make a punch press die for White for $2,500. A one-month delivery time was agreed upon. Black was ready to begin work on the die when White called and told Black to hold up until further notice. White then shopped around in an attempt to improve upon the price. White could not find a better price

and called Black about two weeks later to tell him to go ahead on the die, but Black refused, saying that his work schedule was now such that he could not complete the die within six months. White claims breach of contract and threatens to sue. What is the likely outcome of the case? Why?

2. Why is it necessary for courts to recognize anticipatory breach in contracts in which a structure is to be built and installed?

3. Does your state have an arbitration statute? If so, what are the provisions and limitations in the statute?

4. Black, under a contract with White, built an automatic assembly machine to assemble drive mechanisms for automobile window regulators. The contract calls for a machine capable of producing 1,500 assemblies per hour. The resulting machine ran at a speed which would easily produce 1,500 assemblies per hour. However, its longest run since installation a month ago has only been about two minutes before it jammed. Frequently it will run only one or two pieces before stopping. The cause of jamming is slight variations in the dimensions of the component parts of the window regulator assemblies. The parts are manufactured by White in the same manner that they have been manufactured for many years. Black had access to unlimited quantities of the parts while the machine was being built. According to the contract, Black's performance was finished when the installation of the machine was completed. White has paid $54,000 of the $60,000 agreed price of the machine. Black demands payment of the remainder. White claims a right to retain part or all of the $6,000 to compensate him for efforts spent in making the machine work. Has Black substantially performed? Can he get the $6,000? Why or why not?

5. Green leased a building near two metal working plants for a period of five years. The lease had no restrictions as to use of the building. Green set up a tool and die shop which operated profitably for about a year when the first plant left and relocated in another city. Shortly thereafter the second plant was dissolved in bankruptcy. Green wants to avoid his lease, claiming commercial frustration in that the remaining tool and die work is insufficient to be profitable. Is he stuck with the lease or can he get out? Why?

6. In *Minella v. Phillips*, if Minella could have explained satisfactorily what happened to the missing $30,000, is it likely that the court would have given him a discharge? Why or why not?

15 REMEDIES

We have considered the requirements for the formation of a lawful contract. In Chapter 14 we considered the discharge of obligations imposed on the parties by such contracts. We have observed that not all contractual obligations are discharged as the parties originally intended. When the actual performance is materially less than that which was intended, a breach of contract has occurred. Each party to a contract has a right to obtain proper performance for the rights or performance which he gives up. If this right is not satisfied, the law affords a remedy. The extent and type of remedy afforded is determined by the nature and extent of the breach.

We have defined a contract as an agreement enforceable at law. The enforceable-at-law part of the definition sets the contract agreement apart from other agreements. Saying that contract rights are enforceable at law implies that there must be remedies available for their breach. "For every right, a remedy," so runs an equity maxim, and this pertains to contract rights as well as other rights which the law protects.

In law, remedies exist to enforce a right, or to prevent the violation of a right, or to compensate for an injury. Probably the most common remedy sought and obtained is money *damages*. However, there are numerous instances in which damages will not afford an adequate or complete remedy. For this reason other remedies have been developed. Such remedies as *restitution, specific performance,* the *injunction, rescission,* and *reformation* are examples of those available under certain circumstances. In addition, a court of equity, with its origin based on unusual remedies, can combine and select remedies or, if necessary, invent a new one to fit a new circumstance. Here we will consider only the common remedies of damages, restitution, specific performance, and the injunction. One or a combination of these remedies will be appropriate in nearly any case in which an engineer is likely to be involved.

It has become almost standard practice to provide some form of remedy such as liquidated damages in the wording of engineering contracts. Such provisions are enforceable in court if they are made in good faith by the parties and are reasonable in the extent of the remedy provided.

Damages

Damages are compensation in money, recoverable in court by one who has suffered a loss, detriment, or injury. Any breach of contract situation allows a damage action of some sort unless it is very unusual. Even when the breach is not of a nature such that compensation is really justified, the injured party may still win his case and be awarded *nominal damages* (e.g., six cents or one dollar). An award of nominal damages merely means that the court has recognized that there was an invasion of a technical right which the plaintiff had. Of course, as with any other award, the loser will probably be assessed the court costs. The loser pays the court costs but, win or lose, each party usually must pay his own lawyer.

COMPENSATORY DAMAGES.   The usual reason for undertaking a damage action is to obtain compensation for an injury to one's person, property, or rights. To obtain compensatory damages it is not only necessary to prove that a right existed and was invaded. In addition, the amount of damage must be established with reasonable certainty. If the amount of damage cannot be reasonably established, the result is likely to be an award of nominal damages. The amount of compensation to which the plaintiff may be entitled is a jury question. The judge must accept the jury verdict unless he feels that the jury has incorrectly weighed the evidence.

There are two basic theories of damage measurement:

1. The contract measure of damages.
2. The tort measure of damages.

The contract measure of damages attempts to return any out-of-the-pocket costs to the plaintiff. In addition, it tries to compensate for such things as profits missed as a result of the contract breach. The objective of this method is to place the plaintiff in the position he would have enjoyed if the contract had not been breached.

Of course, the damages claimed must be directly connected to the contract breached if the plaintiff is to be compensated. Black has a contract to build automation equipment for White. Gray states that if the automation works properly for White he will be interested in a similar installation. Black may even have submitted preliminary plans and drawings to Gray. White then breached his contract. Black could collect compensation for his costs so far on White's contract plus the profit which he could reasonably expect from White. However, Black could get nothing from White to cover anticipated profit from Gray. The claim here would be termed too speculative.

The tort theory of damage measurement attempts to return the plaintiff to the position in which he would be if nothing had happened. According to the tort theory, the plaintiff's out-of-pocket costs are covered in addition to compensation for any mental anguish which he may have suffered. The results, in terms of money damages, can be quite different depending upon which theory is followed in a particular case. It might be noted that a tort case can look very much like a contract case, and a breach of contract can appear to be a tort. The dividing line is delicate and, at times, not too well defined.

EXEMPLARY DAMAGES.   In certain cases the court will allow more damages than the reasonable compensation for the injury or wrong suffered. Where the right was violated under circumstances such as fraud, malice, oppression or other despicable conduct by the defendant, exemplary damages may be awarded. Double or triple the bare compensation may result. Such damages have a primary purpose of punishing the defendant for his conduct and setting him forth as an example. Secondarily, exemplary damages are added compensation for the shame, degradation, or mental anguish suffered by the plaintiff.

DUTY TO MITIGATE DAMAGES.   If there were no recourse to law when a person's rights have been invaded, he would certainly make every effort to keep the damage as small as possible. All that the law asks in requiring the plaintiff to mitigate (abate or minimize) the damage suffered is that he follow just such a reasonable course of action. If one is injured he must make every reasonable effort to keep the injury to a minimum. For instance, if an employment contract (to run for a certain period of time) is breached by the employer, the employee must actively seek work elsewhere. If he is successful, he will be allowed the difference between the two salaries (assuming his original job paid him more); if he is unsuccessful after a reasonable effort to find subsequent employment, he may sue for his total lost pay. If he does not make a reasonable effort to find subsequent employment, or if he refuses suitable work, he may find himself with considerably diminished damages. He would not, of course, be required to take work for which he was not suited (for instance, an experienced engineer would be unlikely to be criticized for refusing employment as a farm hand); neither would he be required to move a great distance from his community.

Black is a manufacturer of appliance parts, particularly the chrome plated ones. He has a contract with White whereby White is to supply Black with nickel, at a stated price, for use in the copper-nickel-chromium plating process. During the life of the agreement, White raises the price of the nickel supplied, thus breaching the contract. Black could try to find an alternate source of nickel or he could pay White's increased price. He might even use the increased price as an excuse to cease manufacturing appliance parts for his customers, relying on White's breach to cover any losses he might sustain. Either of the first two alternatives might be considered reasonable as an attempt to mitigate the damage. Black would not, however, be allowed to renege on his contracts with the appliance manufacturers and pass along to White damages assessed against him. Neither could he maintain an action for lost profits if he ceased manufacturing parts on this basis. Black's damage suit will get him only the difference between the contract price and the price he actually had to pay for the nickel.

It might appear in the situation above that the equity remedy of specific performance would be available to Black. Such is not the case unless a statute exists to make it available—and some states do have such statutes. Without statutory provision, however, specific performance would be denied on the basis that money damages would be a sufficient remedy. Black could, conceivably, obtain the same quality and quantity of nickel from other suppliers, with the difference in price being the only loss to him.

Restitution

Restitution, as currently applied, is not greatly different from damages. Awards are usually made in money. They are based on the plaintiff's having parted in good faith with his consideration and the defendant's having breached his duty. The difference between restitution and damages is in the purpose and amount of the award. Restitution only restores what is lost or the value of the thing given. There is no attempt, as in a damage action, to compensate the plaintiff for lost profits. Only the out-of-pocket cost is covered. In effect, the plaintiff is required to return whatever consideration he has received from the defendant. The courts, however, do not adhere strictly to this rule. They will not apply it where, by so doing, they offer a shield to the defendant for his wrongdoing. The injured party is required to return what he has received where it is reasonably possible for him to do so, but it is not made an unwavering prerequisite to recovery by him.

Equity Remedies

Specific performance and the injunction are the principal equity remedies. Neither remedy may be used where an adequate remedy at law (e.g., damages, restitution, or a statute) is available. However, either remedy may be used in conjunction with damages where damages alone would be an insufficient remedy. Where either remedy would require extensive supervision of the court for enforcement, an attempt will be made to find a different remedy. Where, for instance, specific perform ance of a contract to maintain something is requested it is likely that the court would deny the remedy. Such a remedy requires supervision the court would look for a more appropriate remedy and only turn to one of the two standard remedies as a last resort.

SPECIFIC PERFORMANCE.   The most common, though not exclusive use of the remedy of specific performance occurs when a unique piece of property is involved. A piece of land, such as a city lot or a farm, is unique. So is an original painting by an old master, or a tailor-made piece of automation equipment. Courts, since ancient times, have considered land as unique (extension of the concept to other property items is of more recent origin). If a contract to sell a particular piece of land is breached by the seller, sufficient money damages might be awarded to allow neighboring property to be purchased. However, no two pieces of land have the same location and it is likely that there would be other tangible and intangible differences; the purchaser's wife, for instance might claim that the view from the location gives her a sense of security or that the trees are appealing.

INJUNCTION.   Originally injunctions were only prohibitive in nature ("thou shalt not"). Now, in most jurisdictions, an injunction may be either prohibitive or mandatory ("thou shalt"). Even where injunctions must be prohibitive, it is possible to write what is, in effect, a mandatory injunction. In one case a tenant, enraged at his landlord, piled garbage on the front lawn of the tenant house before leaving. Though a mandatory injunction could not be issued in that state, a prohibitive injunction did the job just as well. The tenant was prohibited from allowing the garbage to remain on the lawn at his former residence.

The injunction is often used where irreparable injury to real property is imminent. Not just "possible," but imminent or very probable. The probable damage must also be damage which could not be satisfactorily repaired.

A court will not require specific performance of personal service con tracts; such a holding would violate long-established legal policies. Rather, a person who has contracted his services to another might be enjoined from performing the same services for anyone else.

The speed and convenience of the injunction as a means of enforcing a law has appealed to legislators. If a particular law can be made to call for an injunction or a "cease and desist" order to be issued when the law is violated, the time and expense of a jury trial is often avoided. It is only necessary that the order be issued and probable violators informed. Any further violation is contempt of court resulting in a jail sentence or a fine. The speed and simplicity of the injunction is appealing. However, it should be carefully used in the statutes. Wholesale use could deprive us of our jury trial right.

Enforcement of Remedies

A remedy without enforcement would be meaningless. The law must have teeth if it is to be effective. There are three common means of enforcing court awards against the loser in a suit at law: execution, garnishment, and attachment. Equity enforcement usually takes the form of contempt of court.

After a judgment is rendered in court the loser is expected to comply with that judgment. Where security has been posted, the loss may be deducted from it. Where no security has been pledged and the loser does not comply with the court's order, the other party may return to court for an order to confiscate property in satisfaction of the judgment. Such an order is a *writ of execution*. It is addressed to the sheriff or other enforcement officer, giving him the right to seize as much of the loser's property (both real and personal) as may be necessary to satisfy the judgment. The property so obtained is sold at an execution sale, the proceeds being used to satisfy the award of damages, with any remainder going back to the loser.

Garnishment is the means used to obtain the loser's property which is held by a third party. Notice is given to the third party to turn over the judgment debtor's property in satisfaction of the obligation.

Attachment is a process used when the defendant himself is not within the jurisdiction of the court, but some of his property is available. Because the attachment process usually takes place before the court proceedings, the plaintiff is required to post a bond to protect the defendant. Such attachment prevents the defendant from removing his property from the court's jurisdiction prior to the court's judgment. If the defendant wishes to remove the attachment, he may do so by posting a counter bond in sufficient amount to cover the plaintiff's claim.

Execution, garnishment, and attachment are all limited by statutes in the various states. The homestead laws which limited creditor's rights also protect the loser in a damage action. Also, many state laws severely restrict garnishment, particularly when the wages of the head of a household are concerned.

Contempt of court is the principal means of enforcing equity remedies. The extent of the enforcement is pretty much within the court's discretion. Frequently statutes limit the length of contempt-of-court jail sentences and the amount of fines. However, repeated offenses mean repeated sentencing. Each day in which the court order is avoided represents a separate offense, so the confinement could run for years.

FAIRFIELD v. AMERICAN PHOTOCOPY EQUIPMENT CC

291 P. 2d 194, 138 C.A. 2d 82 (Cal., Dec. 20, 1955

VALLEE, Justice.

Appeal by plaintiff from a judgment of nonsuit in an action for damages for the unauthorized use by defendant of plaintiff's name in advertising its product and for an injunction.

The following facts appear from admissions in the pleadings, the evidence and reasonable inferences therefrom. Plaintiff is an attorney at law admitted to practice in New York and California. Defendant is an Illinois corporation doing business in California. Defendant is engaged in manufacturing and selling a photocopy machine known as "Apeco Systematic Auto-Stat." On July 1, 1954 defendant, without the permission of plaintiff and for the purpose of promoting sales of the machine and for gain and profit, circulated among the legal profession in the United States a printed advertisement indicating that plaintiff was a satisfied user of "Apeco Systematic Auto-Stat." The advertisement contained this statement: "Here's just a partial list of the thousands of leading law firms using the" machine, followed by a list of lawyers and law firms in various cities in the United States, including the name of plaintiff and "Los Angeles." Plaintiff was the only Los Angeles lawyer listed. About 30,000 copies of the advertisement were circulated in the major cities throughout the United States.

Prior to the time defendant circulated the advertisement, plaintiff purchased one of the machines from defendant, returned it to defendant, and defendant refunded the purchase price.

The judgment of nonsuit was granted on the ground there was no proof of damage. The rules governing the granting of a motion for judgment of nonsuit are axiomatic, have been frequently stated, and need not be repeated. . . . It is error to grant a motion for a judgment if the plaintiff is entitled to any relief.

We accept the parties' appraisal of the nature of the action as one for damages for the invasion of plaintiff's right of privacy. The doctrine that there is a legally enforceable right of privacy has been definitely settled in California . . . The right is distinct in and of itself and not merely incidental to some other recognized right for breach of which an action for damages will lie. Violation of the right is a tort. . . .

One concept of the right of privacy is the right of a person to be free from unauthorized and unwarranted publicity. . . . The unauthorized use or publication of a person's name may constitute an actionable invasion of the right . . . The exploitation of another's personality for commercial purposes constitutes one of the most flagrant and common means of invasion of privacy. . .

The gist of the cause of action in a privacy case is not injury to the character or reputation, but a direct wrong of a personal character resulting in injury to the feelings without regard to any effect which the publication may have on the property, business, pecuniary interest, or the standing of the individual in the community. . . . The right of privacy concerns one's own peace of mind while the right of freedom from defamation concerns primarily one's reputation. . . . The injury is mental and subjective. It impairs the mental peace and comfort of the person and may cause suffering much more acute than that caused by a bodily injury. . . . The desire of a business concern for publicity or advertising does not justify its invasion of the right of privacy. . . . The motives of a person charged with invading the right are not material with respect to the determination whether there is a right of action, and malice is not an essential element of a violation of the right. . . . Inadvertence or mistake is no defense where the publication does in fact refer to the plaintiff in such manner as to violate his right of privacy. . . .

The facts proven established an invasion of plaintiff's right of privacy. Defendant, without plaintiff's consent, advertised far and wide that plaintiff was a satisfied user of the machine. Plaintiff was not a satisfied user. The representation was false. The record warrants the inference that when defendant circulated the advertisement it knew plaintiff was not a satisfied user. The advertisement amounted to a pretended endorsement or recommendation of defendant's product. It was an unauthorized and unwarranted appropriation of plaintiff's personality as a lawyer for pecuniary gain and profit. The advertising use of plaintiff's name, without his consent, is comprehended within the narrowest definition of the right of privacy. It was clearly shown that a legal wrong had been done. It was error to grant the motion for judgment of nonsuit.

Defendant says that, at most, plaintiff was entitled to nominal damages only and that a judgment will not be reversed simply to permit a recovery of nominal damages, citing 14 Cal. Jur. 2d 637, sec. 8. We cannot say as a matter of law that plaintiff is only entitled to nominal damages. Nominal damages are awarded to a plaintiff where the evidence shows a breach of duty owed to him or an invasion of his legal rights, without showing that he has thereby sustained a material injury. A judgment for nominal damages must always involve a trivial sum. Such damages are damages in name only and not in fact; they are the same as no damages at all. . . .

Civil Code, section 3281, reads:

Every person who suffers detriment from the unlawful act or omission of another, may recover from the person in fault a compensation therefor in money, which is called damages.

Section 3333 provides that the measure of damages for a tort "is the amount which will compensate for all the detriment proximately caused thereby, whether it could have been anticipated or not." Invasion of privacy for advertising purposes may afford the basis for an inference of improper motive. . . . The advertisement necessarily carried the implication that plaintiff endorsed the machine and had permitted defendant to use his name as a lawyer in its advertisements. He had done neither. Plaintiff is entitled to compensation for injury to his peace of mind and to his feelings. The recoverable compensation for these items is difficult to determine since they afford no definite criteria for the ascertainment of damages. In a case of this character there can be no direct evidence of the amount of damages sustained, nor the amount of money which will compensate for the injury. The measure of damages therefore is for the trier of fact, and in assessing such damages he is accorded a wide and elastic discretion. . . .

The Supreme Court of Oregon in *Hinish v. Meier & Frank Co.*, 166 Or. 482, 113 P. 2d 438, at page 448, 138 A.L.R. 1, stated:

The damages (in an action for the invasion of the right of privacy) may be difficult of ascertainment, but not more so than in actions for malicious prosecutions, breach of promise of marriage, or alienation of affections, and in many cases of libel, slander and assault. The law has never denied recovery to one entitled to damages simply because of uncertainty as to the extent of his injury and the amount which would properly compensate him. . . .

The fact that damages resulting from an invasion of the right of privacy cannot be measured by a pecuniary standard is not a bar to recovery. . . . While special damages may be recovered if sustained, general damages may be recovered without a showing of specific loss. . . . Dean Pound says that "the activities of photographers, and the temptation to advertisers to sacrifice private feelings to their individual gain call upon the law to do more in the attempt to secure this interest than merely take incidental account of infringements of it." . . .

In *Kunz v. Allen*, 102 Kan. 883, 172 P. 532, L.R.A. 1918D, 1151, the defendants used a photograph of the plaintiff without her consent to advertise their business. The trial court sustained a demurrer to plaintiff's evidence, the equivalent of our motion for a judgment of nonsuit. On appeal the court said, 172 P. 532:

The principal ground upon which it is claimed the demurrer was sustained is that the plaintiff failed to prove any actual damages. This was not necessary . . .

Reed v. Real Detective Pub. Co., 63 Ariz. 294, 162 P. 2d 133, was an action for invasion of the right of privacy. The court said, 162 P. 2d 139:

The gravamen of the action here charged is the injury to the feelings of the plaintiff, the mental anguish and distress caused by the publication. In an action of this character, special damages need not be charged or proven, and if the proof discloses a wrongful invasion of the right of privacy, substantial damages for mental anguish alone may be recovered. . . .

In *Goodyear Tire & Rubber Co. v. Vandergriff*, 52 Ga. App. 662, 184 S.E. 452, a right of privacy case, the court observed, 184 S.E. 454:

'In some torts the entire injury is to the peace, happiness, or feelings of the plaintiff; in such cases no measure of damages can be prescribed, except the enlightened conscience of impartial jurors. The worldly circumstances of the parties, the amount of bad faith in the transaction, and all the attendant facts should be weighed.'

One whose right of privacy is unlawfully invaded is entitled to recover substantial damages, although the only damages suffered by him resulted from mental anguish. In such an action, the damages to be recovered are those which the law authorizes in cases of torts of that character, and if the law authorizes a recovery for wounded feelings in other torts of a similar nature, such damages would be recoverable in an action for the violation of this right. (41 Am. Jur. 950, sec. 34.)

The Supreme Court of Washington in *State ex rel. La Follette v. Hinkle*, 131 Wash. 86, 229 P. 317, at page 319, observed:

Nothing so exclusively belongs to a man or is so personal and valuable to him as his name. His reputation and the character he has built up are inseparably connected with it. Others can have no right to use it without his express consent, and he has a right to go into any court at any time to enjoin or prohibit any unauthorized use of it. Nor is it necessary that it be alleged or proved that such unauthorized use will damage him. This the law will presume. . . .

The rule with respect to damages for a libel is analogous. . . . One of the elements entering into damages for a libel is injury to the feelings of the person libeled. That injury may be inferred by the trier of fact from the testimony with relation to the social status of the person libeled. This inference may be supplemented by the direct statement of the plaintiff to the effect that his feelings were injured. . . . In an article by Louis D. Brandeis (later Mr. Justice Brandeis) and Samuel D. Warren which first focused the attention of the profession on the right of privacy, it is said:

The remedies for an invasion of the right of privacy are also suggested by those administered in the law of defamation, and in the law of literary and artistic property, namely:

1. An action of tort for damages in all cases. Even in the absence of special damages, substantial compensation could be allowed for injury to feelings as in the action of slander and libel. . . .

Plaintiff attempted to prove that he had sustained more than nominal damages but was foreclosed from doing so. He testified he had received telephone calls from other lawyers and that he had had conversations with other lawyers pertaining to the advertisement. His counsel asked him how the calls and conversations had affected him and whether they had caused him any mental anguish. On objection by defendant that the questions were immaterial, the court precluded plaintiff from testifying to his feelings resulting from the publication. The rulings were erroneous. The questions were not only material, they were directly pertinent to proof of damage. Plaintiff sought to prove that he had been ridiculed by other lawyers on account of the advertisement. On defendant's objections the court excluded the evidence. The rulings were erroneous. What had been thus said to him was competent to show his mortification of feelings. . . .

Shortly after plaintiff returned the machine he had purchased to defendant, and long before defendant circulated the advertisement using plaintiff's name, some correspondence relative to the machine passed between plaintiff and defendant. The correspondence shows that plaintiff returned the machine because it was unsatisfactory and that defendant knew it. Plaintiff offered the correspondence in evidence. Its authenticity was not questioned. On defendant's objections it was excluded. The correspondence was admissible for the purpose of showing that plaintiff had returned the machine because it was defective and unsatisfactory, and that defendant knew at the time it circularized the legal profession that plaintiff was not a satisfied user.

Other assigned errors are not likely to arise on a retrial and need not be considered.

Reversed.

REVIEW QUESTIONS

1. Black hired White Automation to build a special machine to be used by Black in the manufacture of automobile door handles. The door handles were to be sold to Gray Motor Company. The price of the special machine was to be $100,000. Shortly before work was to begin on the special machine Gray cancelled his order for door handles and Black immediately cancelled the contract for the special machine. Does White have a right to resort to legal action? If so, against whom and for how much?

2. What is the purpose of: a) nominal damages, b) compensatory damages, c) exemplary damages?

3. Distinguish between damages for tort and damages for breach of contract.

4. Green bought a new car from Brown Motor Sales for $2,800. A few days after he bought the car he attempted to pass another vehicle, but the steering linkage locked when he turned his wheels to the left. The resulting crash destroyed the car and sent Green to the hospital. Green's hospital bill amounted to $1,200; the first month away from his job was covered by his employer, but the next two months were not (at $700 per month). When he returned to work with a 20% disability he was asked to take a lower job paying $550 per month because of his inability to perform his former job. He is 45 years old. Examination of the wrecked automobile showed that one joint in the steering linkage appeared too tight and that there was no grease fitting at the joint and, apparently, there never had been one even though a hole had been drilled and tapped for the fitting. Does Green have a right of action against anyone? If so, for how much? Based on what theory?

5. According to the views expressed in *Fairfield v. American Photocopy Equipment Co.*, what are the measures of damages in cases where no certain loss of a particular monetary value can be shown, but a right has been invaded causing suffering to the plaintiff? Could Fairfield reasonably expect to get an injunction against further use of his name in American Photocopy's advertising if he requested it?

16 CONTRACTING PROCEDURE

Before discussing contracting procedure several terms and relationships between the parties involved should be defined.

OWNER. The owner is the party for whom the work is to be done. He is the one to whom the others look for payment for services. He is the final authority in questions as to what is to be included or left out of a project being undertaken for his benefit. He may be a private individual, president of a corporation, chairman of the board of directors, or a public official charged with the responsibility for the project.

ENGINEER OR ARCHITECT. As the terms will be used here, engineer and architect are virtually interchangeable. There is, at present, considerable controversy (including court cases) over the meanings of the terms and the work to be considered the proper field of each. No attempt will be made to add to that controversy here. It will be assumed that the person is properly employed whether he be architect or engineer. The function of such a person is that of agent of the owner. He furnishes the technical and professional skill necessary in the planning and administration of the project to accomplish the owner's purpose. He is the designer, supervisor, investigator, and adviser of the owner. Most state laws require him to be registered as a professional in his field. He may be a consultant or an employee of the owner. He is the one with whom the contractor deals directly.

CONTRACTOR. The contractor is the one who undertakes the actual construction of the project. He furnishes the labor, materials, and equipment with which to complete the job. The term "contractor" is frequently further broken down into *general contractor* and *sub-contractor*. The general contractor agrees to accept the responsibility for the complete project, frequently undertaking the major portion of it himself. Subcontractors are hired for a particular specialty by the general contractor and, in effect, work for him while completing the portion of the project for which they were hired. The general contractor still has the responsibility for the entire project, even though the wiring or the plumbing or the roofing was completed by a subcontractor.

Types of Construction

Much of the capital wealth of our country is constructed by independent contractors. Most of the buildings, machines, bridges, utilities, production facilities, and other items of wealth which are primarily responsible for our standard of living were built under contract. There are two major branches of such construction—public and private. There are significant differences in the motives and relationships involved.

PRIVATE WORK. Private projects are those which are undertaken for an individual or a company. The restrictions imposed upon the parties are those of contracts in general. The agreement may be achieved by advertising and then choosing the best bid, or by direct negotiation without advertising. The acceptance may be oral or in writing; in fact, the entire contract could be oral if the parties so chose.

The profit motive is the usual reason for construction of private works. The owner believes that the project will give him a desirable return on his investment. However, this need not necessarily be the reason for the project. In private work, the reason could be nothing more than a personal whim of the owner. The desirability of the project is not open to question by the public as long as no one is harmed by it.

PUBLIC WORKS. In public projects much of this is different. The motive for construction of public works is public demand or need. Financial return sufficient to justify the investment is frequently of less than primary importance.

Money for private works comes either from direct payments from available funds or from loans (e.g., bonds). Payment for public works comes from tax receipts or from loans (bonds or other obligations) to be retired from future tax receipts.

Voluminous statutes govern the letting of public-works contracts. From a review of these laws, certain restrictions become apparent. Generally, formal advertising and bidding is required to insure competition among the bidders. The "lowest responsible bidder" gets the job. Usually the means of advertising and the length of time the advertisement is to run are specified. Changes in plans or specifications usually cannot be made after the award of the contract even though such changes might be beneficial. Acceptance of a bid may not be effective until it has been ratified by a legislature or a legislative committee.

Once a contractor's bid on a public project has been accepted, the amount he will get is fixed. The official in charge of the project cannot agree to pay more, regardless of the apparent justice of the contractor's claim.

The purpose of the restrictions in letting public projects is, of course, to prevent dishonesty, collusion, or fraud among bidders or between bidders and public officials. Sometimes the restrictions seem unfair; the result is less than might have been accomplished without some of them. Or, perhaps, a well-meaning contractor fails to survive his ignorance of the law. The results in general, though, seem beneficial to the public.

CONTRACTING AND MANUFACTURING. A construction project and the manufacture of goods for a market are basically similar. Each is concerned with the use of labor and equipment to turn raw materials into a finished product of some sort. Each has economic problems concerned with the sources of raw material and labor. Each is concerned with efficient management in an effort to show a profit. Both are concerned with production schedules which must be met if penalties of one nature or another are to be avoided. Quality must be maintained but costs must be minimized.

The main distinction between construction and manufacturing stems from the location of the product. In most construction, whether it is a building or a piece of productive equipment, the place where the product is built is the place where it will stay. Usually the construction product is custom-made, built to specific requirements and not to be reproduced. Such a product does not lend itself as well to the economies of standardization of method as do the products of most manufacturing companies.

DIRECT EMPLOYMENT OR CONTRACT

After the decision has been made by the owner to undertake a construction project, the question frequently arises as to whether the work should be done by the available staff, by contract, or by a combination of both. The decision involves many factors; two very important ones being the relative size of the job and the skill of the staff. Many jobs are too large for the present staff or too small to be submitted to an outside contractor, hence there is no problem. But there are also many projects of intermediate size which could be completed either way. It is with these jobs that the present discussion is concerned. There are a number of benefits and disadvantages which the owner (or engineer) should consider in choosing the best procedure.

COST. Certain savings in cost are apparent when direct employment is used: 1) the owner does not have to pay the contractor's *profit* margin if he does the work himself; 2) the amount added in by the contractor for *contingencies* is saved if no contingencies arise. The expected cost saving here is really anticipation of winnings from a gamble and, if the owner's staff is inexperienced, the odds are against him. The experienced contractor can often see and avert incidents which would otherwise be contingencies; 3) the cost of making *multiple estimates* is avoided if the owner's staff undertakes the job.

FLEXIBILITY. A project undertaken by direct employment is more flexible if it becomes necessary to make changes while the job is under way; the owner has only to order the changes made. Where a contractor is hired to build according to plans and specifications and work is under way, change proposals will usually meet with resistance. The contractor is interested in completing the project as soon as possible in order to earn his money and go on to the next job. He will be tempted to charge heavily for the delay caused by a change.

SUBSEQUENT MAINTENANCE. There is something to be said for subsequent maintenance as an inducement for the owner to use as many of his own people as possible. A machine or other structure is more readily repaired by the original builders than by maintenance men who have had no experience with it.

GRIEVANCES. Union problems are usually somewhat reduced by use of present crews. There is the possibility of jurisdictional disputes but the likelihood of these and other issues arising is minimized. The individuals forming the nucleus of the crew, at least, have learned to live with each other and with others employed by the owner in different jobs.

SPECIALIZATION. The great and sometimes decisive advantage to the owner in hiring a contractor for a project is that the contractor is a specialist. His specialty is in labor, supervison, and procurement of materials—the so-called "know how" of that particular kind of contracting. It is probably this factor, more than any other, which gives the contractor an advantage.

PUBLIC RELATIONS. The public relations programs of many large concerns tip the scales in favor of hiring contractors to undertake jobs for them. This is especially true when a company sets up an operation in a new community. To establish itself in a favorable light in the community, the company hires local people to set up the facilities, even though the company may have a staff capable of doing the job.

PAYMENT ARRANGEMENTS

There are four basic ways in which an owner may pay for work undertaken by a contractor. In addition to the basic payment arrangements, there is an infinite number of variations and combinations of them, each adjusted to a given project. The features of each basic arrangement will be considered primarily from the owner's standpoint.

Lump-sum

If a manufacturer or an individual purchases a product manufactured by a company, he usually knows the price before he makes the agreement to purchase. The price of an automobile is arranged between the dealer and the buyer, for instance, before the sale is actually made. The lump-sum contract arrangement gives the owner the same assurance as to the price he will have to pay for the job. It is this aspect of the lump-sum contract which appeals to people. It is also the main advantage of the arrangement from the owner's standpoint.

There are several inherent disadvantages in the fixed price or lump-sum contract. Probably the main one is the antagonistic interests of the owner and the contractor. Once the contract is signed, the contractor's main interest is in making a profit on the job and in doing it as quickly as possible. There is an incentive for him to do no more than the minimum requirements set forth in the plans and specifications. With an unscrupulous contractor the results may be shoddy workmanship and a poor structure. Even a responsible contractor may be tempted to cut corners if contingencies start eating into his profit margin or if he is already losing on the job. The owner's interest, on the other hand, is to obtain the best possible structure he can get for the money he has agreed to pay.

Changes, under a lump-sum contract, can be quite costly. The change represents an impediment to the contractor's speedy completion of the job. He is in the position where he is able to dictate the cost of changes if he so desires. The owner has hired him to do the job, he is on the premises with his equipment to render the service called for in the contract. The owner's alternative to paying the contractor's price for a change is to wait for completion of the job and then hire someone else to change. This is often very costly.

A lump-sum contract requires that considerable time and money be spent by the contractor in examining the site, estimating, and drawing up and submitting a bid before the job can start. The delays may run to months or even years. The cost can be considerable. If the job is to be started as quickly as possible, the lump-sum contract is not indicated.

If the work required is at all indefinite or uncertain, the lump-sum contract should not be used. The contractor will have to add in a sufficient amount to cover the uncertainty if he is to show a profit. The greater the degree of uncertainty, the greater the probable spread in bidder's proposals. Prices on a 500 ton press, for instance, might vary as much as 6 or 7 percent between high and low bidder among five or six press manufacturers. If the equipment were a piece of automation with only the raw material and the end product known, the highest bid might be four or five times that of the lowest. Each contractor would try to cover himself as best he could against a large number of unknowns and gamble that the amount submitted would result in a successful bid for him.

Lump-sum contracts are used commonly and successfully, but their successful use is pretty well restricted to situations in which unknowns are at a minimum. They are not appropriate: 1) where uncertainties exist; 2) where a speedy start is necessary—emergency work, for instance; 3) where plant operations to be carried on will interfere with the contractor's work.

To overcome these objections people have, at times, gone to one of the two basic cost-plus types of contract.

Cost-Plus-Percent-of-Cost

The most rapid means of starting a project is through the use of the cost-plus-percent pricing arrangement. In an emergency an owner may be faced with the necessity of starting work immediately, while the plans for the completed structure are still being drawn up. Using a cost-plus-percent arrangement, today's phone call can result in action today. It is this feature which prompted the widespread use of such contracts by the federal government during World War II. Valuable time would have been lost in estimating and bidding if they had not been used.

According to the cost-plus-percent arrangement, the owner usually pays all the contractor's costs plus an added percentage (often 15%) of these costs as his profit. "Cost" means the cost of materials and services directly connected with the owner's structure. Such items as the contractor's overhead, staff salaries, and the like are usually excluded unless direct connection to the project can be shown.

A major advantage in the cost-plus-percent contract is its flexibility. Changes may be made readily when the owner desires them. Since the cost to the owner for making changes includes profit to the contractor, the contractor has little reason to object to them.

The risks involved in construction are assumed by the owner in the cost-plus-percent contract. He does not know with any certainty what the project will cost until it is completed. On the other hand, if no adverse conditions (contingencies) arise, the benefit is his rather than the contractor's.

The cost-plus-percent contract is not an unmixed blessing to the owner, though. Since the contractor's profit is tied to costs, those costs may be quite high. Gold-plated doorknobs may show up. The contractor has what amounts to an incentive to dishonesty—a financial reward for running up costs. The most honest of contractors (or people in any profession, for that matter) would be tempted to be inefficient under the circumstances. The need for the owner to police the project is apparent. It is because of this one disadvantage in the cost-plus-percent contract that the federal government now looks with disfavor on the cost-plus-percent type of contract. Renegotiation of contracts and the recapture of excess profits on government contracts following World War II left the government with a rather bitter attitude toward the arrangement.

Even if the contractor pursues the completion of the project in the best interests of the owner, efficiency is not assured. Supervisors and workers alike are not likely to put forth outstanding effort for their employer if nothing will be gained for him as a result.

Cost-Plus-Fixed-Fee

The cure for the main undesirable feature of the cost-plus-percent contract is found in the cost-plus-fixed-fee arrangement. Here the contractor is paid a fixed fee as profit for his services, but the owner picks up the tab for all the contractor's costs of undertaking the project. The amount of the fixed fee is subject to negotiation between owner and contractor or bid by the contractor based upon estimates of the cost of the completed project. The settlement of the amount of the fixed fee in the beginning precludes an immediate start on the project, but the time required is not nearly as great as would be necessary for a lump-sum contract.

The cost-plus-fixed-fee contract is probably the best basic arrangement from the standpoint of all parties concerned. The contractor has no incentive to run up costs or work inefficiently. In fact, with a view toward maximizing his profit in a given period of time, he has an incentive to hasten the completion of the project to obtain his fee.

The element of flexibility may suffer somewhat from the contractor's desire to complete the job rapidly. The proposal by the owner of a major change in the project which will require more time to complete is likely to be met with objections and the "outstretched hand." If the contractor is required to spend a longer time in pursuit of his fee, it is only fair that the fee should be increased.

As in the cost-plus-percent contract, the owner runs the risk of contingencies, but he is in a somewhat better position. Under the cost-plus-percent arrangement, the occurrence of contingencies tends to increase the contractor's ultimate profit. There is incentive to bring about contingencies or, at least, not to actively avoid them. In the cost-plus-fixed-fee arrangement, the desire for early completion is an incentive for the contractor to avoid contingencies if possible. Thus, the owner's interests are better protected.

Unit Price

Certain kinds of structures may be conveniently built under a unit-price type of arrangement. This scheme applies best where there is a large amount of the same kind of work to be done. In the building of a road, for instance, the main elements consist of excavation, fill, and pouring of concrete. A unit-price contract could be conveniently used. The contract would specify so much per cubic yard of excavation (plus an extra amount if rock formation is encountered), so much per cubic yard of fill, and so much per cubic yard of concrete. The price per unit includes the contractor's cost per unit plus any amount for contingencies, overhead and profit. The engineer or architect usually estimates the quantities required ahead of time for the benefit of both owner and contractor. The actual quantities may be considerably different from the estimate, but the contractor is paid according to the actual quantities required.

Usually the unit-price arrangement is used in conjunction with a lump-sum contract. In nearly every job there are some elements (such as clearing, grading, and cleaning up the site) which do not lend themselves to unit pricing. The combination is usually quite beneficial, largely because it is flexible.

In a unit-price contract much of the contractor's uncertainty is relieved which is reflected in a lower estimate for contingencies. The risks not assumed by the contractor, though, must be borne by the owner. The owner has no precise knowledge of cost of the job to him until termination of the job.

Just as is true with a lump-sum contract, the job cannot begin immediately under a unit-price arrangement. The contractor requires time to examine the premises and prepare an estimate for the owner. Normal bidding procedure is usually used in the award of such contracts.

Variations

The types of contracts described above are the four basic forms. In addition to these there are many variations, or hybrids, often tailored to a particular need on a project. Probably the most common variation is the addition of an incentive system of some sort. Profit-sharing and percentage of cost saving are examples. One variation is the addition of a kind of reverse liquidated-damage clause. That is, the contractor is offered a fixed amount per day additionally if he finishes ahead of schedule.

Another form of contract is the *management contract*. In such a contract, the owner hires the contractor, not necessarily to undertake the work with his own organization, but to oversee the job, often hiring others to do the work. Frequently this includes managing work to be done with the owner's labor force. Work undertaken by the owner's people is said to be work under a *force account*. The contractor, under a management contract, is still in the status of independent contractor. He agrees to produce a result. His actions do not bind the owner under a management contract as an agent would bind his principal. The management contract is, therefore, distinct from the agency relationship, which exists between an owner and his engineer or architect. Usually the services of an engineer or architect are not used.

STAGES OF A PROJECT

A project starts as an idea or a dream of the future. If soundly conceived, planned and developed, the dream may be realized. Failure in any of these things may turn it into a nightmare. To follow the development of a project let us consider the lump-sum or the unit-price type, since each requires extensive preliminary work.

Feasibility Studies

Regardless of how beneficial a project may seem to its originator it is nearly always advisable to conduct a preliminary investigation. It is recognized that wars and other emergencies may preclude such an investigation, but in most organizations a state of emergency is somewhat unusual. The purpose of the feasibility study is to obtain preliminary information on several things:

1. What is the cost of undertaking the project? This cost is determined usually on the basis of either annual cost or present worth (or capitalized cost if perpetual service is contemplated);

2. Can the objective be attained better (or cheaper) in some other way? The comparison is made on the basis of annual cost or present worth;

3. What benefits will result from the use of the various alternatives? In most private projects and some public projects the ratio of economic benefit to cost must be sufficient to justify the project. In many public works, a crying need may push consideration of economic benefit into the background.

The preliminary investigations and reports are usually not intensive. Some schemes can be shown to be obviously impractical after obtaining only a minimum of data. Where the scheme appears to be profitable, though, the expenditure of considerable time and money on the feasibility study may be justified. Surveys and investigations of such elements as markets, sources of raw material and labor, cost of transportation, and laws and ordinances involved, may become necessary. Even when the tentative decision has been made to go ahead with the project, based upon reports which show that it will pay off, it is usually worth while to spend some time and money investigating whether or not there is a cheaper way of achieving the same end product. Most such studies can be undertaken at a reasonable cost. However, the more closely balanced the evidence, the more detailed must be the study. Wise use of investigations can save money in the long run, but wisdom also dictates a point at which a study should be terminated. When a course of action (or inaction, as the case may be) is clear, the feasibility study has usually served its purpose.

Design

If the feasibility study indicates that the project is desirable and the decision is made to go ahead, the next step is the design of the structure. Normally, all designs are complete in some detail before work is started. A complete feasibility study usually must include sketches of layouts considered. The design completes consideration of functional requirements, layouts, and the dimensions involved. Preparation of the drawings is a part of the engineer's or architect's task. When the drawings and specifications are completed, they combine to give the basic information on the project.

The design drawings are completed directly after the decision to undertake the project. Actual shop drawings or working drawings are not normally made until the project has been awarded. The shop drawings are those used in the manufacture or assembly of component parts of the project.

Legal Arrangements

If such arrangements have not already been made, land must be obtained by purchase or by exercise of eminent domain if it is to be a public project. Railroad sidings, highway connections, and utility services must all be considered.

In the design drawings the owner and engineer have a picture to be used in talking to others about the project. In construction of a building zoning is likely to be involved and building codes must be satisfied. A copy of the design drawings of the proposed construction ordinarily must be filed with the proper authorities in order to obtain a building permit.

Another legal matter is the engineer's or architect's right to practice in the state. State licensing laws generally require that a registered professional engineer sign construction plans or have them issued under his seal. It is not required that all members of the engineering staff be registered. If a member of the staff who is registered takes the responsibility for the plans, the law is satisfied.

If the project is to be undertaken for the public, strict adherence to laws governing such projects is necessary. It is necessary that the order and appropriation for the project be passed before the work is under

ken. In many types of public construction there are minimum standards
which must be met.

Preparation of Contract Documents

During these preliminary stages of a project it is necessary to prepare
the contract documents to be used through the remainder of the project.
One of the main purposes of these documents is to set forth the relationships between the parties. If this purpose is to be accomplished adequately, the preparation of these documents must be undertaken with
great care and skill. The engineer's task of preparing these documents
often seems dull and routine, a hurdle to be taken to get to something
more interesting. Dull and routine it usually is, but also important. Careful attention to this task prevents many future controversies and may
make any controversies which do arise easier to settle.

The pieces which fit together to make up a construction contract are
known as: 1) the advertisement, 2) instructions to bidders, 3) the proposal, 4) the agreement, 5) bonds, 6) general conditions, and 7) the
specifications and drawings.

Each component of the array of documents which comprises a construction contract has a name or heading. The parts are not called by the
same names in all contracts, and the material covered under the headings
is not always the same. That is, what is covered in "general provisions" in
a federal government contract might be covered in "general conditions"
where a state or a private party is owner, or the coverage might be found
under "information for bidders." There seems to have been only one
major attempt at a general standardization—The American Institute of
Architects has drawn up and copyrighted contract documents for use in
building construction contracts. Although these do not entirely fit the
picture here, the discussion will center around them since they are
national standards in closely analogous construction. The federal government and most of the state governments have standardized contract
components; the same is true of most large companies. Only a short
indoctrination is necessary to familiarize a new engineer with his employer's particular terms and usages.

Certain instances of overlapping may be noted. Ideally, a subject
should be thoroughly treated in only one place and reference made to
this treatment whenever the occasion arises again in the documents. In
larger projects, though, duplication of coverage is fairly common.

ADVERTISEMENT.   The advertisement is usually the last contract document prepared, but is the first one seen by the contractor.

The primary purpose of the advertisement is to obtain competitive
bidding on the project. In public contracts three bidders on any project
are normally required and it takes a special authorization if an award

is to be made otherwise. In private work there is, of course, no legal requirement to advertise. Contract awards are often made to contractors with whom the owner has successfully dealt on previous occasions. Many companies consider competitive bidding to be desirable, however, and formal procedures have been established by them to require it.

A second purpose to be accomplished by the advertisement is to attract only prospective bidders who would be interested in the type of work involved. The advertisement should not attract those who have insufficient capacity or who are not interested in the type or location of the work. To accomplish this end the wording of the advertisement should give a clear, general picture of what is to be done.

The title of the advertisement has two functions. It must attract attention and it should also state very generally what is to be built. The phrase "Notice to Contractors" or "Call for Bids" together with a phrase describing generally the type of structure, as "Elementary School," serves these functions well. A glance attracts the qualified contractor and prompts him to read further.

The information to be included in the advertisement varies with the type of project contemplated, but the following details are often found desirable:

1. The kind of job.
2. Where it is to take place—construction equipment is rather costly to move.
3. Who is owner and who is engineer—previous contacts with owner or engineer may influence a contractor.
4. Approximate size of the project.
5. The date and place for receipt of bids, and the date and place of opening and reading bids.
6. If an award is to be made, e.g., "to lowest responsible bidder," or if the owner reserves the right to reject any and all bids; and when the contract is to be signed.
7. Deposits to be required, bid bonds, performance bonds.
8. Procedure for withdrawing bids if withdrawal is to be allowed.
9. The place where copies of the contract documents may be obtained.
10. Any special conditions.

To accomplish the purposes of advertising for bids, the advertising medium should be carefully selected. Public contracts must be advertised in local newspapers. In private contracts, local newspapers and trade journals make good advertising media.

See Appendix, page 358 for the advertisement used by the State of

Florida Board of Control to attract bidders on the Administration Building for the University of South Florida.

INSTRUCTIONS FOR BIDDERS. The purposes of advertisement are best served by brevity. The contractors who remain interested in the project after reading the advertisement are given an opportunity to obtain more information, usually from the engineer. It is customary to require a deposit (usually from $5.00 to $50.00) from the contractor when he obtains a set of the contract documents.

The contract document known as "Instructions for Bidders" or "Information for Bidders" may be a separate document. Probably just as frequently it is the beginning portion of the specifications. Much of the information contained in Instructions for Bidders is the same as that given in the advertisement, but in expanded form—in other words, the "what," "where," "when," "how," and "for whom" in more detail.

Additional inclusions in the Instructions for Bidders vary considerably from one project to another. Items included in Instructions for Bidders in one project may be found in the general conditions document or in the general provisions section of the specifications in other projects. Additional items usually included in the Instructions for Bidders section are listed below:

1. A requirement that the bidders follow the proposal form.

2. A statement as to whether or not alternative proposals will be considered.

3. The proper signing of bids; e.g., the use of a power of attorney.

4. Qualification or pre-qualification of bidders. This is a requirement to satisfy the owner that the contractor has the necessary skill, financial means, staff, and equipment to do the job.

5. Discrepancies—provision is usually made for review with the engineer of any discrepancies which appear in the contract documents.

6. Examination of the site. An invitation is normally extended to bidders to examine the site with a warning that no additional compensation will be allowed as a result of conditions of which the bidder could have informed himself.

7. Provision for return of required bid deposits to unsuccessful bidders.

See Appendix, page 359 for the Instructions for Bidders used in building the University of South Florida Administration Building.

THE PROPOSAL. The proposal is a formal offer by the contractor to do the required work of the project. Acceptance of the proposal makes it a binding contract so considerable care must be exercised by the engineer in drawing it up.

Proposal forms are usually standardized for all bidders on a particular job. If the proposal is broken down into components (as in a unit-price contract), it is necessary for comparison purposes that the breakdown b. the same for all bidders. Where just one lump-sum bid is requested, it is still necessary for the proposal form to be the same for all, since bid should be on an equivalent basis. The following elements may be con. tained in a proposal form:

1. The price or prices for which the contractor agrees to perform the work involved.

2. The time when work is to start and when it is to be finished.

3. A statement that no fraud or collusion exists. Of particular concern is the possibility of fraud or collusion among bidders or between any bidder and a representative or employee of the owner.

4. A statement that the bidder accepts responsibility for having examined the site.

5. Proffer of any required bid bond or guarantee and agreement to furnish whatever other bonds may be required as well as an agreement to forfeit these bonds or portions of them under conditions stipulated.

6. Acknowledgment that the various other documents are to become parts of the contract.

7. A listing of subcontractors if required.

8. Signature and signatures of witnesses.

See Appendix, page 368 for the Proposal Form used by contractor bidding on construction of the University of South Florida Administration Building.

AGREEMENT. To a lawyer the agreement probably would be the most important of the contract documents. It is the focal point of the entire relationship between owner and contractor which the remaining contract documents are drawn to support.

The term "agreement" is used advisedly for this document because it is preferable to use the term "contract" for the complete array of contract documents.

Usually the agreement is quite short—one page or, possibly two—in which the work to be done is described largely by reference to the other contract documents. The owner's consideration (the price to be paid for the work) must be shown as well as the means and time of payment.

Although they are included in the other contract documents which are incorporated by reference, there are a few items which are usually repeated in the agreement. If time of completion is an essential element of the project, that time and liquidated damages for failure to complete on time are mentioned. If there is to be a warranty of the work by the contractor for, say, a year after completion, such a warranty is usually ncluded. Any amounts to be held back from payments to the contractor re set forth.

See Appendix, page 371 for the Standard Form of Agreement between contractor and owner. Reprinted with permission of the American nstitute of Architects.

BONDS.   A bond gives the owner financial protection in case of default y the contractor. There are three types of bonds in common use in ontracting—the *Bid Bond*, the *Performance Bond*, and the *Labor and 1aterial Payment Bond*. Each protects the owner by assuming a risk vhich he would normally run in hiring a contractor to undertake work or him.

The function of a bid bond is to assure the owner that the bidder will ign the agreement to do the work if his bid is the one accepted. In heory the amount of the Bid Bond is supposed to cover the owner's loss f the lowest responsible bidder fails to sign the agreement and the wner must then turn to the next higher bidder. Usually the owner does ot require a Bid Bond as such. He requires a deposit which may be atisfied by a Bid Bond or a certified check or some other security by the ontractor that the owner will be reimbursed in case of failure to sign. The bid security is forfeited only if the chosen bidder fails to agree to the roject. It is returned to the bidder after the agreement is made. The bid ecurities of unsuccessful bidders are, of course, returned to them.

See Appendix, page 375 for Bid Bond Form, reprinted with permision of the American Institute of Architects.

Through the Performance Bond the owner's risk that the contractor nay fail to complete the project is passed on to a surety company. The isk involved may be very slight—most contractors are in business to stay. Iowever, a contractor deals in the future and predictions of what will appen sometimes go awry. Risks are involved. The contractor may meet vith insurmountable obstacles. Such things as unforeseen price rises, trikes, fires, floods, storms, or unsuspected subsoil conditions can finanially ruin even the best-backed contractors. If the contractor is faced vith such disaster, insolvency may result and the owner, if he has not rovided for a performance bond, may be left trying to obtain blood rom a stone. However, if a performance bond has been required, comletion of his structure is guaranteed. Many surety companies maintain heir own facilities to be pressed into service on such occasions; more requently the surety company hires another contractor to complete the ob.

The cost of a performance bond will, of course, be passed on to the wner in the price he pays for the work. This price normally runs somevhat less than one percent of the bid price for the contract. For this rice the owner not only gets risk protection, but a preselection of conractors. Surety companies are quite choosy about the contractors that they agree to back. The irresponsible and the "fly-by-nights" are poor risks and a reputable surety company will not back them. The requirement of a performance bond, then, allows the owner to select from the best.

See Appendix, page 376 for Performance Bond reprinted with permission of the American Institute of Architects.

The third type of bond offers protection against labor and material men's liens, known generally as mechanics' liens. The lien laws of the various states differ considerably. In any state, though, if a contractor fails to pay for his labor or material, a lien may be obtained against the property which they were used to improve. In addition to the labor and material supplier's liens, the contractor, subcontractor, engineer, or architect may secure payment by recording a lien. Based upon the assumption of the owner's honesty and integrity in dealing with his contractor and engineer or architect, discussion here will be confined to labor liens and material suppliers' liens.

Mechanics' liens secure payment for anything connected with the improvement of real estate. The security is an encumbrance upon the property which then makes it more difficult to sell or mortgage. Technical procedures and delays are necessary in following the lien laws to remove encumbrances. There are two ways in which the owner may protect himself:

1. By withholding sufficient funds from payments to the contractor to pay for labor and materials if the contractor fails to do so, or

2. By requiring the contractor to obtain a labor and material payment bond.

Withholding part payment requires that the owner know the amount he may have to pay. This, in turn, usually requires a sworn statement from the contractors as to his outstanding bills before payment to the contractor is made. Some state lien laws require such a sworn statement if a payment bond has not been provided in the contract. The procedure can become somewhat cumbersome.

Requirement of a labor and material payment bond from the contractor is much simpler for the owner. According to the bond the surety company assumes liability for the contractor's unpaid bills.

When the federal government is owner in a project, a performance bond and a labor and material payment bond are automatically required. The Miller Act (passed in 1935) requires such bonds for federal contracts exceeding $2000.

A Labor and Material Payment Bond is reprinted with permission of the American Institute of Architects in the Appendix, page 377.

GENERAL CONDITIONS.   In a set of contract documents the document which states the general relationships among the parties is usually known as the *General Conditions*. The General Conditions deal in rights reserved and assigned among the parties, authority and responsibility. Topics covered in the General Conditions vary from contract to contract, but some are almost invariably present.

There is nearly always a statement near the beginning of the General Conditions as to the unity of the contract documents—that a requirement in one document is just as binding as if it appeared in all of them. Such unity is necessary since the specifications for even a small project would reach tremendous size if each specification item had to be followed by all conditions pertaining to it.

The right of inspection by the owner or his representative at any time is usually reserved. It is common also to allow inspection by public officials as a General Condition.

Conditions for termination of the contract by the owner and by the contractor are set forth in the General Conditions. Bankruptcy of the contractor and failure by the owner to make scheduled payments to the contractor when due are conditions for termination.

The insurance program for the project is usually outlined in the General Conditions. Provision is made for workmen's compensation to cover medical costs and partial wage payments in case of injury to a worker as a result of his employment by the contractor. The owner's protective liability insurance protects the owner from contingent liability if the contractor's operations should injure anyone. Fire insurance and vehicle liability are among many other types of insurance commonly required in the General Conditions.

The engineer or architect is to make decisions on the work involved in the project. He has the right to stop the work when it appears necessary to do so. The extent or limits of his authority should be spelled out clearly. Provision is often made for arbitration as a final step in an altercation between the owner and the contractor.

Finally, the General Conditions usually include a requirement that the contractor keep the site clean as work progresses and that he clean up the site thoroughly when he finishes.

See Appendix, page 378 for General Conditions, reprinted with permission of the American Institute of Architects.

The Final Steps

TIME. Almost invariably there is considerable pressure by the owner to get things started after the decision has been made to undertake a project. Advertising and bidding procedure require time, however, and to shorten the time required in the initial stages is nearly always an act of folly. The prospective bidders need time to investigate the work site and to plan their work. If there is not enough time for the investigation and planning stage, many unknowns will remain. Generally, the more that is not known by a bidder, the higher will be the bid price. There are few fears greater than fear of the unknown, and fear of a proposed project drives the price up.

COLLUSION. Most owners, engineers, and contractors are honest people. There are some of each, though, who will eagerly forget ethics and the law to seize an unfair advantage. Unfair advantages take many forms, and there are many shades of gray between fair and honest practices and illegal ones. One is the preference of one contractor over another, either by giving him added vital information privately or by writing the specifications so as to give him an advantage. Another form of collusion occurs occasionally when there is a limited number of responsible bidders on a project. The bidders get together and decide who will take the job and for what price; the other bidders then submit prices higher than that submitted by the "successful" bidder. The result of these and other forms of collusion is higher cost to the owner. The existence of such practices is the main reason for governmental restrictions in letting public contracts. Collusion is, of course, against public policy and the Sherman Anti-Trust Act. It is punishable by both fine and imprisonment. In addition, up to triple damages can be recovered in a civil action by those injured.

The time for receiving proposals should be fixed and inflexible. It is unfair to give one contractor a longer time to prepare his proposal than the others had. Similarly, the opening of the proposals should take place at the time specified.

LOWEST RESPONSIBLE BIDDER. A contract award normally goes to the "lowest responsible bidder." Many factors enter into the determination of the contractor who is to be awarded the contract. If prequalification has been required, the decision is based upon price alone. The non-monetary factors used to determine the lowest responsible bidder are those which indicate a reasonable likelihood of completing the contract. The chief factors to be considered are:

1. The contractor's *reputation*. Such things as shoddy work, constant bickering for extra payments, and an uncooperative or lackadaisical attitude are cause for caution. Rejection of a bidder on the basis of reputation often leads to arguments, but each person builds his own reputation and should have to live by it.

2. The contractor's *finances*. Inadequate finances or credit can be a source of trouble in a project. Even though a bond is required of the contractor, finding a substitute will cause a delay, and the work may suffer.

3. The contractor's *experience*. If the project is a new field for the con-

tractor, he may have to experiment where an experienced contractor would automatically know the answers. There is, of course, the possibility that the results from this inexperience might be better because of a new approach or new ideas. The best guide is the contractor's past performance. The size of the project is also of importance. A contractor's success on a $40,000 job does not insure success on a million-dollar project.

4. The contractor's *equipment*. Most contracting work requires expensive equipment, which is often quite specialized. Without access to the proper equipment, the contractor may be doomed to failure despite good intentions. A trip by the engineer to examine the contractor's machinery and equipment may be recommended.

5. The contractor's *staff*. The skill of each of the contractor's staff members in his respective area of specialization can mean the success or failure of an enterprise. Purchasing of materials and supplies, for instance, can add to profit or be an excessive addition to cost. There are many instances of the same or similar items being sold for widely divergent prices by different suppliers.

Disqualification of a bidder is a rather serious step and the engineer should be sure of his reasons before taking this action. Charges of favoritism and the prospect of debates over qualifications prompt the engineer to overlook any personal feelings he may have toward a bidder. In all bids the right to reject any and all proposals should be reserved for use if needed.

CONTRACTOR'S COSTS

What is the major reason why contractors lose money on jobs which they undertake? Probably the best answer is that they bid too low. And why should a contractor bid too low? Because he has overlooked one or more of the elements which make up a proposal. There are five basic categories necessary in any proposal if the contractor is to "make out" on the job. These are 1) direct labor, 2) materials, 3) overhead, 4) contingencies, and 5) profit.

Direct Labor

In putting together the necessary ingredients for any kind of structure, be it a special machine or a building, direct labor is an important item. The cost-per-hour for tool makers, carpenters, bricklayers, and other specialists is a significant amount. This direct payment cost can be anticipated and is usually estimated with reasonable accuracy. There are other costs, though, which are tied to direct labor but which are often overlooked.

FRINGES.   The costs involved in direct labor which are often overlooked are those which are usually termed *fringe benefits*. Fringe benefits are payments (other than direct wages) by an employer caused by the presence of the worker on the payroll and imposed on the employer in compliance with a governmental requirement or by collective bargaining. Many payments are fringes according to this definition.

Workmen's compensation is one such payment. To conform with a state's workmen's compensation law, the employer usually pays an insurance company or a state agency a set amount per $100 of payroll. The amount paid by the employer is determined either from a rate manual or according to the employer's injury experience. These costs run from a few cents per $100 on office employees to nearly $20 per $100 of payroll on certain types of construction work.

Social security is another governmental-required fringe benefit. Employer's payments to social security are equal to those deducted from the worker's wage; e.g., at 6 percent total deduction, the employer would pay 3 per cent and the employee 3 per cent of the employee's wages. When the Social Security Act was passed, these payments were little more than a trivial annoyance; now they constitute a significant cost to the employer.

Holiday pay and vacation pay are common fringe costs to the employer. A recent collective bargaining goal has been the inclusion of each employee's birthday as a holiday for him. Although these payments are made for time when no work is performed, they are still costs of direct labor.

It is the policy of many employers to share the cost of medical insurance and life insurance with their employees. Overtime premiums and shift premiums add to the cost of direct labor. Maintenance of a retirement fund for employees, payments from which are to be added to social security benefits, is common.

Two of the means used to increase employee interest in the company are stock-buying plans and profit-sharing plans. In a stock-buying plan, the employer usually helps the employee become a part-owner in his or other companies. Frequently, this takes the form of making deductions from the employee's wages and then adding to the employee's investment a few years later. Turnover is reduced if the employee must wait for the employer's addition to the investment. Profit-sharing plans work in many ways, one way being the division of company profits after the first, say, $100,000 of profit in a particular year. The increased incentive and company loyalty which result from such plans cannot be denied—but neither can the added cost.

AVAILABILITY AND TRANSPORTATION.   With increased automation, it has become more and more possible—and even desirable—to locate plants without reference to labor supply. Structures are being built in the frozen regions near the Arctic Circle and the Antarctic and in desert regions, for example. The contractor who undertakes such installations has a problem of getting people to go with and work on the project. Often this requires relocation expenses and housing to be furnished. In less spectacular instances the cost is often overlooked. There are many locations where, though there may be an abundance of people, there is a shortage of particular specialists. Getting these specialists may entail payment by the contractor for daily time in transit or for moving them to the location.

Materials

One of the largest costs of a project is the cost of materials which go into it. Purchasing can make or break a contractor. There is, in effect, an added profit for the contractor who, because of his knowledge of sources of materials and supplies, is able to make fortunate procurements throughout his project. One characteristic which often marks an efficient contractor is prompt payment of invoices. It is common practice among suppliers to offer discounts for prompt payment, such as 2 per cent off for payment within 10 days, net in 30 days. Although 2 per cent on any one bill may not amount to much, the accumulation is significant.

AVAILABILITY AND TRANSPORTATION. Local availability of materials and supplies is important. Even apparent local availability may not be sufficient. The local market may be closed to an outsider. The legality of such local agreements is quite questionable, but the practical results are apparent. One story runs something like this: It seems that the Black Construction Company, in a neighboring state, was successful bidder on a local contract, bidding in competition with local contractors. The bid was made on the basis of cement, mortar sand, and gravel being locally available (suppliers in the area were quite plentiful). Black set up to begin operations on the site but, when he tried to buy concrete ingredients, he found that they were "earmarked" for his former bidding competitors. As a result, Black had to transport cement, mortar sand, and gravel several hundred miles, resulting in a loss to him on the contract. Other contractors have run into very high local prices. Usually, it pays a contractor to investigate and make sure of local supplies before bidding on work in unfamiliar settings.

STORAGE. The owner often allows use of his storage facilities if such facilities are available. In many contracts, though, such facilities are not available or are inadequate. The successful bidder should include storage in his planning.

Overhead

A discussion of all of the items which normally constitute overhead would be beyond the scope and purpose of this book. These are the costs that many small contractors or those new in the field often tend to overlook; as a result, they seem to "make out" on their contracts, but lose money in the long run.

The contractor's overhead consists of many things: maintenance of his office, equipment maintenance, taxes, supervision, depreciation on equipment, utilities and others.

COST OF ESTIMATING.   Of particular interest is the cost of investigation, planning, and estimating. This cost usually runs somewhere around 2 per cent of the bid price on a project. Two per cent isn't bad, but very few contractors get every job on which they bid. It is likely that the average would be about one successful bid out of every six or so submitted. If these figures are accepted, then the actual cost of making an average successful bid is about 12 per cent of the bid price. If the bidding is realistic, the cost is passed on to the owner. It is worth noting that this cost constitutes one of the wastes of competitive bidding practices. There have been instances in which owners solicited bids with no real intention of going through with their project. Such practices should be discouraged.

Contingencies

Very few projects run smoothly from start to finish. It is rare that every day is a weather-working day or that delays do not occur for one reason or another. To cover the unexpected events the contractor usually adds an item known as "contingencies" into his bid. The cost of the item runs anywhere from 5 per cent to 15 per cent of the total, depending upon the likelihood that hazards will occur. If liquidated damages are in prospect, contingencies may be quite high. If all work to be done is clearly and completely shown, and the probability of hazards is small, the amount for contingencies will be reduced.

Profit

People who work for others as independent contractors do so in an endeavor to make a profit. Much of the growth of our economy can be attributed to the intent to make such a profit. The contractor is entitled as is anyone else to be paid a reasonable return on the projects he undertakes. The percentage of profit varies with such things as the size of the job, competition, and other factors, but profit there must be if the contractor is to survive.

HAYNES v. COLUMBIA PRODUCERS, INC.

344 P. 2d 1032 Washington (Oct. 15, 1959)

FINLEY, Judge.

E. R. Haynes, a general contractor, brought this action to recover money allegedly due him from the defendant, Columbia Producers, Inc., under four contracts entered into between the parties.

At the trial the work done pursuant to each of the four contracts was referred to by a separate job number. For convenience, we will refer to the contracts in the same manner. The first contract (Job 5-14) was the only one of the four in writing. It provided for the construction of a grain elevator and was a "fixed-price" contract. The second contract (Job 5-16) was also for a fixed amount. It was for the construction of a foundation and concrete slabs for a steel warehouse to be erected adjacent to the elevator. The third and fourth agreements were both "cost-plus" contracts. One of them (Job 5-19) provided for the labor and material for the construction of an under-tunnel and foundation, and a slab, for a storage warehouse. The fourth contract (Job 5-26) was for the installation of machinery to be used in the storage warehouse building.

One of the principal causes of the difficulties between plaintiff and defendant was that all four contracts were being performed simultaneously, and the work was being done at the same location. During the trial, the corporation contended, *inter alia*, that the contractor had billed many items to the cost-plus contracts, whereas, in fact, these items should have been charged to the "fixed-price" contracts.

Plaintiff Haynes performed all work required under the contracts. The sole dispute at the trial concerned the amount, if any, which defendant corporation owed the plaintiff. The trial court entered judgment for the plaintiff in the sum of $28,052.99, plus interest. Both parties have appealed, the plaintiff claiming a greater amount than was awarded to him, and the defendant claiming that the amount of the judgment was too large. For convenience, we shall herinafter refer to the appellant as Columbia Producers and to the respondent—cross-appellant as Haynes.

Under the machinery installation contract (Job 5-26), Haynes agreed to install certain machinery in Columbia Producers' elevator. Columbia Producers purchased this machinery from a third party, the Carter-Miller Company, thereby receiving a discount of $1,948. Columbia Producers directed Carter-Miller to credit the $1,948 discount to Haynes, who had an account with Carter-Miller for other purchases completely independent from the work he was then doing for Columbia Producers. The obvious effect was, of course, that Haynes owed Carter-Miller $1,948 less than he had owed before the discount was credited to his account.

Columbia Producers contended that the "plus" amount agreed to as the contractor's fee on Job 5-26 was the discount that the corporation caused to be credited to Haynes' account with Carter-Miller. The trial court found that the parties had agreed that the "plus" amount would be ten per cent of cost, and made no finding relative to the Carter-Miller discount.

The appellant, Columbia Producers, does not assign error to the finding of the trial court that the parties agreed to a contractor's fee of ten per cent. Its assignment of error is directed to the failure of the trial court to make any finding relative to the discount. It is urged by Columbia Producers that the effect of the trial court's decision on this point is to give a double allowance to Haynes. With this we agree.

Columbia Producers directed Carter-Miller to credit Haynes with this discount, under the mistaken impression that this was what the parties had agreed to as the contractor's fee on Job 5-26. The fact that Columbia Producers was mistaken on this point does not entitle Haynes to a ten per cent fee and the discount. Haynes' contention that Columbia Producers gave him this discount merely as a gratuity is not supported by the record, and is not consistent with the business relationship existing between these parties. In short, Columbia Producers' first assignment of error is well taken, and it should be allowed $1,948 as an offset against the judgment awarded Haynes.

As part of Haynes' costs on the machinery installation contract (Job 5-26), the trial court allowed him $1,061.30 for labor used to install certain bin dividers. Columbia Producers contend that the obligation to install these dividers existed under Job 5-14, and that, consequently, it was error to allow these costs as a part of Job 5-26. This is not merely a dispute without substance, as it will be remembered that Job 5-14 is a "fixed-price" contract, whereas Job 5-26 is a "cost-plus" contract.

The contract entered into between these parties for the construction of the elevator (Job 5-14) obligated Haynes to furnish labor and all other costs necessary to complete a reinforced concrete elevator as shown on certain plans. These plans were introduced into evidence, and it is readily apparent that they provided for the construction of bin dividers.

The oral contract made for the installation of machinery (Job 5-26) was subdivided as follows: (a) hopper bin bottoms; (b) spoutings; (c) belt conveyors; and (d) general machinery installation. It will be noticed that there was no obligation under this contract for installation of any bin dividers. Rather, this obligation clearly existed under the contract entered into for the construction of the elevator. Accordingly, the judgment awarded Haynes should be reduced in the further amount of $1,061.30 (independent of any interest calculation).

Columbia Producers next contends that the trial court erred in refusing to credit it with $2,467.18, representing the amount charged by Haynes for certain sheet steel, and the transportation thereof, for use in the construction of bin bottoms and hoppers on Job 5-26. The total bill for this item was $4,164.18, representing 38,352 pounds of steel, plus transportation. Columbia Producers claims that only 20,000 pounds were actually used on Job 5-26. The trial court, faced with conflicting testimony, found for Haynes on this issue. We have carefully examined the record and conclude that it supports this finding.

Finally, Columbia Producers urges that the trial court erred in allowing Haynes interest on the amount found due him. In this connection it asserts that a trial of this case was necessary in order to determine how much was owing from it to Haynes, and that, consequently, this amount was not liquidated in the sense that it could have been determined prior to trial. Columbia

Producers bases this assertion on the fact that Haynes allegedly failed to furnish adequate or proper billings, in that many items were being charged to the cost-plus contracts which should have been charged to the fixed-price contracts. Columbia Producers asserts that, in addition, many other items on the bill were overcharges. Even assuming these facts to be substantially true, we conclude that the trial court was correct in the allowance of interest.

In *Mall Tool Company v. Far West Equipment Company*, 1954, 45 Wash. 2d 158, 273 P.2d 652, 659, this court quoted with approval from McCormick on Damages 213, para. 54, that

'A claim is liquidated if the evidence furnishes data which, if believed, makes it possible to compute the amount with exactness, *without reliance upon opinion or discretion*. Examples are claims upon promises to pay a fixed sum, claims for money had and received, claims for money paid out, and claims for *goods or services to be paid for at an agreed rate*.' [Emphasis supplied.]

and that

'If the claim is one of the kinds mentioned above, it is still "liquidated," by what seems the preferable view, even though it is disputed in whole or in part.'

In further explanation of the above, McCormick continues by stating:

'Doubtless all courts would agree that a specific sum of money named in and covenanted to be paid by an express contract, where the liability to pay the principal sum is undisputed, is a "liquidated" sum. Such admitted claims rarely give rise to any controversy interest. Is the claim for such a sum still a "liquidated" demand, where the defendant denies all liability under the contract, *or disputes liability for certain items and admits others?* It would seem that the existence of a dispute over the whole or part of the claim should not change the character of the claim from one for a liquidated, to one for an unliquidated, sum. And this conclusion finds support in the cases. . . .

'. . . In short, *it is the character of the claim* and not of the defense that is determinative of the question whether an amount of money sued for is a "liquidated sum."' [Emphasis supplied.]

We are convinced that the *character of the claim* in the case at bar is liquidated. Two of these contracts were for fixed amounts. The other two were for costs, plus ten per cent of costs, as the contractor's fee. All were subject to mathematical computation to arrive at the amount owed. It was not necessary to rely on opinion evidence. In short, the amounts owed were determinable within the meaning of the Mall Tool case, supra. The trial court did not err in allowing interest.

We turn now to a discussion of the assigments of error raised by Haynes on his cross-appeal, only one of which we need to discuss in detail.

The written contract entered into for the construction of the elevator (Job 5-14) provided that Haynes should be allowed extra compensation if it became necessary for him to excavate any "rock." The trial court found that Haynes had expended $1,814.11 for extra excavation within the terms of the contract. However, the trial court also found that, under the original plans, Haynes was obligated to construct a basement, size 40' by 40'. It is admitted that the basement as it was finally constructed was only 20' by 40'. The trial court determined that there was a saving to Haynes of $1,690 in the construction of the smaller basement; consequently, the $1,814.11 allowed for the rock excavation was reduced by the amount of $1,690.

Haynes contends that there is no substantial evidence in the record to support the trial court's finding that, under the contract, he was originally obligated to construct a basement, 40' by 40'. Haynes argues that the agreement between the parties was originally for a basement 20' by 40'. We believe there is merit to this contention.

The written contract did not specify what the dimensions of the basement were to be. The contract merely required Haynes to construct the basement in accordance with certain plans. From the plans it is difficult to ascertain the actual size the basement was to be. For example, one of Columbia Producers' witnesses, an engineer, testified that the plans called for the basement to be 40' by 40'; on cross-examination, however, he admitted that the plans showed only a one-sided view of the basement. The only probative evidence concerning the agreement between the parties which we have found in the record is the testimony of Haynes. He testified that, originally, it was agreed the basement would be 40' by 20'. As there appears to be no evidence to contradict this testimony, it follows that the trial court erred in finding that the original plans specified the basement should be 40' by 40', and in awarding the amount of $1,690 as a credit to Columbia Producers.

The remaining four assignments of error raised by Haynes are all directed to the trial court's findings of fact. By his pleadings, as modified by a pretrial order, Haynes claimed (1) that he was entitled to $3,874 for extra work done on Job 5-16 for the reason that he was required to level certain ground before commencing construction of the warehouse required by that job; (2) that he was entitled to $980.27 for cement delivered, and (3) to $982.25 for excavation done on Job 5-19 over and above the amount allowed by the trial court; (4) that he had filed a claim of lien against Columbia Producers within ninety days after the termination of work as required by statute. The trial court found adversely to Haynes on each of these claims. Our examination of the record discloses that the evidence amply supports these findings.

The net effect of our decision is to allow Haynes $1,319.30 (independent of any recalculation of interest) less than was allowed him by the trial court. Under the circumstances, neither party shall recover costs on this appeal.

The cause is remanded with directions to the trial court to enter judgment in accordance with the views expressed herein.

REVIEW QUESTIONS

1. Describe the relationships between the parties to a construction contract.

2. How do public projects and private projects differ?

3. In what ways are contracting and manufacturing similar? How do they differ?

4. If you planned to build a two-car garage on your lot, what factors

would you consider in deciding whether to attempt to build the garage yourself or hire a contractor to do it? How does this differ from an industrial situation in which a company is trying to decide whether to build a special machine or hire someone else to build it?

5. Summarize briefly the advantages and disadvantages of: 1) a lump-sum contract; 2) a cost-plus-percent-of-cost contract; 3) a cost-plus-fixed-fee contract; and 4) a combination of unit-price and lump-sum contract.

6. In *Haynes v. Columbia Producers, Inc.,* what caused the court action? How could it have been prevented in the original arrangement?

7. What purposes are served by a feasibility study? When should it end?

8. Why do governments so strictly regulate competitive bidding practices? What formal procedures are required in your state?

9. Locate in a local newspaper an "advertisement" or "call for bids" on a construction project. What details does the advertisement give its reader?

10. What are mechanic's lien laws? How do your state statutes call for such liens to be established and removed?

11. What are the purposes of each of the three types of bonds commonly required of contractors?

12. What nonmonetary factors determine the qualifications of a bidder?

13. Your employer is about to bid on the building and installation of a shuttle mechanism to automatically move 2" diameter hollow cylinders 1" high from a lathe to a punch press, to locate them in the press die and actuate the press to extrude the cylinders. What are the cost elements likely to be encountered in the work and which, therefore, should be included in the price bid?

17

SPECIFICATIONS

As the term is used here, a specification means a description of work to be done or things to be purchased. Specifications are most frequently heard of in building construction, but they apply to every area of engineering. The definition is broad enough to include many things which we do daily in dealing with others. If you hire a painter to paint your house and tell him that the house is to be white with gray trim, you have made a specification. If you take your car to an auto mechanic to be repaired, telling the mechanic to do whatever is necessary to remove the "grind" from the transmission, you have made a specification. A person ordering four $\frac{1}{4}$-inch stove bolts, 3" long, from a hardware store clerk is using a specification. The specifications mentioned so far have been oral rather than written, but they are just as truly specifications as are the voluminous written ones for such a construction project as the Hoover Dam.

There are two basic reasons for putting specifications in writing rather than giving them orally:

1. To obtain a permanent record for resolving disputes.

2. To insure planning.

If the purchase involved is of sufficient money value so that a breach of the conditions specified could cause the purchaser substantial injury, the specifications should be written. The written record of what is specified defines the duties of the parties. The specification is part of a contract. It is likely to be interpreted in court or by an arbitration board if a dispute arises between the parties. Lawsuits on construction projects have been undertaken years after completion of the projects. Without a permanent record of the rights and obligations of the parties, the result is likely to be confusion. Written specifications frequently prevent costly lawsuits because they act as a ready reference in controversies between the parties. It is not often that building construction is undertaken without specifications. However, almost as commonly, process engineers, project engineers, accountants and purchasing agents toil over specifications for machinery and equipment. Very few government purchases are made without reference to written specifications. In fact, the only occasions in which the federal government purchases without such specifications are isolated instances of purchases of services.

The second reason for requiring written specifications is that writing a specification almost necessarily requires planning. It is easy to specify something orally without giving it much thought. However, when it becomes necessary to reduce the specification to written form, the very knowledge that a permanent record is being made induces caution. When one writes, he tends to examine his reasons for whatever he puts on paper. The result, in specification writing, is usually a more efficient purchase. The likelihood that the thing specified will do the job required at a lower over-all cost is improved greatly by the writing. In specifying 30 strokes per minute for a punch press he is about to purchase, a process engineer may well be led to question his decision as he writes the specification. Under certain conditions a variable speed press (say 20 to 40 strokes per minute) might be more appropriate. The writing of the specification calls his attention to the question again.

SPECIFICATION WRITING

The specification has a communications job to do. It must communicate to the reader what is required by the writer. It is essentially quite a simple job. As such, it can be done best by the use of simple language. Complex sentence structure and complicated wording may often be interpreted more than one way. With simple structure and simple wording this is much less likely to happen. It is best to avoid jargon, abbreviations, and symbols unless they are of a recognized standard, and fully understood in the trade.

Specifications, together with the drawings, show the contractor what is to be done. Each supplements the other. In addition, the specifications indicate the relation between the parties in greater detail than does the agreement. The working drawings show the work to be accomplished, but, frequently, not the quality standards required. The quality standards are usually more conveniently stated in the specifications.

Style

Specifications should be written with the greatest clarity of which the author is capable. The more clear and concise the writing, the better the comprehension. A specification is not the place for flowery language or complicated legal terms. Although it is difficult to overemphasize brevity and terse presentation in writing specifications, the specifications still must be complete. Completeness should be considered the limit to which brevity can be taken. In other words, the writer should strive to be brief up to the point where further brevity may be accomplished only by sacrificing some of the meaning in the specification.

Novels and other literature written to be read for entertainment frequently refer to the subject in terms of "he" and "his," and other such pronouns. The use of such words adds considerably to the ease and enjoyment of reading such material. The vast majority of the readers will understand the meaning intended by the author. Those who do not will usually pass over the sentence without hesitation in order to maintain interest in the story. The writer of anything which is likely to be interpreted in a court of law cannot afford to be so entertaining. Where it is at all likely that there may be a misinterpretation, the subject should be repeated. Consider the sentence: "In case of controversy between the contractor and the inspector, he shall immediately refer the question to the engineer." Who is to refer the question? The contractor could say "I thought the inspector was to contact the engineer," and vice versa. Replacement of the word "he" by "the contractor" or "the inspector" clears up any doubt.

Precise Wording

Our language consists of many words with similar meanings. There are general words and specific words. The word "property," for instance, has a very broad meaning, including all items of personal possessions as well as real estate. Many other terms have broad meanings and should be used very carefully in the wording of a specification. The words used should indicate what is to be accomplished so precisely that no doubt can exist. Commonly-used words frequently are not exact enough in meaning. For instance, it is quite common to hear someone say that something should have an addition on either side of it, as "a light on either side of the gateway," when what is intended is that the addition must be present on each side, as "a light on each side of the gateway." Many other words are commonly used interchangeably, such as "any" and "all," "amount" and "quantity," "malleable" and "ductile," and "hardness" and "rigidity," for example. The inexactness of meaning in conversation usually causes no problems; but in specification writing the result can be trouble, measured in dollars. There are few instances in the English language where one word will mean exactly the same thing as another. Care in wording is definitely indicated where the writing may have to be reviewed in court.

Reference Specifications

With the wealth of old specifications, texts on specification writing, and standards published by various organizations, it is a rare specification today that is entirely original. As a practical matter this is desirable. Previous specifications have been tested, errors removed, and the language improved. If the rewriting for the new specification is carefully done, other potential problems may be discovered and eliminated. In addition, there is less likelihood of overlooking something in the present specifications if a pattern can be followed. However, a word of caution is necessary. Wholesale clipping of paragraphs and requirements from previous specifications can result in problems. While frequently there is considerable similarity between specifications, it is unlikely that any two will be exactly alike. If caution is not exercised in adapting paragraphs and clauses from old to new, the requirements for certain features of the new job are likely to be different from what was intended. There may be features of the new job which are found to be completely omitted from the new specification.

Many organizations have written standards for various items of equipment or elemental components, making it unnecessary for the specification writer to do more than incorporate these standards by reference. The United States government has a vast array of published standard specifications. For instance, when the government buys women's slacks for use in the armed forces, the specification consists mainly of references to military standards and other standarized specifications. The buttons are covered in Federal specification no. V-B-781; the fasteners by V-F-106; the shipping boxes by NN-B-631, and so on for the cloth, the stitches, the labels, and all the other elements of the purchase. The writing of a specification where such standards exist consists largely of determining the appropriate elements and listing the standards in logical order. The advantage of such standardization is quite obvious. A specialist in one element of the entire assembly has specified the appriate quality to be used. It is impossible for one person to be a specialist in everything. The specification resulting from a combination of several specialists is quite likely to be better than it would be if the total specification were to be written by any one of them.

ARRANGEMENT

The specification usually consists of at least two parts, one general and the other specific and detailed. The first part is known by many names (such as general conditions, general provisions, or special conditions) in various specifications, and the information included is not well standardized. In most contracts there is a separate document, previously discussed, known as the "General Conditions," dealing with very basic rights and responsibilities of the parties. To avoid conflict with the more basic document, we will use "general provisions" as the name of the general portion of the specifications.

General Provisions

In the relationships between the parties to a construction contract there is a vast middle ground between the provisions in the agreement and general conditions and the detailed specifications. The general conditions are general enough so that they apply to any contract work which the owner may want and to any contractor he may hire. The general provisions part of the specification pertains to a particular contract or type of contract. It sets the owner's policy as to control of the work, the scope and quality of the work, and any special requirements or precautions. It is here that answers are found to many of the day-to-day questions that arise between the parties. To cover these questions the general provisions must consider many topics. A few of the topics appear frequently enough to justify consideration here, these being representative of the contents of a general provisions section.

SEQUENCE OF WORK.   One topic which is almost certain to be covered (usually by a requirement for consultation) is the sequence of work. It is poor policy, from a legal and from a cost standpoint, to control rigidly the details of the work to be accomplished. However, there are occasions when some control must be exercised by the owner in the public interest (as in highway construction) or to dovetail the project with the work undertaken by other contractors. Usually a work schedule is called for in the specifications to aid the engineer and contractor in planning the work to the best advantage of the owner. Such a work schedule is

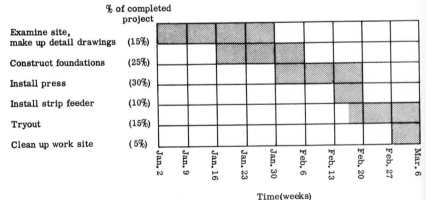

Work Schedule for Press Installation

made by showing graphically the starting and completion dates for the component parts of the project. The work schedule resembles the Gantt Charts so commonly used in production scheduling in industry. The figure shows a simple work schedule chart for a multistation, strip-feed punch-press installation. A schedule such as this provides the engineer with the means of obtaining a weekly (or daily or monthly) check against actual performance. It may be noted that the schedule also contains percentages assigned to each component of the job. These percentages represent estimated portions of the total job for each component and are usually agreed upon by the engineer and the contractor prior to starting work. Such schedules are frequently used in a progressive payment scheme (so much per week or month according to accomplishments during the period). The schedule allows a realistic estimate of progress to be made. For instance, assume that the contractor installing the presses shown in the figure is on schedule on Feb. 4 (the end of the week beginning Jan. 30). At this point he would be entitled to payments totalling 50 per cent of the total contract price less whatever amount may be withheld until final completion and acceptance. The amount to be so held back is another thing which is occasionally specified in the general provisions. Frequently this is set at 10 per cent. In the foregoing case, assuming a 10 per cent holdback, the contractor should receive 45 per cent of the total contract price.

CHANGES AND EXTRA WORK. Very few large contracts are completed without changes being made during the course of the work. Questions of payment for such changes can cause severe disagreement if nothing is provided in anticipation of them. A provision for changes and extra work is usually made in either the general conditions or the general provisions portion of the specification. Just as there are four basic means of paying for a contract, there are also four means of paying for extra work:

1. Lump sum.
2. Cost plus percentage.
3. Cost plus fixed fee.
4. Unit price.

The cost plus percentage and unit price types of contract present little or no problem as to compensation for changes or added work. The extra work is compensated at the fixed rate in the unit price contract; in the cost-plus-percent contract changes are easily made. In the lump-sum and cost-plus-fixed fee contracts, though, the necessity to prearrange a way to compensate for extra work is apparent. The contractor is already on the job; it is usually inconvenient and costly to get someone else to replace him for the added work. If the contractor is unscrupulous and the engineer has not provided adequately for changes, the contractor can make these changes costly. To illustrate this point there is a tale (of rather doubtful veracity) on the subject. It seems that a rather prominent builder of homes made his living a few years ago by capitalizing on the very human desire to change the structure while it is being constructed. He had a large selection of standard homes which he offered to build for any married man at cost. The customer would agree to a structure and work would progress to the point where the rooms were laid out and partitioning begun. At this point almost invariably the customer or his wife would require one or a series of changes to be made. The cost of the changes was, of course, quite high, for this was where the contractor made his profit. A few of the more cost-conscious customers managed to resist the temptation to change and were rewarded by getting an adequate house at a very low cost, but these were the exceptions. The engineer's attention to this detail in the contract documents may well be worth his time.

OTHER SUPPLIERS.   Work or materials to be supplied by others (either by the owner or other contractors) should be shown in the specification. Frequently this takes the form of one or more "right of supply" clauses in which the owner reserves the right to supply motors or other components (often salvaged from worn-out machines). When more than one contractor is to work on a project, the dividing lines must be clearly drawn in the specification. This is necessary to avoid conflict and to provide assurance that someone will be responsible for the details of each item; in other words, to avoid overlap or gaps in the contracted work.

DRAWINGS.   The drawings are an integral part of a construction contract. The following statement is commonly included in the general provisions of the specification: "The Contract Documents are complementary, and what is called for by any one shall be binding as if called for by all." The drawings and specifications, particularly, supplement each other as everyday working documents. Occasionally a conflict between a drawing and the specifications will become apparent. To resolve such conflicts, the general provisions frequently state that: "In case of difference between drawings and specifications, the specifications shall govern." Some provision is usually made for submission of working drawings and sketches for the engineer's approval during the course of the construction. Such details as the number of copies of drawings, even the size and type of paper to be used, are sometimes specified.

INFORMATION GIVEN.   Usually, considerable information pertinent to the proposed project is passed along to the bidders and thus, eventually, to the contractor. Some of the information may be of such a nature that the owner and the engineer will not want to warrant its completeness or the indications given by it. This is commonly true of test borings, for instance, where a defect in the subsoil might not show up in the samples taken. To protect the owner in such circumstances, the general provisions usually state that neither the owner nor the engineer will warrant that the information given shows the entire true picture. Generally, the contractor is held responsible for having made his own examination of the site.

SERVICES FURNISHED. When an addition to an existing structure is made, or when machinery or equipment is installed, certain of the services necessary are commonly supplied by the owner. Such services as water, compressed air, electricity, and crane service to unload equipment are frequently furnished by him. It is in the owner's interest to mention the availability of such services in the specification to give the contractor a true picture of some of the costs he will not have to cover.

RECEIPT AND STORAGE OF MATERIALS. By similar reasoning, if the contractor is to be allowed to use the owner's receiving and storage facilities, this should be made clear to him in the specification. Such facilities constitute a considerable addition to the cost if the contractor is to supply them himself. The cost will be passed along to the owner if he does not supply such facilities.

WAGE RATES. Particularly in government contracts, the wages paid the contractor are important. There are several federal statutes (and, usually, similar state statutes) which regulate wages, hours, and even sources of materials on public contracts. By way of example, many federal contracts cite the Davis-Bacon Act (wages), the Buy American Act (purchases of materials), and the Eight-Hour Laws (wages and hours) in their specifications.

The wages paid to workmen are of importance, even when the owner is a private party. Wages and working conditions poorer than those to which the area is accustomed can cause strikes and other labor problems. The owner may find the project delayed or even partly destroyed as a result of labor strife. It is unpleasant to find oneself the innocent victim in such circumstances. To avoid trouble of this nature, many specifications for private contracts provide for wage rates and working conditions to be equal to or better than those prevailing in the trade or locality.

SAFETY. A requirement as to safety and accident prevention is also a usual inclusion in the specifications. "The contractor shall, at all times, exercise reasonable precautions for the safety of employees in the performance of this contract, and shall comply with all applicable provisions of federal, state, and municipal safety laws and building construction codes."

Detail Specifications

The second major division of the specifications gives the details of the work to be undertaken. These detail specifications, together with the engineer's drawings, state how the job is to be done and what is to be accomplished. In writing the general provisions portion the engineer has

access to guideposts and instructions. When he writes the detail specifications, though, the engineer has fewer guideposts and must rely on his
knowledge of what can be accomplished and his ability to express himself.

Detail specifications are concerned with the materials and workmanship in the finished project.

MATERIALS.   When something is purchased, the purchase is made
with the intent of obtaining some service which the thing purchased is
capable of rendering. All a possession can do for one is to give service of
some kind. When a lathe or a punch press is bought, the purchaser is
really purchasing the capability of turning or bending or blanking or
performing other operations on materials as long as he owns the machine.
Much the same is true in the purchase of materials for a construction
project. The materials purchased must render a service. It is up to the
engineer to obtain the best service available for the owner at the most
favorable cost to him. There are, then, two factors which normally oppose
each other in the selection of material: cost and service. There are many
instances in which the same or similar service can be rendered by two
quite different materials (or pieces of equipment or machines). Part of
an engineer's stock in trade is his knowledge of various means of obtaining services for his employer.

Materials are commonly called for in specifications according to established standards. SAE 1090 steel, for instance, indicates a steel with 90
points of carbon, which will harden with proper heat treatment and has
some unique physical properties. The various physical properties, such as
strength, elasticity, conductivity, and the appearance of materials, are
important in determining the service which the material will render in a
specific application. The factors of transportation and storage cost and
inspection costs join other costs to be weighed against the service available
from a particular material.

Very often, specifications are written with "or equal" clauses. "Electrical
controls to be XYZ or equal." What is meant by the "or equal" is not
literally exact equality. Probably a more proper way of stating the meaning would be "or equivalent." In this, as in other language used, the
courts interpret wording according to trade usage.

WORKMANSHIP.   When one takes an automobile to a mechanic for a
valve job, he usually isn't interested in the order of removal and replacement of the screws, nuts, and bolts. Similarly, it is rare for the owner to
be greatly interested in how a particular result is accomplished, providing the result is satisfactory. It is usually far better to specify results to be
accomplished rather than the process of accomplishing those results. For
instance, it is much better to state the compressive strength of concrete
a week after pouring than to specify the quantities of cement, sand, and
broken stone or gravel, and the method of mixing.

There are exceptions, of course, to the principle of specifying only results. A particular method may interfere with the rights of others (e.g., blasting, in place of air hammers). It may also be necessary to specify a method or process if interference with other contractors is likely to occur.

Usually it is sufficient in specifications to require the workmanship to be equal to the best available without going into the details of the method. "All sheet-metal work shall be performed and completed in accordance with the best modern sheet-metal practice, and no detail necessary therefor shall be omitted, although specific mention thereof may not be made either in these specifications or on the drawings."

Arbitrary Specifications

Generally, there are two possible relationships between the owner and the contractor. The relationship of owner-independent contractor indicates that the contractor has been hired to produce a particular result. The employer-employee, or master-servant, relationship is present where the owner (employer) or his agent, the engineer, supervises too closely the work of those employed. There are two principal advantages to the owner in retaining the owner-independent contractor relationship. Probably the primary advantage is that the contractor retains liability for his acts. There are many cases on record where, because the supervision was too close or the specifications made the contractor a mere employee of the owner, the owner was held directly liable for the acts of the contractor. Statements such as: "The contractor shall begin and continue work on whatever parts of the project the engineer shall direct, at whatever time the engineer shall direct" sound like the contractor is to be an employee of the engineer (and, hence, an employee of the owner). Such statements leave the door wide open for a court finding against the owner in a case of public liability.

There is another advantage to specifying results to be obtained rather than specifying the means of attaining them. If a contractor follows a particular procedure specified, he cannot be held responsible if the result proves faulty. On the other hand, if he agrees to produce a result, with the means of accomplishment left up to him, he must produce the result specified. Failure to produce the result according to the specifications may give rise to a damage action against the contractor or repair by him.

The following specification was written and used in the purchase of the described automation. The process engineer who wrote these specifications had helped to plan the impact bar manufacturing process. Later he supervised the installation of the automation and worked out production problems concerned with it.

X COMPANY

MANUFACTURING ENGINEERING

DEPARTMENT SPECIFICATION NO. _____

P. N. NO. _____

SUBJECT _____ AUTOMATIC SHEET LOADER FOR IMPACT BARS.

PLANT _____ Y PLANT _____ PROJECT _____ ITEM NO. _____

INCLUDED DRAWINGS _____

APPROVALS _____   /s/ ......   /s/ ......

_____   /s/ ......   /s/ ......

_____   /s/ ......

_____   /s/ ......

_____   /s/ ......

_____   /s/ ......

_____   /s/ ......

——— REVISIONS ———

DWG. NO.	SHT. NO.	LOCATION	DATE	REMARKS

ISSUED BY _____ /s/ ......

SHEET NO. 1 OF 7 SHEETS   Y PLANT

INSTRUCTIONS

Information

Contractor shall consult the Manufacturing Engineering Department of the X Company Y Plant in regards to working procedure, production line operations, reference drawings, plant layout drawings and these specifications.

Responsibility

Contractor shall be responsible for all field dimensions including interference with adjoining machines, building structure clearances and installation location. Dimensions, speeds, machine sizes and locations described in these specifications are only approximate. Reliable data must be ascertained by contractors and be verified by the person or persons concerned before proceeding with questioned phase of automation and machine construction.

Testing

Contractors shall completely design, fabricate, machine, deliver and install special machines and automation described in these specifications. This equipment shall be tested for performance after installation and shall simulate actual production rates, as set forth in these specifications. The contractor shall be responsible for the proper functioning of all contracted equipment. The validity of such functioning shall be borne out in the prescribed test phases herein explained. Test phases shall be conducted under the supervision of suitable representatives of the X Company and the approval of all equipment will be forthcoming from these representatives.

Drawings

After contract is awarded, (5) sets of preliminary prints representing proposal drawings of the equipment contracted shall be submitted to the Manufacturing Engineering Department for consideration, subject to approval. One set of submitted proposals will be approved by the X Company, and returned to the contractor together with proper contract authorization. The remaining prints shall become the property of the X Company. Errors, omissions and/or changes affecting these drawings that are discovered or made as the equipment is manufactured, shall be corrected by the contractor and submitted to the Manufacturing Engineering Department for approval before altering contracted construction.

The Manufacturing Engineering Department will issue the necessary drawing numbers and titles as required for the various components making up the complete unit. All working drawings shall be supplied by the contractor and shall be made on tracing cloth. Such drawings shall be made on sheets conforming to X Company Standard sizes. They shall be intelligibly drawn and cross indexed for reference purposes.

Tracings or tracing reproductions, comprising all drawings of the complete project shall be delivered to and become the property of the X Company on or before filing completion notice. These shall include piping diagrams, electrical diagrams, detail and assembly drawings of all mechanical and structural components of the contracted equipment.

All drawings must conform to the X Company Standards, A.I.S.C. and J.I.C. Electrical, Pneumatic and Hydraulic Standards.

Rights of Supply

X Company reserves the right to supply any items on the proposed automation and equipment or motors which may be available from their source. Therefore, an itemized list of all standard commercially manufactured equipment shall be submitted to the X Company for approval before purchases are made by contractor.

Consultation

Immediately after the contract is awarded, the successful bidder shall confer with the Manufacturing Engineering Department, X Company, Y Plant and discuss details of time scheduling and working procedure.

Contractor shall then prepare a progress schedule of his work, complete with starting and completion dates for each phase of the machine set-up and equipment he expects to manufacture and submit it to the Manufacturing Engineering Department, Y Plant, for approval.

Procedure for Delivery

All equipment and machines, either assembled or knocked down shall be plainly marked with the vendor's name, a description of the article and X Company Purchase and Item Number. Miscellaneous or loose items shall be crated and marked in a similar manner with a list of contents enclosed in each package. All items or packages shall be listed on the Bill of Lading.

The X Company will receive items and furnish crane service, if available, to unload. Contractor shall move equipment to job site. X Company assumes no responsibility for any loss or damage in transit.

X Company "general conditions" shall become part of the contract.

GENERAL

Purpose

The purpose of these (2) sheet loaders is to load sheets singly onto a press feed shuttle from a conveyor on which 14" high stacks of 125 sheets each are placed.

Work

All work shall be performed in accordance with X Company Standards and all workmanship shall be equal to or better than the best modern practices. Job site must be completely cleared of all debris caused by the contractor before completion notice can be accepted. Installation and field work shall be done under the direction of the Y Plant Engineering Department.

Power

Contractor shall furnish all wiring from the X Company Distribution panel, to the machine control panels. Contractor shall be responsible for all wiring and control devices within his contracted equipment, including mounting, labeling and operation of all switches, relays and solenoids. All electrical, pneumatic and hydraulic installation shall conform to X-J.I.C. Standards. A minimum number of air and water supply lines to any and all equipment shall be furnished by X Company when necessary. 440/220 V., 3 Ph., 60 Cy., A.C. power.

Materials

Machines and allied equipment shall be constructed mainly of casting, rolled structural shapes, gears, chain and fixtures of good quality, free of rust.

Fabrication shall be accomplished by bolting or welding. All holes must be drilled or punched. Burning of holes will not be permitted. All supports shall be properly spaced for uniform transfer of load to floor. Means of securement shall be fixed anchor bolts set in lead or sulphur. All parts shall be designed and detailed with due regard to allowable stresses in materials used.

Contractor shall shop paint all materials with (1) coat of M-426 Red Lead and field paint with (1) coat of M-340 Grey. Inside of all removable drive guards shall be painted with (1) coat of M-314 Alert Orange.

Machines and automatic equipment shall be suitably equipped with alemite or equal hydraulic lubrication fittings wherever necessary. Manifold lubrication lines shall be provided on all equipment wherever feasible, employing alemite or equal lubrication manifolds.

All air or hydraulic cylinders, valves, motors, speed reducers, relays, starters and other commercial items shall be of approved X Company selection.

All exposed drives, couplings, belts, sprockets, chains and/or other moving parts shall be completely guarded with enclosed type easily removable metal guards. All guards to be designed and fabricated in accordance with X Company Sheet Metal Standards. All guards to have the approval of the X Company Local Safety Engineer.

AUTOMATION DESCRIPTION

A. Machines and automation equipment shall be fully automatic, wherever possible and interlocked electrically or mechanically.

B. Automation equipment shall be designed in such a manner that conveyed parts can be removed from it at any phase of its operation without difficulty. Exception to this rule must have individual approval.

C. Machines and automation equipment shall be provided with guards wherever necessary to prevent loose parts from falling or bouncing from proper locations.

D. All wipers, diverters or other moving equipment shall be designed and built in a manner which will prevent jamming or damaging of machine parts.

E. All metering devices and automatic equipment must be designed and constructed in a manner which will cause an even and regular distribution and flow of parts.

F. All air cylinders supplied by contractor shall be cushioned at both ends and be provided with suitable speed control valves wherever necessary.

DETAILED DESCRIPTION

1. (2) magnetic (pneumatic) sheet leaders will be required. They shall be located relatively to the 2,300 ton presses and four chain stack conveyors as shown in the attached sketch. Contractor shall furnish department 240, Manufacturing Engineering, with the approximate overall dimensions of these machines and their allied equipment as soon as possible for Plant Layout purposes.

2. The machines shall be designed to load the 2,300 ton press dies with single sheets removed from stacks of 125 sheets previously placed on a four chain conveyor. The machines shall be interlocked mechanically or electrically with the 2,300 ton presses and the four chain conveyors to provide a continuous flow of production. The machines shall be capable of handling single sheets up to 144″ in length, 48″ in width and .125″ in thickness. Sheet sizes to be handled are shown below:

Part	Sheet Size
"A" Rear	.110″ x 36″ x 95″
"A" Front	.110″ x 42″ x 118″
"B" Rear	.110″ x 28″ x 103″
"B" Front	.110″ x 46″ x 110″

3. Operator push button station shall be designed and built in such a manner that the machine may be operated as follows:

A. Fully automatic—with machine loaded.

B. Manual—individual push button for each station.

C. One cycle operation—automatic with machine not loaded.

4. Each machine control panel shall contain sufficient excess room to accommodate the installation of six (6) additional relays.

5. *Outside contractor to furnish*

A. Necessary labor and materials to design, fabricate and install two (2) complete sheet loading mechanisms with control panels and operator control stations as described above.

    B. All necessary safety equipment.

    C. All starters, Square "D" type or equal.

    D. Do all field painting.

6. *X Company to furnish*

    A. Crane service, if available, to unload.

    B. Plant layout location of all items.

    C. Electric, air and other plant services to within 40′ of contracted equipment.

7. Assigned "Z" number is 121-ZP-124. Drawing title is "Automatic Sheet Loader for Impact Bars."

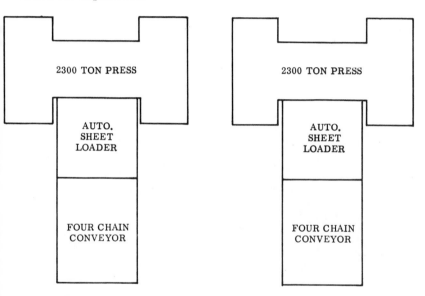

Sketch showing relative location of Automatic Sheet Loaders

SWITZER v. BOZEMAN

106 So. 2d 762 (La., Nov. 21, 1958)

Fruge, Judge ad hoc.

Defendant-appellant appeals from a judgment costing him in the sum of $269.22 in connection with his contract with subcontractor A. Switzer, plaintiff-appellee, herein.

This is a suit, in which the only issue is the interpretation of the provision of the plans and specifications. And that is whether certain electrical work was called for in the plans and specifications.

L.S.U., as owner, entered into a contract with defendant-appellant, Robert

L. Bozeman, a contractor, to remodel the third floor of Nicholson Hall, which remodeling work consisted only in subdividing some of the large rooms and hallways into small offices. The remodeling work was to be in accordance with plans and specifications prepared by architects.

Bozeman then entered into a sub-contract with plaintiff-appellee, A. Switzer, under the terms of which Switzer was to do all of the electrical work required under the plans and specifications for $1,183.

During the course of the job, Switzer claimed that the plans and specifications only called for one new electrical ceiling fixture, whereas, in order for the job to be complete, it was necessary to furnish and install many additional new electrical ceiling fixtures. Switzer then requested the architects to grant him an extra allowance from L.S.U., to enable him to install these "claimed" additional new electrical ceiling fixtures. The architect ruled that the plans and specifications were clear and that all new electrical ceiling fixtures required to complete the job were specified in the plans and specifications.

Switzer, despite repeated demands from Bozeman, refused to complete the job, so Bozeman hired another electrical company to finish Switzer's contract. This latter company completed the job at a cost to Bozeman of $687.59. Bozeman then deducted this amount from the electrical sub-contract price and paid the difference to Switzer. This suit followed, in which Switzer claimed this $687.59, which was the amount deducted from his contract price.

The district court held that Switzer was wrong and that the new electrical ceiling fixtures required to complete the job were all specified in the plans and specifications, and therefore, covered by Switzer's sub-contract; this item included $102.16 paid the new electrical contractor to install the fixtures, and $238.87 paid for the fixtures themselves. The district court also found that Switzer had not "grounded" the outlets to which the fixtures were attached, and recognized the amount paid by Bozeman to this new electrical contractor of $80.32 to have such work done.

However, the district court held that the $269.22 which Bozeman paid this new electrical contractor to install the electrical work for the telephones were not specified in the plans and specifications, and, therefore, not included in the electrical sub-contract that Switzer had with Bozeman. Accordingly, the lower court granted judgment to Switzer against Bozeman for $269.22.

We are not favored with written reasons by the trial court.

The only issue involves the interpretation of a contract. Since the plans and specifications by the architects are made part of the contract, we must determine whether they require that the telephone outlets be connected by conduit with the existing telephone panel in the building.

The plans have a legend thereon where various symbols are listed, with the meaning of each symbol shown opposite thereto. For example, there was a small circle with radiating lines, spoken of during the trial as "rising sun," and opposite which were the words "Elect. Clng. Fixture," meaning electrical ceiling fixture. And there were symbols for bookcase, new partition, electrical base outlet, etc. Additionally, there was a symbol of an inverted triangle, opposite which was the word "Telephone." This inverted triangle, meaning telephone, was shown in six places on the plans, indicating that there were to be six telephone outlets installed.

The question involved is whether, by showing such symbol of an inverted triangle that only the outlet itself was called for, or whether that outlet was also to be connected with the telephone panel already in use in the building. Now, if only the outlets were called for and it was not required to connect such outlets up with the panel so that service could be had, it is obvious that another contract would have to be let to connect the outlets up with the panel in order to use the telephones. It would appear to be an absurd consequence to say that the contract called for the outlets, but did not require that they be connected with the panel, in view of the specifications.

The specifications made it clear that this was to be a completed job "including tying utilities all into existing service," and was to be "ready for immediate use." The plans and specifications called for all "work evidently necessary within the general intent (thereof) . . . for the . . . thorough completion of the work." We quote these provisions of the specifications, viz.:

Scope of work and general items: "Extent of work: It is the intent of these specifications to cover all required labor and materials for the remodeling interior of Nicholson Hall, Third Floor, LSU, Baton Rouge, La.; The contractor shall perform all work required for the completion of this work in accordance with these specifications and accompanying drawings ready for occupancy; including tying utilities all into existing services.

Scope: These specifications, together with the drawings, are intended to cover all labor, materials and appliances of every kind required to provide all necessary electrical work and electrical fixtures for the remodeling job. All the work shall be ready for immediate use before the same will be accepted.

Extra work: No additional compensation will be allowed for work evidently necessary within the general intent of these specifications and accompanying plans for the proper construction and thorough completion of the work.

Arthur G. McLavy, the electrical contractor who completed the electrical work for Bozeman, testified about this conduit to connect the telephone outlets with the existing telephone panel in the building, viz.:

Q. Now what is your other item?
A. That was to furnish the necessary labor and materials to put in a conduit telephone system as required by the telephone company.
Q. To put in what?
A. A telephone system for existing telephone panels to outlets as shown on the plans according to directions by the telephone company and the University.
Q. Was that work the type of work customarily the telephone company did?
A. No, sir.
Q. Was that work called for in these plans and specifications?
A. You are asking for an opinion now.
Q. Well, you read the plans and specifications, didn't you?
A. Yes, sir.
Q. Was that work called for? Can you point out on the plans and specifications where it is called for?
A. It is not called for on the plans and specifications in so many words, but it's the general practice in any commercial building or any building used as an office building to have a continuous conduit system for the telephone company to install their wires.
Q. What requirement is shown on the plans with reference to telephones?
A. Just the outlets are indicated.

Q. Just the outlets are indicated?

A. Yes.

Q. And from that you draw the conclusion that you are supposed to connect those up with the telephone wires from outside of the building?

A. No.

Q. What is that?

A. You would draw the conclusion from that that you would have to extend from the nearest, I would say, panel or junction box in the building in each and every outlet, a continuous run of conduit.

Q. Is that customary and standard practice in the electrical business in this section in a building such as this?

A. Yes.

Q. Any question about this, any room for debate on that?

A. Of course, there would be room for debate on it.

Q. Well, what is the room for debate?

A. Well, I mean in my mind there is.

Q. Say what is in your mind, Mr. McLavy.

A. Nothing.

Q. The plans indicate here on page A-1 the 3-cornered white symbol and marked opposite it is shown telephone, and how many of those do they have on this plan? Will you count them?

A. Six.

Q. When you went on the job what work on the telephone installation had been performed before you got there?

A. The outlet box had been installed. The outlet box had been installed in the partition and the conduit run out at ceiling level.

Q. Then what did you do?

A. I requested a meeting with representatives from Louisiana State University and the telephone company to meet me out there and we laid out how they wanted it done.

Q. What was it that you did?

A. There is an existing panel,—I forget which end of the hall it is on, east end, yes. We ran a one inch conduit from there out into the corridor and down. We could describe it and down close to the west end and from there branched out to the smaller conduits of the existing outlets or close to them as directed by the telephone company.

Q. I ask you again in a building such as this is that work customarily done by the electrical contractor and not by the telephone people?

A. The telephone company does not run any conduit themselves.

The electrical work in connecting the telephone outlets to the telephone panel by conduit was obviously necessary in accordance with the panels and specifications.

It is our opinion that this work was clearly called for in the plans and specifications. It necessarily follows that it was included in Switzer's bid which is as follows:

Confirming phoned price this date . . . Nicholson Hall Elec. per plans and specs. $1183.00.

It is significant that the record reveals no effort by Switzer with respect to any claim with Bozeman or anyone else that the electrical work necessary to connect the telephone outlets to the existing telephone panels in the building was called for in the plans and specifications. Switzer testified that he ran a ½ inch conduit from the telephone boxes as shown on the plans by the symbols to points at, in most cases, ceiling height where he could be instructed to bring them to other places. He further testified that he had met Mr. Wilson on the job once or twice to discuss fixtures and other arrangements. He stated that he had written a letter but upon a close perusal of the record no letter in evidence disclosed any reference to telephone connections; we therefore conclude that there was no controversy whatsoever with respect to the telephone connections prior to the date of trial. The record disclosed that Mr. Switzer took the position all along by the letters he wrote and by his testimony in the record that he should have been permitted to charge extra for new light fixtures to be installed on the job which request was denied by the architect. To clarify this point, we take the liberty of quoting from the correspondence in the record.

Bozeman's letter of August 29, 1956, to Switzer, in part, reads:

. . . we take the position however, that the job must be complete in accordance with the plans, specifications, and job requirements as interpreted by the architect.

We will complete our portion of this job by August 31st, 1956, and unless notified to the contrary, in writing, we shall expect the electrical work to be complete also.

Switzer's answer to Bozeman, dated August 30, 1956, in part, says:

Your letter of the 29th received this date. We appreciate your position in this matter . . . but feel also that the fixtures in question . . . are not specified . . . as part of our work.

It is not possible for us to complete this work . . . other than the installation per plans and specifications . . . which is installed as of this date.

Bozeman's letter to Switzer dated September 4, 1956, by registered mail, in part, reads:

In your letter of August 30, 1956, you have refused to complete the above mentioned job unless you receive from the architect a change order covering five different items. Since the University officials and the Architects have advised us that this building must be ready for occupancy by Monday, September 10, 1956, and in view of the position that you have taken in this matter, it appears to us that we are forced to act as follows:

We hereby notify you that all of your work must be completed by Saturday, September 8, 1956. Further, if you have not shown sufficient effort by 8 am Thursday, September 6, 1956, to complete this job within the time set forth, we will take over and complete that portion of the electrical work as is now incomplete, and deduct from your contract the cost to us. . . .

It is in evidence that Switzer did not examine the site so that he could be in a position to say where the telephone panel was to which the telephone outlets were to be connected. Nor could he know the conditions that were present so that the type and size of conduit could be determined. It is important to quote from the specifications at this point:

Examination of Site: . . . each bidder will be held to have examined the site and satisfied himself as to the existing conditions . . . that will in any manner affect the work under this contract.

The specifications did include tying utilities all into existing services and require the remodeled part to be ready for immediate use after acceptance by L.S.U. and called for all work evidently necessary to complete the job. Thus, it appears to us that if Switzer had looked he would have seen the telephone panel on the third floor, and it is obvious that the outlets were to be connected with this panel, and by so doing he would have known the type and size of the panel. Aside from that, he could have called in the architect, the telephone company and the electrical representative of the University to assist him.

Accordingly, for these reasons, the trial court judgment in favor of plaintiff-appellee is hereby reversed and his suit dismissed at his cost.

Reversed.

REVIEW QUESTIONS

1. Why should specifications be written rather than oral?

2. Distinguish between:
   a. malleable and ductile.
   b. strength and rigidity.
   c. force and pressure.
   d. structure and building.
   e. project and operation.
   f. tool and die.
   g. machine and automation.
   h. precise and accurate.

3. What are the inherent advantages of standardized specifications?

4. What danger is there in requiring a contractor to follow a particular method in his performance?

5. What is the owner's interest in the wages the contractor pays to his employees?

6. What different machines could be used to obtain a 2" x 4" rectangular piece from a sheet of $\frac{1}{16}$" thick aluminum? In what ways could you fasten two pieces of metal together?

7. Write a simple specification for the purchase and installation of a $\frac{1}{3}$ h.p. pedestal grinder.

8. What are the inherent advantages and disadvantages in copying portions of old specifications into a new one?

9. Interpreting from *Switzer v. Bozeman,* to what extent do trade or area practices have a bearing on meanings or omissions in specifications?

18 PROPERTY

Most engineers must work for other people—either for a private enterprise or for the public (a local, state, or federal government). An engineer uses other people's property in his work; hence, he must observe their rights. In numerous instances his work will require him to deal with his employer's property mingled with that of others. Effectively handling the property and rights thus commingled requires some knowledge of property law.

What is property? All of us have things which we consider to be ours: our clothing, books, writing instruments, a watch, perhaps a home in the suburbs. The word property is used in two senses. It denotes *things* owned by a person, which is the usual concept. It also means the *rights* involved in ownership. These rights, known as property rights, signify dominion over things owned. That is, the right to use and to exclude others from using the things we own; the right of control over and enjoyment of them, and the right to dispose of them.

Property may be classed as real, personal, or mixed. In the discussion of the Statute of Frauds, Chapter 12, it was necessary to distinguish between real and personal property. Generally, real property was defined as land and anything firmly attached to it. Personal property is all property other than real, such as goods, chattels, choses in action, money, and accounts receivable, or other evidences of debt. Combinations of real and personal property are mixed property.

Property is either corporeal or incorporeal. Corporeal property exists in a material state—land, money, an automobile. Incorporeal property, on the other hand, does not have material existence. It may be a right-of-way across property, or the good will of an enterprise.

PERSONAL PROPERTY

The term *chattels* is often used synonymously with personal property. *Chattels personal in possession* are the tangible items; e.g. a watch, a truck, or a machine in a factory. *Chattels personal in action,* commonly known as *choses in action,* are intangible rights arising from tort or contract—the right to goods contracted for or the right to recovery for injuries suffered in an automobile collision, for example. A *chattel real* is an interest in land less than fee simple ownership or a life estate—for example, a ten-year lease.

Acquisition

A person may lawfully obtain ownership of personal property by: 1) original acquisition, 2) a procedure of law, or 3) acts of other persons.

ORIGINAL ACQUISITION. Unowned things in their natural state become the property of the first person to obtain possession of them. Most things are owned by someone today, but, for example, the possibility of reducing wild animals to personal property still exists. Obtaining ownership in this way is known as acquiring title by occupancy.

Property which one *creates* by his mental or physical efforts belongs to him unless he has agreed, for compensation, to transfer it to another. Books, inventions, trade names, and other such creations are of this nature.

Property may be acquired by *accession*—adding to other property. A new windshield of a car or a new gear in the transmission becomes the property of the owner of the automobile. This is particularly true where the addition becomes an integral, built-in part of the whole in such a way that it is not readily detachable. Even where the innocent purchaser of stolen property adds value to it, he is merely adding value to property belonging to another. White buys a car from Gray who, unknown to White, has stolen the car from Black. White adds a new motor, transmission, and paint job to the car. Later, Black locates his car. Black is entitled to regain possession of his car in its improved state. Probably there is no other place where the law adheres so strictly to the principle of *caveat emptor* (the buyer beware) than in the purchase of stolen property.

Accession also applies to a natural increase of purchased property. Black sells White a mare. Shortly after the sale a foal is born. White is the owner of both the mare and the foal.

PROCEDURE OF LAW. Property may be distributed according to certain legal procedures. Four of these arise from intestate death, mortgage foreclosure, judicial sale, and bankruptcy.

When a person dies and has not left a will, his death is termed *intestate.* The various states have, by statute, declared how property shall be distributed in case of such intestate death—the laws of descent. There is a great variation in these statutes as to who will inherit the estate. If no relatives of the deceased can be found, the property will go to the state—it "escheats" to the state.

Even when a person leaves a will, he is limited somewhat in the way he may leave his estate to his heirs. He may not, according to most state laws, leave his wife or minor children destitute by willing his entire estate to strangers.

Statutes provide for mortgage foreclosure in case of default by the mortgagor. Although it is common in chattel mortgages to provide for the mortgagee to take and sell the mortgaged property in case of default, a court procedure is usually possible if such provision has not been made.

Sales of property may be undertaken to satisfy a judgment of a court. Certain property of the loser is taken from him (within limits stated in the laws of each state) and is sold to satisfy the judgment.

When abandoned property is found by the police or sheriff's department in a community, it is kept for a statutory period of time and then sold at public auction. Such sales usually must be advertised and public, with the property going to the highest bidder.

Under bankruptcy procedures a trustee is appointed by the court with the duty to convert the assets of the bankrupt into money. The trustee [1] takes over the property with the right and duty to sell it.

Generally the buyer of property does not get any better title than the seller had. In judicial sales, sales of abandoned property, and bankruptcy sales, title is usually not warranted by the seller. The seller sells by virtue of a legal right or duty to do so; the buyer assumes the risk that title may not be good. Black steals White's car and abandons it in a neighboring town. It is held by the local police department for the required period of time and then sold to Gray at a public auction. Later White finds his car in Gray's possession. White can claim and get his car.

ACTS OF OTHER PERSONS.   Title to personal property may be lawfully acquired from others by will, gift, contract, confusion, or abandonment. A person may also acquire possession of property if it is lost or mislaid by another.

The subject of wills is discussed under real property. It is sufficient to note here that, if the testator complies with the law, he may leave his property to whomsoever he wishes.

If property is acquired by gift, title to the property follows possession. Black promises White a gift of $500. At this point White has nothing. The promise of a future gift, either oral or in writing is unenforceable, since it is unsupported by consideration. Of course, if the written promise of a gift were signed and sealed, a consideration would be imputed

---

[1] See Trusts, p. 276.

under common law and the promise would be enforceable. As soon as Black actually gives the $500 to White, though, it becomes his property and Black loses any claim to it. Under a few exceptional circumstances the gift may be recoverable, particularly when a third party has rights in the gift.[2]

The subject of acquisition of personal property by contract is covered in Chapter 19, "Sales and Warranties." Good title to personal property is warranted in any sale unless there is a stipulation to the contrary in the contract.

Property may be acquired by what is known as *confusion* primarily when fungible goods are involved. Fungible goods are goods any unit of which is replaceable by any other unit—e.g., grain of a particular type, crude oil, or screws in a bin. Such goods are usually sold by weight or measure.

If fungible property of two or more owners is mixed together so that the identity of each owner's property is lost, each owner owns an undivided share of the confused mass. After harvest, Black stores 500 bushels of wheat with 700 bushels of wheat belonging to White in a common granary. Each owns an undivided share of the 1200 bushels of wheat. Destruction of a part of the mass will be shared by each party on the basis of his contribution to the total.

If confusion of goods results from the tortious act of one of the parties, the innocent party will, by law, be kept unharmed by the act of the other. If ownership by the *tort feasor* cannot be determined, the innocent party becomes owner of the total.

Abandoned property is unowned. It becomes the property of the first person to take possession of it. Taking possession of abandoned property is about the same as taking possession of something which has never been owned.

Lost and *mislaid* property give rise to some legal problems. In both cases the owner has unintentionally parted with possession of his property. In both cases he still owns the property even though it is no longer in his possession. The finder of lost property has a right to the property as his own against all persons except the true owner. By contrast, the holder of mislaid property has possession of it as a bailee—in other words, he is holding it to give to the owner.

The distinction between lost and mislaid property is derived largely from the circumstances in which it is found. If the property is found in such a location that it is apparent that the owner intentionally placed it there and then inadvertently left it, it is mislaid. A purse left on a store

---

[2] As where the property was stolen from another, or where the donor anticipated impending bankruptcy, or where the donor was dying and diminished the property which would go to his heirs.

counter would be mislaid; if it were found on the floor, it would have been lost.

In many states the problems involved in lost and mislaid property have been cleared up by statute. The requirements of the statutes usually are met by advertising the property in a local newspaper. If no one claims the property within a certain time after publication of the advertisement, the finder obtains title to the property.

Bailment

A relationship which closely resembles property ownership is that of *bailment*. The bailment relationship occurs when personal property is left by the bailor (the owner of·the property) with a second person, the bailee.

REQUIREMENTS.   Distinguishing bailment from similar relationships requires careful definition. A bailment is made up of three elements:

1. Title to the property must remain with the bailor.
2. Possession of the property must be completely surrrendered by the bailor to the bailee.
3. The parties must intend to return the bailor's property to him at the end of the bailment.

Notice the similarity between a bailment and a sale or a trade with a slight delay in it. Black stores a spare conveyor at White's warehouse at an agreed storage rental. Black still has title to the conveyor, White has possession, and the same conveyor is to be returned to Black. Therefore, it is an instance of bailment. With certain other types of property, though, an inherent difficulty exists. If, instead of a conveyor, Black were to store grain in a common granary, he might not expect to get back the identical grain that he stored. The same might be true of animals in a herd and a few other instances where the owner does not expect that the identical property will be returned to him. Courts are not uniform in all jurisdictions in their holdings under such circumstances. Generally, though, it is held that where the owner is not to receive back the identical thing given, it is not bailment. It is held that title passed with possession and that title to other similar goods will be passed back later. It is, in other words, a sale.

It becomes necessary to find out who owns what when one party or the other goes bankrupt or a writ is issued pursuant to a judgment against someone's property. Property being held for a bailor by a bailee cannot be successfully taken for the bailee's debt. It is possible, though, if a judgment were to be issued against the bailor, to obtain his bailed property from the bailee.

DUTY OF CARE. The person entrusted with the property of another has a duty to care for it. Under a particular set of circumstances the degree of care may be great, ordinary, or slight. There are two primary considerations which determine the necessary degree of care: a) the nature of the property involved and b) the purpose of the bailment. As to the nature of the property, it is obvious that a person should take greater care of a new automatic screw machine than of a used anvil.

The bailment relationship benefits someone—the bailor, the bailee, or both. If the bailment is to benefit the bailor only, the bailee need exercise only slight care in protecting the bailed property. He is liable only if he has been grossly negligent. Such a bailment might occur as a result of the owner requesting a friend to care for his property gratuitously.

If property is borrowed for the benefit of the bailee (as one would borrow his neighbor's lawn mower), great care is required of the bailee. The property must be returned in the form in which it was borrowed. About the only damage for which the bailee would not be responsible would be that resulting from an act of God—such as destruction by a cyclone.

Probably the most common form of bailment occurs as a benefit to both bailor and bailee. Whenever the bailor pays the bailee to take his goods and alter them in some way or just to store them for him and then return them, both parties benefit. Thus, mutual benefit bailments would occur in such situations as: leaving a car at a garage with orders to fix the transmission; transferring a machine from Cleveland, Ohio, to Fort Worth, Texas; or storage of an unused machine at a warehouse during a slack period. When the bailment is to benefit both parties the bailee is required to use at least ordinary care. By ordinary care is meant the care that a person would be likely to use in preserving his own property. The bailee is liable for damage resulting from his negligence if negligence can be proved against him.

If the bailee has used the requisite amount of care in preserving the bailor's property, he will not be held liable for damage. Loss of the property or damage to it, then, will follow title and be borne by the bailor.

BAILEE'S RIGHT AND DUTIES. The bailee's right to possession of the bailed property is second only to the bailor's right. The bailee may sue a third party to recover the property if necessary.

The bailee is liable if he gives the bailed property to someone other than the owner or his agent and it is thereby lost. However, if the bailee returns the property to the person who gave it to him originally, assuming that he is still the owner, the bailee is not liable.

The bailor has a duty to disclose any known defects in the bailed property which might harm the bailee or his employees. If harm results from a failure to disclose such defects, the bailor may be held liable for tort.

NEGLIGENCE LIABILITY.   Most bailments are contracts. It is possible, therefore, for the bailee, by contract clauses, to remove any or all liability for his negligence, but only if he is a private bailee. For a public or quasi-public bailee—a hotel or express company, for instance—to make such a contract stipulation would be unlawful. Such a bailee will be liable for negligence when serving the public regardless of contract clauses to the contrary. If a private bailee insists on eliminating his liability, there are only two choices open—to do business with him on his terms or look elsewhere.

Fixtures

A fixture is personal property attached to real property. By the attachment the personal property becomes a part of the real property. The concrete and other building materials that are worked into a plant become real property. Similarly, a heating unit or a television aerial becomes a fixture when it is attached to a house.

Generally, ownership of a fixture goes to the owner of the real estate to which it is attached. There are so many exceptions to this generality, though, that it might be restated: *unless something appears to the contrary* the owner of the real property also owns the fixture. The main condition to the contrary is the intention of the parties when the fixture was attached. If it appears that both parties intended that ownership of the fixture should not go to the owner of the real property, the original owner will have a right to remove it. Black Construction Company undertakes the building of a structure for the White Company. A small building, complete with plumbing and lighting is erected on the premises as a superintendent's office. Although the superintendent's office is firmly fixed to the ground, it may be removed at the end of the project.

The relationship of landlord and tenant often involves the determination of ownership of fixtures. When real property is leased or rented the tenant normally may install his personal property—e.g., machines or conveyors, and then take them with him when he leaves. If the tenant fails to remove one of his fixtures and take it with him, ownership goes to the owner of the land. Black rented a house from White. Requiring hot water, which White's house did not have, Black bought a suitable water heater from Gray Appliance Store, paying 10 per cent down. Black hooked up the water heater to the plumbing and used it for a month, then moved to another state. Gray Appliance tried to get the water heater back, but could not do so since it was now part of White's real property. Gray's only available action is against Black and he may be hard to reach by court action.

REAL PROPERTY

Real property has been defined as land and anything firmly affixed thereto. When an engineer becomes a party to building a road or renovating a manufacturing plant, he is concerned with real property. As a citizen in a community he will either own real property or lease it. Speculation in real estate is nearly as popular a sport as speculation in the stock market. We will consider here the transfer (or conveyance) of real property and some of the rights and duties created.

We may buy real property, use it pretty much as we please, and transfer it to others with very few restrictions involved. The right to "own one's own home" is almost a part of our heritage. It is only when title is threatened or, perhaps, when prescriptive rights are exercised against real property that we become aware that there are limitations.

It has not always been this way. In England, where our ideas about real property originated, no one other than the king could be said to own much of anything a few centuries ago. Under the feudal system there, the land belonged to the crown. The right to hold realty depended upon military service and fealty to the king, and was theoretically terminable at his option. Land was parcelled out to the gentry who, in turn, divided it up among their servants. Originally, when a landholder died another person was appointed to take his place. Very early this was replaced by provisions which tended to insure that the property would remain in the family of the grantee or tenant provided the heir was able to meet the military obligations entailed.

Little remains today in the United States of feudal rights in land. About the only remnant is the state's right of eminent domain, the right of a federal, state, or local government to use private property for public benefit, and escheatment, the return of property to the state upon intestate death of the owner when no eligible relatives can be found. See page 274 for a discussion of eminent domain.

Kinds of Estates

Estates in real property are classed as freehold, less than freehold, and future estates.

FREEHOLD. A freehold estate is an estate of undetermined duration in real property. It may be an estate in fee simple or it may be an estate for life. An estate in fee simple is the highest real property estate known to law. The holder of an estate in fee simple has the right to complete use and enjoyment as long as this does not harm another, and the right to transfer the estate to anyone he chooses. Upon his death his estate will go to his heirs according to his will or according to law if he dies intestate.

A life estate is an estate of undetermined duration and, therefore, a freehold estate. The life upon which the term of the estate depends is usually that of the holder of the estate, but it could be anyone else. An estate which is terminable upon some contingency other than death but is, in some way, dependent upon the duration of a person's life is treated the same as a life estate. Black gives an estate to a young widow, terminable when she remarries. She might die without remarrying, and this would also terminate the estate. It is therefore treated in law the same as a life estate, but with marriage as an added contingency.

The rights in a life estate are not so complete as they are in a fee-simple estate. The holder of a life estate may not sell it to another. Though he is allowed use and enjoyment of the real property, he may not destroy its value. For instance, he may not sell the topsoil or remove ornamental trees, although he could cut and sell ripe timber.

LESS THAN FREEHOLD. An estate in real property which is to run for a fixed or determinable time is less than freehold. In law it is considered as personal property. Thus, a ten-year lease or a grant of property to run "as long as the property is used for educational purposes" would be less than freehold estates. By contrast, a lease for "99 years, renewable forever" would be a freehold estate, since the duration is undetermined.

FUTURE ESTATES. A future estate is an estate which someone will have when a future event occurs. According to Gray's will, Black is to get an estate left to White when White dies. Black has future estate in the property involved.

Transfer of Real Property

Real property and real property rights are transferred in four major ways: 1) by will or inheritance, 2) by sale, 3) by gift, and 4) by legal action. We will consider the documents required in these transfers.

Will

Originally, the word *will* indicated a disposal of real property only— a *testament* disposed of the testator's personal property. Thus the use of the phrase *last will and testament* came to be popular when the testator wished to combine the two functions in one document. By common and legally accepted usage the term *will* today indicates disposition of both real and personal property.

AGE. Anyone of sound mind and 21 years of age may make a valid will in the United States. In some states the age requirement for women has been lowered to 18.

SANITY. An idiot, an imbecile or an insane person cannot make a valid will. The law does not require a towering intellect as a testator, however. The law requires only that the testator have: a) sufficient mental capacity to comprehend his property; b) capacity to consider all persons to whom he might desire to leave his property; and c) understanding that he is making a will. In these requirements there is nothing which prohibits an eccentric person from making a will. A person physically or mentally ill may make a will. Even an insane person could, in his rational moments, make a valid will.

WHO MAY INHERIT. Inheritance is not limited to relatives of the deceased under a valid will. Almost anyone may inherit. Municipalities, universities, and charitable organizations often have benefited from the terms of wills. The law does prevent inheritance by the murderer of the testator. Also, joint stock companies cannot inherit; neither can a corporation, unless the charter granted by the state allows inheritance.

Similarly, the testator has a right to disinherit as he chooses within the limits of the state statutes. Complete disinheritance of the testator's husband or wife cannot be done successfully in most states, and provision for his minor children may be required. Aside from these statutes, though, the testator may disinherit as he pleases.

TYPES OF WILLS. In addition to the ordinary written will with witnesses, two other types of wills are recognized in some states. The *holographic will* is one which is written entirely in longhand by the testator. Usually no witnesses are required. Where the holographic will is recognized—in about half of the states—it has the same standing as any other will.

A *nuncupative will* is an oral will. Such a will must be made to a certain number of witnesses and they, in turn, must reduce it to writing shortly thereafter, according to most state statutes. The testator cannot will real property to another orally. In fact, in the states where nuncupative wills have legal standing, a limit is usually placed on the amount of personal property which may be willed orally.

WITNESSES. A witness to a will must be a disinterested party capable of being a witness in any judicial proceeding. It would be possible for a minor to be a witness. A person who stands to gain or lose by the will, though, would be incompetent as a witness.

ESSENTIALS OF A VALID WILL. There are four essentials or requirements for a valid will:

1. To pass the testator's real and personal property along to others, the will must be *in writing*. The law does not require any special kind of writing such as typing or longhand, so long as the will is written. Neither is there a requirement as to the material on which the writing appears. A will chiseled in stone or etched on glass could be as legally binding as one drawn up on a form prepared by an attorney.

2. A valid will must be *signed* by the testator and *sealed* (in those states requiring a seal). The signature normally appears at the end of a will and its validity may be open to question if it appears elsewhere.

3. Wills (except holographic) must be witnessed. State laws require either two or three persons to attest the signing of a will. The will must be signed in the presence and sight of the witnesses and the witnesses must sign in the presence and sight of each other and of the testator.

4. A will must be published. In wills, the word "publication" means something different from its ordinary sense. By publication of a will it is meant that the testator must declare that it is his last will and testament. The witnesses must know that it is a will being signed; not necessarily the terms of it, only that it is a will.

CODICILS.   A codicil is a change in a will. It is used to explain, modify, add to, or revoke a part of an existing will. If there is any question as to the date of the making of the will, the time when the last codicil was drawn is the effective date of the will. The making of a codicil to a will requires the same formality as is required in making a will.

PROBATE.   After the death of the testator the will is presented for probate to a probate (or surrogate) court. State statutes determine the next steps, but the laws follow a general pattern. Opportunity is given to question the validity of a will. It may be held invalid for fraud, undue influence, improper execution, forgery, mistake, or incapacity of the testator. If the validity is unchallenged or any challenges attempted are unsuccessful, it is admitted to probate—i.e., received by the court as a valid statement of the testator's intent. If the will is successfully challenged, a previous will may be reinstated or, if no previous will exists, the result is the same as intestate death.

In drawing up a will it is customary to name someone as executor or executrix. Upon the death of the testator and probate of the will, the executor is called upon to carry out the terms of the will. This must be done *under bond* unless the testator has specifically exempted the executor from bond. If no will was left or if no executor was named in the will, the court will appoint an administrator or administratrix. The functions of an administrator are similar to those of an executor. However, if the decedent left no will, the administrator must follow state laws for distributing property following intestate death.

Deed

Conveying real property by sale or gift requires a formal transfer. Each state has jurisdiction over the real property within its boundaries. Each has set forth the formalities required to convey ownership from one person to another. Although the statutes vary from state to state, there is a general uniformity in the requirements.

KINDS OF DEEDS. There are two kinds of deeds in common use in the United States today: *warranty* and *quit-claim*. There are occasions when each may be used, but the better title is obtained in a warranty deed.

A warranty deed warrants that the title obtained by the grantee is good. In any deed the grantee gets only the title that the grantor has to give; but if grantee's title under a warranty deed is ever successfully attacked, the grantee may recover any damage suffered from the grantor. Specifically, the grantor warrants three things: 1) that he has good title and the right to convey it; 2) that there are no encumbrances other than those mentioned in the deed; and 3) that grantee and his heirs or assigns will have quiet, peaceful enjoyment of the property conveyed.

A *quit-claim* deed transfers title but does not warrant it. In effect, it is the conveyance by the grantor of whatever title he may have to the property. Such a deed might be used where inheritance of the property by several members of a family sometime in the past has left a clouded title.

ESSENTIALS OF A DEED. For a deed to be valid it must be composed of several essential elements. The deed must name grantor and grantee and the consideration involved; the property must be described or otherwise identified; some words of conveyance must be used; it must be signed, sealed (in many states), witnessed, delivered, and then be accepted by the grantee.

Description of property within a city is likely to be by lot number and plat. Rural property may be described according to metes and bounds, or by the Torrens System of sections and fractions. In interpreting a deed the court will endeavor to carry out intents of the parties even though there is an error in the description. Corner markers or monuments and natural land marks show this intent better than descriptions, since these can be seen by the parties. Thus the presence of such a marker may cause the court to disregard the technical description. If descriptions conflict in a deed, the court will interpret the wording in the grantee's favor.

RECORDING. Any instrument involving real property must be recorded. The recording of a deed does not pass title to the property; the making of the deed took care of that. It is still essential to record it, though, because if the grantor were to make a second deed to another fraudulently, the first grantee to record his deed would have valid claim to the property; the other grantee would be left with only his action against the grantor.

TITLE SEARCH AND TITLE INSURANCE. The law requires any proceeding that affects real estate to be recorded as a notice to the public. Thus, to have full force or standing at law, a deed, mortgage, lien, attachment or other encumbrance must be filed at the local recorder's office or registry of deeds.

A title search involves following the changes in title to a piece of property from the initial grant from the state to the present. The result of the search should show an unbroken chain; a break is cause for suspicion and further search. A will leaving the property to more than one person may be questioned. Any encumbrance on the property is questioned to determine whether or not it has been cleared up. Of course, there is a point in time beyond which it is usually felt it is not necessary to go. If, because of destruction of records or for some other reason, ancient title cannot be cleared it will usually be certified despite the void.

In most communities title insurance may be purchased to warrant title to real property. The title insurance company will search the title and issue insurance for a one-shot fee based on the outcome of the search.

MORTGAGES. A large proportion of the buyers of real property today do not have sufficient assets to pay cash for their real estate. Money to buy the property must be borrowed from someone. The money might be borrowed on a personal loan or a note, but the problem of securing the loan exists. Black borrows $12,000 from White on a note, the money to be used to buy a house and lot. If Black, at some future time cannot pay an installment on the note, White may obtain a judgment in court for the remainder of the note. However, under most state statutes execution or attachment could not be levied upon Black's homestead and much of his personal property. Thus, White would have little real security. A mortgage offers the lender substantially greater security.

A real estate mortgage is a contract between the mortgagor (the borrower) and the mortgagee (the lender). The mortgagor borrows funds from the mortgagee, perhaps for the purchase of real estate, promising to return the money with interest, and offering the real estate as security.

MORTGAGE THEORIES. Mortgages began under common law as defeasible conveyances. The mortgage took the form of a deed from mortgagor to mortgagee. The mortgagor could defeat the deed (get it back) by paying the loan on which the mortgage was based in the time specified. If the mortgagor missed a payment, though, he had nothing. Any default gave the mortgagee absolute right of ownership. The results seemed rather harsh and the treatment has become more lenient.

In equity jurisdiction, where mortgage foreclosures are normally handled, certain mortgagor's rights have come to be recognized. Where common law considered the mortgagee as owner, allowing him to collect rents and profits from the property, mortgagor now has the rights of ownership. A missed payment no longer terminates forever the mortgagor's right; he has a certain time in which to redeem the property under a right known as *equity of redemption.*

In equity the view is taken that the whole idea of the mortgage is security for a loan—that it is nothing more than a lien. This *lien theory* is now the accepted reasoning on mortgages in the majority of the states. Some states, though, still hold to the older common law ideas in modified form, under the *title theory* of mortgages.

FORMALITY. Since a real estate mortgage is an interest in real property, it must be in writing. The form of a mortgage, even in *lien theory* states, is similar to that of a deed, and the same formal requirements usually pertain to both. The mortgage must be signed, sealed (where the seal is recognized), witnessed, and recorded. When the mortgage is satisfied, this too must be recorded. Recording of the mortgage and its discharge serves as notice to the public of this type of property encumbrance.

MORTGAGOR'S DUTIES. Security is the reason for a mortgage. While the mortgagor is owner of the mortgaged property, his right of ownership necessarily must be somewhat restricted. He cannot tear down all buildings, sell off the trees and topsoil, and then allow the mortgagee to take over the worthless remainder. To do so would diminish the mortgagee's security and constitute the tort of *waste*. With his security so threatened, the mortgagee has reason to institute foreclosure proceedings.

As the loan balance declines, the mortgagor's right to unlimited use and disposal of the property increases, since less security is required to protect the mortgagee's interest.

The mortgagor usually must pay all taxes, assessments, and insurance on the mortgaged property. Unpaid taxes and assessments become liens and endanger the mortgagee's security. Insurance on the property protects mortgagee and mortgagor alike. In case of near total destruction, the mortgage balance is paid and any remainder paid to the mortgagor.

The mortgagor must, of course, make his mortgage payments when they are due. Nonpayment constitutes default and gives the mortgagee the right to institute foreclosure. Generally, early tender of payment of the balance due need not be accepted by the mortgagee; he has a right to the interest which he has contracted for. The standard FHA and Veteran's Administration mortgages have provisions for early payment, but many other mortgages do not.

MORTGAGEE'S RIGHTS. The mortgagee may assign the mortgage note together with the mortgage to a third person who, then, has the same rights as the mortgagee or "stands in the mortgagee's shoes." Mortgagor must, of course, be notified of the assignment if he is to be required to pay the assignee. If the mortgagor, lacking knowledge of the assignment, pays the original mortgagee, he will diminish the amount of the note by the amount of the payment.

In case of default in payment or a diminishing of the security, mortgagee may foreclose. Generally, foreclosure begins as a bill in equity.

The bill outlines the mortgagee's rights and the mortgagor's breach of the agreement. If foreclosure is allowed, the court will appoint a master of chancery to sell the mortgaged property. The purchaser gets a deed to the property; court costs are paid first from the proceeds, then the mortgage balance; any remainder after this is applied to inferior liens, e.g., second mortgage; and, finally, if anything remains it is returned to the mortgagor.

If the foreclosure sale of the property does not return enough to pay off court costs and the mortgage, the court may issue a deficiency decree. Such decree holds the mortgagor personally liable for the unpaid balance of the obligation. Enforcement by execution or attachment will be likely to follow. The courts lately have exhibited some reluctance to issue deficiency decrees. This is especially true where the loan was for the purchase of the real property security. It is felt that the mortgagee lent the money on the security of the realty and not on the mortgagor's personal credit. In other words, the mortgagee must have evaluated the risks involved and the mortgagor's security when the loan was made. Recovery, then, should be limited to the price this property will bring— part of the value of the interest charged is payment for risk.

MORTGAGOR'S RIGHTS. The presence of a mortgage on real property does not, of course, prevent reasonable use of the property by the mortgagor or disposal of it subject to the mortgagee's rights. The mortgagor may use and enjoy the mortgaged property in whatever way he wishes as long as he does not harm another thereby, including the mortgagee.

The mortgaged property may be willed to another or sold or given away. The transferee takes the place of the mortgagor except as to personal liability on the debt. If the grantee takes the property merely *subject to* the mortgage he will not be held to have assumed personal liability. In other words, in case of default a deficiency judgment might still be obtained against the original mortgagor. On the other hand, if the grantee *assumes* the mortgage, he is held to replace the mortgagor in all respects.

LAND CONTRACTS. An arrangement commonly used in the purchase of real property is the land contract. It resembles quite closely a mortgage under the title theory. According to a land contract the purchaser, in addition to his down payment (if any), agrees to make a series of payments. When the balance is reduced to some agreed amount, frequently half the purchase price, the seller will deed the property to the buyer and take a first mortgage.

Land contracts typically include the right of the seller to declare all payments due immediately if a payment is missed or is late. This, of course, has the effect of forcing forfeiture by the buyer since, if he has missed one payment, it is hardly likely that he could pay the entire balance. If the buyer gives back the land upon default, the seller takes it back with no problem of foreclosure proceedings and public resale. The seller is still owner and he merely takes over his property.

This removal of the buyer and repossession of property by the seller with no balancing of the equities involved is known as strict foreclosure. Strict foreclosure is allowed in connection with both mortgages and land contracts where the prospective buyer has acted very improperly or is insolvent. State laws govern the handling of land contracts as well as mortgages. Where the buyer has acted in good faith under a land contract and has made only a slight default, the equities will usually be balanced in some manner—but the buyer must ask for his relief. If the buyer merely returns the land to the seller he gives up any chance he may have to recoup a part of his loss; his equity is cut off.

Eminent Domain

The right to possession and use of property is a lesser right than the right to take such property for public necessity. The right to take private property for public use is known as *eminent domain* (or *condemnation*). The right of *eminent domain* may be exercised by the state or municipality or other public entity but it is not limited to these. Quasi-public enterprises or private businesses whose functions serve the public at large, e.g., railroad or power companies, also may petition for and be granted this right.

Only such private rights as are necessary to the public will be taken by eminent domain. If the taking of these rights will disturb the private owner in his use and enjoyment of the property, he will be compensated for his loss. Compensation is made according to an assessment of the market value of the right lost. Either party may appeal the assessment if he is dissatisfied.

DEDICATION. When land is required for public use such as a road or school playground many owners will donate land for the purpose. Such donations are known as *dedications*. Although dedications are usually made expressly by the owner to the public officials involved, they may also be implied. If public use of private property is made continuously for a period of twenty years or longer, dedication may be conclusively presumed.

No formality is required in the offer to dedicate a piece of property to public use. Similarly no formality is required for acceptance. To complete a dedication, though, there must be some kind of acceptance. When the offer is expressly made, it is usually answered by expressed acceptance. Acceptance may be implied, though, from public activities, such as maintaining the dedicated property. Public maintenance of a privately owned, but publicly used road, for instance, would indicate acceptance of the road.

It may seem unnecessary to determine whether or not a particular piece of property has been dedicated to the public use. The question of tort liability, though, makes title determination important. If someone is injured because of a large hole in a road the question arises as to who owned the road and who, therefore, had the duty to maintain it.

ADVERSE POSSESSION. Title to real property may be acquired by *adverse possession*. The legal requirements make it quite difficult to acquire title to land in this manner; however, if the requirements are met, a new title to the land is issued to its possessor. That is, adverse possession results not in a transfer of present title, but in an entirely new title being issued.

The right to take title by adverse possession results from the theory in law that doubt and uncertainty as to title to anything should be removed. Reasoning from this, owners should be compelled to be reasonably diligent in defending their rights. The compulsion afforded is adverse possession.

There are four general requirements for adverse possession: 1) possession must be open and notorious actual occupation. The possessor must occupy the realty in the same manner as one might expect of the true owner; 2) the possession and occupation must be adverse to the interests of the owner. Thus, a tenant or leaseholder could not obtain title to the realty by adverse possession; 3) the adverse possession must be continuous over the statutory period required. If the state statute requires twenty years (as a large number do), two ten-year periods separated by a period when the property was occupied only by the true owner would not suffice; and 4) there must be either a *claim of right* or *color of title* by the possessor. *Claim of right* is interpreted from acts of the possessor such as improving the land or fencing it. *Color of title* is some symbol or claim of ownership which is in some way defective. Payment of taxes on the property possessed is required by some statutes.

PRESCRIPTION. Prescriptive rights are just about the same as title from adverse possession. About the only major difference in most states is that prescriptive rights do not give a person ownership of real property. Instead, prescription deals in rights involved with real property, particularly easements. As with adverse possession, the use of the property must be open and notoriously adverse to the owner. Black, for many years (a sufficient number according to the state statute), has crossed White's land to get to his own. Black has established an easement by prescription. He does not own the path across White's property, but he has a right to continue to cross it in the same manner in which he is accustomed to crossing it.

Trusts

Titles to both real and personal property may be involved in a trust relationship. Trusts involve at least two people—the trustee, who either holds or sells property, and the beneficiary, who is to benefit from the trust. In courts of equity two titles to trust property have developed. The trustee is held to have legal title, with the right to sell or otherwise use the property involved. The beneficiary has equitable title to the property. Equitable title is regarded by equity as the real ownership, even though legal title is vested in someone else.

Rights in Common

Ownership of property by several persons arises under five situations: partnership, joint tenancy, tenancy in common, tenancy by the entireties, and community property. In each situation the rights of more than one person are involved in any property dealings.

PARTNERSHIP. People often join their assets to more effectively carry on an enterprise. Each of the partners has rights in the joined property and in other property acquired by the partnership. Each has attendant liabilities. Every partner has a right to act as agent in the business of the firm, thus adding to or disposing of assets in the particular types of transactions for which the partnership exists. Transactions outside the normal course of business, though, require agreement of all the partners.

Partners in an enterprise have what is known as *unlimited liability* for the debts of the partnership; each stands to lose some or nearly all of his personal fortune if the enterprise folds. However, for many purposes the property of individual partners is separate from that of the partnership. When a solvent partnership is dissolved—possibly because of the death of a partner or agreement to dissolve—each partner has a claim to a share of the partnership assets, but no claim upon the property individually owned by other partners. If a partnership becomes bankrupt, the firm's creditors have first claim upon the partnership assets; the creditors of the bankrupt partner have first claim against his individual property.

JOINT TENANCY. A joint tenancy is created by a will or deed naming two or more parties as joint tenants. Under joint tenancy each tenant has the right to use the property and may not exclude the other joint tenants from it. The right of survivorship is a main feature of joint tenancies. It is for this reason and certain abuses of it that some states take a dim view of joint tenancies.

A joint tenant may sell his share in the property to another, but the buyer then becomes a tenant in common with the remaining joint tenants. The buyer is tenant in common, but the remaining joint tenants are still joint tenants. Since survivorship acts before a will does, a joint tenant cannot successfully leave his interest in the property to his heirs.

TENANCY IN COMMON.   A tenancy in common is about the same thing as a joint tenancy except for the complications of survivorship. A tenant in common may leave his interest in the property to heirs or sell it to someone. The result is merely a substitution of one or more tenants in common.

Each tenant in common has an undivided part interest in the whole property. Each is entitled to a proportionate share in possession, use of, and profits from the property. If one tenant pays property costs, say taxes, he has the right to contribution from the others.

TENANCY BY THE ENTIRETIES.   Tenancy by the entireties might be thought of as a special case of joint tenancy. The relation is created by conveying to husband and wife by the entireties. Neither husband nor wife can destroy the relationship without consent of the other. Real property held in this manner cannot be taken to satisfy the debts of either party under an individual judgment. It may be taken, though, to satisfy a judgment against both of them.

COMMUNITY PROPERTY.   Some nine of our states [3] have a somewhat exceptional treatment of property owned by husband and wife. Property which is acquired by the couple after their marriage is known as community property. Each has an equal share in it. Upon the death of either party the other is entitled to at least half the community property or to the entire amount if there is no will to the contrary. If they agree to disagree by way of the divorce court, each is entitled to half of the community property (with a few exceptions in some of the states).

Community property is property acquired after marriage. It is possible, though, for either husband or wife to have and acquire separate property either before or after marriage. That property which each has when he leaves the unmarried status is his. Also, if property is acquired by one of the two after marriage by gift, will, bequest, or descent, it is his separate property. Property obtained by trading separate property for it remains separate from community property.

Real Property Leases

CREATION AND CHARACTERISTICS.   A lease is a contract by which a tenant acquires something less than complete rights in real property owned by another, the landlord. The lease, itself is a *chattel real*, that is, personal property. Although it is a contract, it involves an interest in land, so it is treated somewhat exceptionally in a lease. The original

---

[3] Arizona, California, Idaho, Louisiana, New Mexico, Nevada, Texas, Washington, and, to a lesser degree, Oklahoma.

Statute of Frauds considered leases as real property transactions and required them to be in writing. The Statute of Frauds has been changed in the various states, however, so that an oral lease contract to run for a year or less (three years or less in some states) is binding.

A lease creates the relationship of lessor and lessee or, more commonly, landlord and tenant. The relationship created is not the same as that between a roomer and proprietor of a rooming house or innkeeper and guest. It involves more than these. The tenant is placed in possession of the property to use as he pleases, and as long as he abides by law and the lease, his rights to use and enjoyment are about the same as that of ownership.

The provisions of the lease contract bind the parties. This, of course, is fundamental—but it should be noted that if the lease is written, any oral provisions not reduced to writing are valueless. They are unenforceable. Black leases a building from White for the manufacture of boat trailers. White orally promises to rewire the building, but the written lease is silent about the wiring. If White does not rewire the building Black is likely to be in the market for some extension cords. Black might be able to use the oral promises to show fraud in the creation of the contract, but this would be about the only value of the oral promise.

Those covenants expressed in the lease agreement will be adhered to strictly in a court interpretation. If the Black and White lease above contained a statement that Black "agreed to return the building in as good condition as when received, save for normal wear and tear and natural decay," such clause would hardly sound ominous. However, if the building burned down, Black might find himself replacing it or paying for it under this clause in the lease.

A lease runs for a definite period of time or is terminable at will by either party. It is this feature which makes it something less than a freehold estate. There are four general types of leases: 1) a lease for a definite period of time; whether for one week or for 99 years, it is still a lease; 2) a lease from year to year, month to month, week to week; 3) a tenancy at will; or 4) a tenancy at sufferance.

A lease for a definite period of time, say two years, needs little explanation. The tenants' rights end with the passage of time.

A *lease from month to month*, might arise from the expiration of a lease that was taken for a definite period of time. If the tenant continues to hold the property with the consent of the landlord after expiration of the original lease, he has a lease of this nature. The rent periods in the original lease dictate how long the tenant's new lease right will last; e.g., if the expired lease was to run a year at a fixed amount per month, the new lease runs from month to month.

When the tenant is given possession in such a way that a lease would be presumed and yet no term is called out, he is said to have a *tenancy at will*. It may be terminated at any time by either party.

A *tenancy at sufferance* occurs when the tenant remains in possession of the property *without the landlord's consent* after expiration of the lease. The landlord may terminate a tenancy at sufferance at any time.

Unless law or lease prohibits it, rights under a lease contract may be assigned to another. The result is known either as *assignment* or *sublease* depending on how much of the lease contract was assigned. If the entire remainder of the lease is assigned to another, it constitutes an *assignment;* if the lessee fails to assign all rights under the lease—assigns only part of them—it is a *sublease*. In a sublease the original lessee still has property rights in the lease. Consider the Black-White lease again. Black, finding the manufacture of boat trailers quite seasonal and rather unprofitable, assigns the remaining term of the lease to Gray. If Black has reserved nothing to himself and has assigned the full remainder of the term, Gray is now bound by the terms of the original lease. If Black had assigned to Gray only a part of the building, or had assigned to him only two of the remaining, say, four years under it, this would constitute a sublease. In such a situation Gray would not be bound by the terms of the original lease, but by the terms of the new one between himself and Black.

LANDLORD'S RIGHTS.   The landlord is, of course, entitled to the agreed compensation for the use of the premises. He has the right to come peaceably upon the premises for purposes of collecting the rent when it is due. In certain states he has the statutory right to exercise a lien against the tenant's personal property if other efforts to collect the rent fail. As a last resort, the landlord may obtain an eviction order against the tenant, thus removing him, if the rent is not paid when due. If the lease only designates a patch of ground, as many do, the destruction of a building there will not reduce the amount of rent, even though the leased property may become untenantable as a result.

At the end of the term the leased premises must be returned to the landlord in substantially the same condition as when leased. Though the landlord is not allowed to interfere with the tenant's enjoyment of the property, he may, after notice, inspect the premises for waste. Also he has a right to come upon the premises for purposes of repairing damage.

The landlord has available an action for waste against his tenant if waste can be shown. But the landlord's available action does not end with his tenant. The land is still owned by the landlord—he is *remainderman*— he is said to have a reversionary interest in the property. He, therefore, has a right to prevent third persons from injuring the property or obtaining easements upon it. The law will support an action by him for recovery or preventive relief as the case may be.

TENANT'S RIGHTS. The tenant has a right to the property he has leased free from interference by the landlord. He has a right to the appurtenances on the property, such as buildings, if such was the intent of the lease. Whether the leasehold will serve the tenant's purposes or not is beside the point unless fraud or concealment can be proved. Here the rule of *caveat emptor* applies—if the property would not serve the tenant's purposes he should not have leased it. The tenant, of course, is at liberty to use the property for any purpose he wishes as long as the use does not violate the law or a provision of the lease.

The tenant often must improve the premises to suit them to his purpose. When the term of the lease expires, who owns the improvements? The answer depends upon the intent of the parties when the improvements were made. How much improvement could be made? The extent of improvements depends upon two factors: the purpose of the lease and the length of its term. Generally, the landlord is entitled to the return of his property substantially in the same form that it was when he leased it. A lease to run 100 years would allow a great deal more alteration than a one-year lease. If the stated use of the premises or restrictions in the lease make changes obviously necessary, agreement to those changes will be implied.

Taxes and assessments are normally paid by the landlord. If the tenant finds he must pay real estate taxes or assessments to retain the leased property, he has a choice of two remedies; he may either pay the agreed rent and maintain a damage action against the landlord or set off the payments against the rent he has contracted to pay. Of course, the landlord could shift responsibility for taxes and assessments to his tenant as part of the lease agreement if he so desired.

LIABILITY. The tenant is liable for injuries to his employees, guests, or invitees to nearly the same extent as an owner of the property. He has a duty to keep the premises in a safe condition, a duty owed to third persons.

Unless a covenant in the lease requires it, the landlord is under no duty to repair the premises. It follows, then, that he is not liable to outsiders for injuries sustained by them. It is only rarely that the landlord may be held liable for injury to his tenant; only where a defective condition of the premises was known to the landlord and he did not reveal it to the tenant is he liable.

Easement

An *easement* is an interest in land. It gives a person a right to do something with the real property of another or a right to have another avoid doing something with his property.

As an interest in land, an easement requires a writing to be enforceable under the Statute of Frauds. It is heritable, assignable, and irrevocable. It is these features which distinguish an easement from a license. A license is revocable and unassignable permission or authority to use the property of another. A valid license may be given orally. Black and White own adjoining property. Black has secured written permission to cross White's land. The writing states that the right to cross White's land pertains to "Black, his heirs or assigns." Such a grant would be held an easement since it is capable of being assigned to another. If Black sells his land to Gray the easement may be transferred to Gray in the sale. A license, on the other hand, could not be transferred.

There are several types of natural easement. An owner of a building owns a right (in the form of an easement) to prevent his neighbor from excavating in such a way as to cause his building to tend to fall into the hole. This is known as the right of *lateral support*. If Black sells White a piece of property which is completely surrounded by Black's property (no other means of access except by air travel) there is an implied natural easement across Black's property. This is known as a *way of necessity*. Although the idea did not become popular in the United States, a natural easement to light and air developed in English law; no structure could be built which interfered greatly with the natural light available to a neighbor.

Easements, other than natural, are created by grant or prescription. The grant may be in the form of a deed of the easement right, itself, or a covenant in the deed which transfers to real property. All manner of easement rights are created by grant or prescription—roads, power lines, gas lines, or sewers may cross land under such easements. Even raising the water level and inundating part of someone's land by damming a stream may involve an easement.

A person cannot have an easement in his own land. There must be a *dominant estate* (the owned property) and a *servient estate* (the easement)—this, of course, would not be possible if an owner of a piece of property could possess an easement in the property in addition to complete ownership of it.

WATER RIGHTS

When a person owns a piece of real property, his ownership ordinarily extends to things on it, over it, and under it. From this the conclusion might logically be drawn that water on and beneath the land belongs to the owner of that land. Actually, the rights may or may not extend to ownership of the water depending upon the jurisdiction. There are several different ways in which water rights are handled, ranging from individual ownership to state ownership. The question of water ownership has lately become more and more pressing, as our population has increased considerably, bringing with it an increased demand by each individual for water. As public demand for water increases still further we are likely to see continued legislation in this field. Although there is a lack of uniformity in laws and court cases on water rights, some generalities may be stated. When a problem involving water arises, it is advisable to check local legislation and court decisions.

Boundaries

The extent of real property is often limited by a watercourse or a body of water. Under common law the defining of property limits in such a manner has several meanings, depending on the nature of the body of water.

If a nonnavigable stream separates the property of two riparian owners,[4] each owns to the center of the stream channel, or to the "thread of the stream" as it is known. Shifting of the stream to a new channel does not change the rights of the two owners. The property line remains as before if the channel change comes about suddenly or in such a way that the old channel may continue to be identified.

Riparian owners are entitled to additions to their property which come about gradually as a stream adds to one shore or another. If, as a result of these natural accretions, the channel gradually changes, the dividing line of the properties will also change; the property of one riparian owner will be extended at the expense of his neighbor, across the stream.

The owner of property bordering on water affected by the tides owns only to the high-water mark. The foreshore (the land between the high-water mark and low-water mark) is public property, belonging to the state.

Land which borders upon navigable lakes or streams is owned to the low-water mark. In addition, the owner has the right to build a pier extending to the line of navigability. The difficulty of establishing a fixed property line by the concepts of high-water or low-water marks have led some of the states to establish riparian property lines by other means. Lines so established are not so apt to fluctuate with droughts or floods.

When a stream divides two states, state ownership does not follow any general pattern. One state may own all of the stream or none of it; or the center of the stream or the channel may be the dividing line.

RIPARIAN RIGHTS AND DUTIES. A riparian owner generally has the right to *reasonable use* of water bordering his property. *Reasonable use*

---

[4] Riparian owners are owners of property bordering upon a stream or other body of water.

is a little difficult to define, however, and each controversy over the right to use water must be decided on its own merits. Generally, it means that the owner may use the water as long as he returns it approximately the same in quantity and quality as it was when it came to him. He has a duty not to pollute the water on which his property borders. For instance, he cannot dump garbage or sewage into a stream bordering his property. Such would be an unreasonable use since this would infringe upon the right of downstream riparian owners to have the water in its natural state. Domestic use of water (for drinking or bathing) is held to be more important than either agricultural or industrial uses.

UNDERGROUND WATER. Water and the rights to its use are not limited to the rivers and lakes on the surface of land. Who owns water in the soil (percolating water) or underground rivers? Generally, the right to use and the duty not to pollute extend to underground streams as well as surface streams.

A large quantity of water is present beneath the soil—water which has no appreciable direction of flow, which is known as percolating water. The results of tapping this source of water are often quite unpredictable. The owner of land generally has the right to drill a well and capture a quantity of this water for his own use. However, if in so doing he lowers the level of the water table so that his neighbor cannot get water, an injury is apparent and the neighbor's cause is actionable. Where a watershed supply is quite limited the court will have a tough time assigning the rights to the water.

Irrigation has been the salvation of many areas of our country. If water must be pumped from a watershed, though, the lowered level of the water table may harm neighboring communities. Not all of the water returns to the soil; much is lost in evaporation from the ground surface and leaves of the plants fed.

A property owner cannot lower a water table, and thus harm his neighbor; neither may he raise the level of groundwater and do harm. The damming of a stream could result in flooded basements nearby.

PRIOR APPROPRIATION. Our western states have far more serious water problems than the eastern states. The common law rights mentioned above seem satisfactory where water is plentiful, but other rules have developed in the West.

The rights of prior appropriation (roughly—first come, first served) and prescription predominate in the West. The first of two or more persons to appropriate water to his own use has the superior right to continued use. Continued use of water for an extended period of time, even by a nonriparian owner, gives him the right to further use. Currently, the states which adhere to the doctrine of prior appropriation are: Alaska, Arizona, California, Colorado, Idaho, Kansas, Montana, Nebraska, Nevada, New Mexico, North Dakota, Oklahoma, Oregon, South Dakota,

Texas, Utah, Washington, and Wyoming. If a person wishes to appropriate a large amount of water to his own uses he must first obtain a permit to do so. In this way, use of the water is controlled for the benefit of the public.

BRIDGES v. THOMAS

Fla., 118 So. 2d 549 (March 14, 1960)

ALLEN, Chief Judge.

The appellant, as plaintiff in the lower court, filed an action to have a deed and purchase money mortgage between her and the appellee-defendants reformed so as to reduce the quantity of land that plaintiff intended to convey to defendants. The complaint also stated that "should said defendants be dissatisfied with said transaction" that the same be cancelled. The defendants answered admitting the transaction with plaintiff but averred that it was an arm's length transaction and that the plaintiff instead of setting up any mistake had only manifested a change of mind in regard to the width of the land sold to defendants. After a hearing on the merits and examining the documents involved, the lower court entered final judgment in favor of defendants.

The plaintiff was the owner of two parcels of land contiguous to each other extending from the Florida East Coast Railway across U. S. Highway No. 1 to the Indian River. The parcels are designated as No. 1 and No. 2. The creek, at its confluence with the Indian River, was believed by plaintiff to divide parcel No. 1 from Parcel No. 2.

In the latter part of 1956, plaintiff negotiated with the defendants for the sale of part of parcel No. 1. Plaintiff did not have a survey of her land nor did she have an abstract of title, but based on the assumption that the creek was supposed to be the boundary between the two parcels, the plaintiff had defendant draw, in the presence of plaintiffs, a map of the land to be sold. This map showed the north-south limits of the land along the river to be 150 feet, the northern boundary meandering westerly along the creek to a point where the creek is 60 feet north of the southern boundary line and then along this 60 foot line west to the railroad. A price of $3,500 was set with $300 to be paid down as a binder. On October 20, 1956, the binder was paid and a receipt given. The deed conveying this land to defendants was dated and acknowledged on November 14, 1956.

Sometime in May, 1957, a survey was made for defendants and plaintiff by one Heath. This survey showed the center of the creek to be 193.55 feet (instead of 148 feet as listed in the deed) north of the south boundary of parcel No. 1, with a meandering river frontage of 220 feet. Upon discovery that the creek was actually in parcel No. 2, retained by plaintiff, the defendants were requested to adjust their north boundary to 148 feet north of the south boundary. The defendants refused and this suit was filed.

To better understand this transaction, a copy of the survey sketch is attached. The defendants contend the transaction was to cover from the center of the creek to the south boundary. Plaintiff contends it was to cover from the south boundary north 148 feet, but in no event was the conveyance to cover any land north of the creek. Plaintiff also contends that she relied on a mistaken assumption that the creek divided the two parcels of land. It appears from the record, however, that the plaintiff told the defendants, ". . . I want you folks to have what is south of the creek, but I don't want you to come across the creek . . . that is the reason I am putting this 148 feet to keep you south of the creek." It also appears that plaintiff furnished a map to an out of state mortgagee prior to this transaction showing the creek to be the dividing line and subsequently a similar sketch was furnished to an abstract company by plaintiff. It should be noted that this abstract was not available when the conveyance in question was negotiated and consummated thus could not be the basis of the mistake.

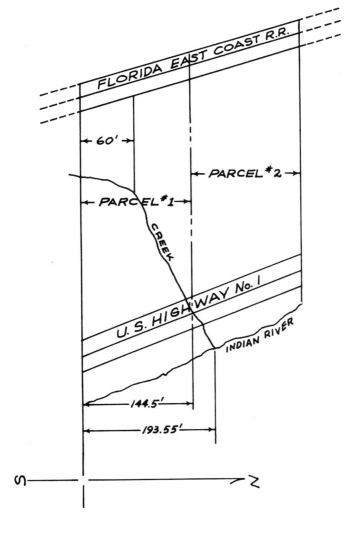

The deed from plaintiff to defendants provides:

Begin in center of Creek at confluence with Indian River at a point approximately 148 ft. North of South line of land owned by Mae D. Bridges; thence Westerly along center of said Creek to a point which is 60 ft. North of South line of said land owned by Mae D. Bridges; thence Westerly parallel to South line of said property aforesaid and 60 ft. distance therefrom to Florida East Coast Railway right-of-way; thence Southerly along East boundary of Florida East Coast Railway right-of-way to South line of said property of Mae D. Bridges; thence East along South line of Mae D. Bridges property to the Indian River; thence Northerly meandering the West bank of Indian River to point of beginning. Together with riparian and littoral rights thereunto belonging, excepting right-of-way of U. S. Highway No. 1 as now located. Said land being part of Government Lot 2, Section 21, Township 29 South, Range 38 East, Brevard County, Florida.

For the purpose of determining whether equitable relief should be granted in this type situation the courts have divided the cases into two general classes: (1) where the sale is of a specific quantity which is usually denominated a sale by the acre, and (2) where the sale is of a specific tract by name or description, which is usually called a sale in gross. Inasmuch as the present transaction was clearly a sale by description with no mention of price per foot or acre, our discussion will be limited to sales in gross and the principles applicable thereto.

The question whether a sale is one in gross or by the acre is to be determined from the terms of the contract or deed and the surrounding circumstances. It is noted that the deed in question provides a point of beginning at the center of the creek at the confluence with Indian River but then further describes this point of beginning as being ". . . a point approximately 148 ft. North of South line. . . . It has long been held that monuments and natural landmarks as a general rule prevail over courses and distances for the purpose of determining the location of a boundary even though this means either the shortening or lengthening of distance. . . . The basis for the rule is that mistakes are deemed more likely to occur with respect to course and distances than in regard to objects which are visible and permanent and are accordingly more reliable evidence than courses and distances. Consequently, if marked trees or water courses be called for in the deed, distances must be lengthened or shortened and courses varied so as to conform to those objects.

The case of *Pierce v. Alexander*, Tex. Civ. App. 1945, 189 S.W.2d 16, involved a factual question similar to the instant case. The deed in question in the Pierce case provided that the east line of the parcel was to be 385 varas [5] in length with its southern terminus at Wallace Creek. The evidence established that the creek was actually 405 varas from the northern terminus of the east line, or some 20 varas south of the 385 varas point as set forth by the distance call in the deed. The Court of Civil Appeals of Texas held that since the call was for Wallace Creek, the boundary line must be extended to the creek even though the stated length thereof falls short of the creek.

It would therefore appear that in order to give effect to the entire description of the tract of land in the instant case, the approximate distance must give way to the superior call of the confluence of the creek with the river as

---

[5] A vara is a Spanish-American measure about 33 inches long.

the point of beginning. The land having been sold in bulk for a lump sum with no mention of quantity being the essence of the contract, the parties are deemed to have assumed the risk of deficiency or excess in the absence of fraud. . . . This principle has been stated by the Florida Supreme Court in *Citizen's State Bank v. Jones,* 100 Fla. 1492, 131 So. 369, 373, as follows:

'The rule denying relief in case of a deficit or an excess is frequently applied in equity as well as at law, but a court of equity will not interfere on account of either a surplus or a deficiency where it is clear that the parties intend a contract of hazard, and it is said that although this general rule may not carry into effect the real intention of the parties it is calculated to prevent litigation.' 27 R.C.L. 434 para. 147. . . .

The parties having dealt at arm's length and the deed being silent as to the specific quantity of land conveyed, any excess over and above the approximated distance must be deemed to have been precipitated by plaintiff's own conduct in failing to know the extent of property she offered and undertook to sell. If one's mistake is due to his own negligence and lack of foresight and caution, in the absence of fraud or imposition, equity will not grant relief. . . .

Finding no error by the chancellor and for the reasons assigned herein, the judgment of the lower court is affirmed.

Affirmed.

REVIEW QUESTIONS

1. Distinguish between:
   1) personal property and real property.
   2) sale and bailment.
   3) warranty deed and quit-claim deed.

2. In what ways may personal property be lawfully acquired?

3. What are the requirements for a valid will?

4. Why must real estate transactions be recorded?

5. In what ways are a mortgagee's interests in real property similar to those of a landlord?

6. How are water rights controlled in your state?

7. List the points made by the court leading to its decision in *Bridges v. Thomas.*

8. The deed in *Bridges v. Thomas* mentioned *littoral* rights. What are littoral rights?

19 SALES AND WARRANTIES

The building of any kind of structure, be it a productive machine, a process or a building to house it, a road, or a bridge, requires the purchase of a good many things. In a large organization a purchasing department buys what the engineer needs; in a small concern the engineer may find that he must do a part of the buying job. In either case the engineer is concerned with the purchasing activity. The engineer's job includes at least effective recommendation of items to be purchased. The manufacturing engineer or process engineer may not be charged with the responsibility of actually purchasing; nevertheless, he is very much concerned with the items to be bought, since they are to be components of his final structure. A target date for completion must be met and delay in receipt and installation of components may be quite costly. Financial arrangements and transportation indirectly concern the engineer.

The engineer is also concerned with the adequacy of the components of his structure. The vendor said the product would render the service intended, but the product simply will not perform. Is there any recourse? Are we stuck with the purchase or do we have rights based on warranty? Such problems do arise and the engineer is involved with them.

The term "sale" could refer to transfer of either real or personal property but it means here a transfer of the ownership of personal property only, for a price in money. The sales law which has developed to govern such transfers is set forth in most states by the Uniform Sales Act.

Ownership

It is often desirable to know who owns goods at a particular time. One who does not own goods cannot lose them. When goods are stolen or destroyed by fire, flood, or other catastrophe the one to suffer the loss is the owner. Consequently, the time when title passes from seller to buyer is important.

SPECIFIC AND IDENTIFIED. For title to pass, the goods must be specific and identified. They must exist and be in a deliverable state such that no material thing remains to be done to them by the seller. If any of these requirements is not met, the sales contract is interpreted not as a "sale," but as a *contract to sell*. Title does not pass in a contract to sell until the seller unconditionally appropriates the goods in the buyer's behalf. Black, in need of 20 cooling fans for shop use, visits White's warehouse where White has about 100 such fans stored. After examining sample fans, Black agrees to take 20 of them at an agreed price per fan. At this point there is no sale; White still owns the entire 100 fans and, should anything happen to them, the entire loss is White's. Now let us assume that the two men separate out 20 fans. Now, if no other material thing remains to be done, Black has title to the 20 fans so separated. If the parties agreed to have White deliver the fans to Black, and if it appeared to be their intent to have title pass upon delivery, title would not pass until delivery had taken place. Of course, if the fans were not yet in existence and were purchased merely by a description or a sample, title could not pass until the fans were made and appropriated to Black's contract.

F.O.B., F.A.S., C.I.F., AND C.A.F. Several three-letter abbreviations are commonly used in shipping goods from seller to buyer. They specify the point at which title passage is to take place. For instance, F.O.B. San Francisco indicates that when the seller has delivered goods into the carrier's possession in San Francisco, to be delivered to the buyer, title passes to the buyer. F.A.S. means the same thing with respect to delivery by ship. C.I.F. and C.A.F. also indicate title passage points, but require more performance by the seller than just handing over the goods to a common carrier. In a C.A.F. (cost and freight) sale the seller is required to obtain a negotiable bill of lading for the goods and pay the freight cost. C.I.F. (cost, insurance, and freight) requires him not only to do the things required in a C.A.F. sale, but to insure the goods as well.

Where the parties have used one of these sets of initials but it is clear from the remainder of the contract that title is intended to pass somewhere else, the courts will disregard the initialed terms.

C.O.D. AND ORDER BILL OF LADING DRAFT ATTACHED. There are several means by which the seller may secure a sale to insure payment. Two such means are represented by C.O.D. (cash on delivery) and order-bill-of-lading-draft-attached sales. In a C.O.D. sale the carrier acts for the seller in collecting for the goods upon delivery to the buyer. Despite this, the buyer has the risks of ownership of the goods while they are in the hands of the carrier.

The order-bill-of-lading-draft-attached sale is similar to the C.O.D. sale. The main difference is that a bank takes over the duty of collecting for the seller. The seller (or the seller's bank) sends a bill of lading together with a bank draft for the price of the goods to a bank in the buyer's city. The buyer pays the bank draft to obtain the bill of lading. With his bill of lading the buyer now obtains his goods from the common carrier.

In these sales as with any other sale the buyer has a reasonable time in which to inspect the goods to determine whether or not they are defective. In the C.O.D. type of sale the buyer must usually pay for the goods before he receives them, but he still has a right to the return of his consideration if the goods prove defective upon examination.

Conditional Sales

In our economy, credit buying accounts for a large number of sales. People (and industries) frequently purchase according to present needs or desires and agree to pay later. Often the seller, in order to have more than just a promise of future payment, will require some kind of security. Two common means used by sellers to gain this security are the conditional sale and the chattel mortgage.

The conditional sales contract is one in which title to the goods sold is retained by the seller (or vendor) until some condition is met. Possession of the goods is surrendered to the buyer; they are his even to running the risks of ownership, even though actual title is retained by the seller. The condition to be met by the buyer is usually the full payment of the purchase price (plus accrued interest). However, the condition to be met may be anything that the parties may stipulate as a condition precedent to title passage. When the stipulated condition has been met, title to the goods passes to the buyer. If the condition is not met the seller has a right to repossess his goods.

Most states require that both conditional sales and chattel mortgage contracts be in writing and recorded. Neither of these requirements existed under common law. The recording of such contracts in the recorder's office constitutes notice to the public that the vendor has rights in the goods. Since title remains with the seller under a conditional sales agreement, the buyer cannot resell and pass good title along to a third party. The seller still has the right to reclaim his goods wherever he may find them. There are two exceptions to this rule: 1) where the purpose of the conditional purchase was resale in the usual line of the buyer's business, a third party purchaser obtains title to the goods even against the conditional seller, and 2) where the goods have been sold to a third party and have become an integral part of some larger thing as, for instance, steel becoming part of a machine.

Upon default by the conditional buyer the conditional seller may elect one of two remedies under common law. He may either exercise his right to repossess the goods, or affirm the sale and bring action against the buyer for the unpaid balance. If the goods are repossessed, the seller has a right to resell them. The goods, when resold, are likely to bring a price different from the amount still owed by the conditional buyer. Under common law, if the resale of the goods brings less than this balance the conditional seller has no action available for the remainder. If the resale brings more, the difference belongs to the seller, not the conditional buyer. The common law on conditional sales is modified by statute in most states. Under the Uniform Sales Act the seller has an action available against the conditional buyer if an insufficient amount is realized upon resale of the goods.

Black buys a machine from White on a conditional sale contract. According to the arrangement he is to pay the $2,000 price of the machine (including interest) by paying ten percent ($200) down and $90 per month for 20 months. He defaults after having made the down payment and six monthly payments. White repossesses the machine at a cost of $40. Resale of the machine costs White $50, and White obtains $1000 for the machine when it is resold. He has an action available against Black for the $350 deficit under the Uniform Sales Act, but no action available under common law unless he has reserved that right in the sales contract. If resale of the machine had brought $1500, the extra $150 would have been White's under either common law or the Uniform Sales Act. Statutes have been passed in some states which would have the effect of returning any surplus on resale to Black, making the conditional sale similar to a chattel mortgage in this respect.

Chattel Mortgage

A second means of securing payment for goods sold is the chattel mortgage. Historically, mortgages began as defeasible conveyances of property. That is, the mortgagor gave title to the mortgaged property to the mortgagee with the condition that if the mortgagor paid back the money borrowed, the title would be returned to him. Our present mortgage laws deviate from this principle. In most states the holder of a chattel mortgage is considered to have a lien on the mortgaged property rather than title to it. Usually it makes little difference whether the title theory or the lien theory is followed in a chattel mortgage case. The end results are similar. The mortgagor has the right to possession and use of the property unless and until he defaults in payments. When the buyer defaults, the seller has the right, either under title or lien, to take the property and sell it in satisfaction of the debt. The buyer is entitled to any excess over remaining payments, interest, and cost of repossession and sale which the property may bring. Similarly, the buyer is still responsible for the remainder if sale of the property does not cover the remaining payments and costs.

Generally, property, to be mortgaged, must exist. A mortgage specifying goods not yet in existence is interpreted as a contract to mortgage rather than a mortgage. Property which will come into existence naturally (not at the hand of man), such as a planted field of wheat is treated as an exception.

Mortgaged goods can be resold by the mortgagor, with the purchaser taking the goods *subject to* the mortgage payments. It is necessary that the mortgagee be informed of the transfer and give his approval. Without the consent of the mortgagee the sale would be incomplete. That is, the original mortgagor would be obligated to pay the mortgagee. The mortgagee must approve of the substitution if the original mortgagor is to be released from his obligation.

In case of default on a chattel mortgage the mortgagee is entitled to bring a foreclosure suit against the mortgagor. If the foreclosure action is successful a court officer (usually the sheriff) is directed to sell the mortgaged property to satisfy the debt. To avoid the time and cost of a foreclosure suit chattel mortgages commonly contain a clause giving the mortgagee the right, upon default, to repossess the property and sell it. Many state statutes, however, require that resale of such property be public and only following public notice. Without such requirement the mortgagee could conceivably sell the goods to a friend or relative for a pittance and sue the mortgagor for the remainder.

Sale on Approval and Sale or Return

A device frequently used to sell goods is to place them in the prospective buyer's hands for a period of time. The buying motive of possession is strong in most members of our society, and when we have goods on a trial basis it is often difficult to surrender possession of them at the end of the trial period. The law concerned here determines title passage in two distinct types of such sales activity.

In the *sale on approval* the buyer is given possession of the goods for a period of time to become his if he approves of them. While the goods are in the buyer's hands the title to them rests with the seller. Thus, any loss of the goods is the seller's loss with, of course, the right to recover if the prospective buyer caused the loss. Approval may be either express or implied. Expression by the buyer of willingness to take title to the goods is approval. If a time limit is stated and the goods are held beyond the time limit, approval is implied. If there is no time limit and the goods are held beyond a reasonable period of time, approval is also implied. The third implication of approval occurs when goods are used as the buyer's own, in such a way that a reasonable trial of them is exceeded in their use. Until he has registered his approval, though, the prospective buyer in a sale on approval arrangement is merely bailee of the seller's goods.

A *sale or return* is treated by the courts as a sale—with the privilege of returning the goods. The title to the property passes to the buyer. A sale in which the seller states that the buyer "may return the goods if he is not completely satisfied" is a sale or return transaction. Return of the goods revests the title in the seller. If a time limit is stated and the goods are not returned in that time, the sale is final. If no time limit is stated the buyer has a reasonable time in which to return the goods. The seller regains title to the goods if the buyer makes a timely return of them, even though the seller refuses to accept them back.

Sale by Non-owner

Ordinarily a seller cannot give the buyer better title to goods sold than he (the seller) has. Unless you are an agent, you can't sell things you don't own. There are three exceptions to this rule.

If the buyer of goods leaves them in the seller's possession and the seller resells them to a third party, that third party will get good title. Black buys a drill press from White, temporarily leaving it with White. White's agent, lacking knowledge of the sale, sells the drill press to Gray. Gray will get good title to the press and Black is left with a breach of contract action available against White. This exception has a good practical foundation in that, since most sales of personal property are not required to be recorded, the third party has no means of knowing that a prior sale of the property was made. White was in possession of the drill press and appeared to have a perfect right to sell it.

If a seller is induced by fraud to sell goods, he has a right to rescind the agreement. However, if the goods are resold by the buyer to a third person before the seller rescinds, the third person gets good title to the goods. The seller is left with his action against the original buyer for fraud.

If the true owner, by some act or neglect on his part, leads a purchaser to believe that another person has the right to sell the goods, the buyer in good faith will receive good title. The acts or neglect on the owner's part are not spelled out, but the title passage appears to be based on the theory of *estoppel*. After such a sale the owner is *estopped* from denying that he gave the seller the right to sell the goods.

WARRANTY

Warranty and Representation

EXPRESS WARRANTIES.   A statement of warranty is a promissory statement. It is here that the main distinction can be made between statements which may be fraudulent and warranty statements. You recall that fraud involved a false representation of a fact—something past or present. Warranty has to do with either the present or future. When Black sells White an automatic screw machine and tells White that it has just been overhauled, when in truth it has not been, such a statement is fraudulent. If Black, on the other hand, promised to repair the machine if it should break down in the first year White uses it, this statement constitutes a warranty. Statements having to do with the present, though, are a little harder to distinguish. A statement by Black that all the collets and pushers had been replaced and were new would be factual; if untrue, it should be the basis of fraud. In contrast, a statement that the machine was in such a condition that it would be useful in the manufacture of White's product would constitute warranty. Another distinction between warranty and fraudulent representations is that a warranty becomes part of a contract, whereas the representations are inducements to contract. Clarity of this distinction, though, may be questionable in many situations. In certain cases where a false representation has been made, the buyer may elect either his remedy for fraud or breach of warranty.

OPINIONS.   A warranty is a statement other than opinion or judgment. With very rare exceptions a statement made as the seller's opinion cannot constitute warranty. A statement by the vendor that the merchandise is "first rate" or "the best" or "superior quality" is usually construed as sales talk or "puffing" the goods. The courts have long adhered to the doctrine of *caveat emptor,* popularly interpreted as "the buyer beware." This principle is based upon the idea that the buyer is free to inspect goods before he buys them and free not to buy if he is not allowed to inspect, or if he finds something wrong.

A recent tendency in the law is to place more responsibility upon the seller. It might even be called *"caveat venditor."* The trend is based upon the notion that many statements made by a vendor actually have the effect of relieving the buyer of the duty to ascertain the value of the goods for himself. An affirmation of value having this effect has often been held to be a warranty in recent decisions.

In making a warranty of his merchandise, a vendor makes a contract somewhat similar to insurance. He agrees to assume a risk which would normally be borne by the buyer. In the example above if Black warranted the automatic screw machine for a year as to breakdown, he would be promising to take over White's risk of repairing the machine for a year.

WARRANTY AND SALE. A warranty is necessarily connected to a sale. In fact it cannot exist unless it is based on a sale. If the warranty is made at the time of the sale, the consideration for the warranty is part of the sale price. However, if the warranty is made later it must, as any other contractural promise, be supported by separate consideration to be legally binding.

WARRANTY BENEFITS. Earlier in the text mention was made of privity of contract. One who is not a party to the formation of a contract does not have the legally enforceable right to reap the benefits of it. This is also true of warranty promises. The original promisee is the only one who has a legal right to the benefits of a warranty. When goods are resold the warranty is not passed along to the new buyer. The rule is a general one and there is a prominent exception to it. Where the goods in question consist of food or drugs, public policy and many statutes dictate the protection in the law.

Implied Warranties

In addition to express warranties which may be made by the seller at the time of sale, there are several implied warranties. These implied warranties exist in all sales contracts unless they are expressly omitted by the parties.

GOOD TITLE. In a present sale the seller warrants by implication that the title which he passes along to the buyer is good. In a contract to sell, the implication is made that the seller will be able to pass good title to the buyer at some later date. By warranty of good title is meant the implied promise that no other person has valid claim to the merchandise in question. Specific exceptions to the warranty of good title exist in the form of sheriff's sales, auctions, mortgagee's sales, and the like. Such sales are often authorized by law, but there is no assurance that a prior owner or lien holder does not exist to disturb quiet enjoyment of title to the goods. The title obtained is, in some respects, similar to the quit-claim deed in real estate where the seller, in effect, says "I give you my claim to title however good it may be."

DESCRIPTION OR SAMPLE. When goods are purchased according to a description or a sample only, there is an implied warranty that the goods will match the description or sample. Since the buyer normally does not have an opportunity to examine the merchandise he is buying, the seller would have a chance to short change him. The warranty is meant to prevent this. Goods must conform in all respects to the kind, quality, and condition described or as shown by sample.

SUITABILITY FOR DESCRIBED PURPOSE. The seller is assumed by the courts to be more familiar with his goods than is the purchaser. For this reason, if the purchase is made on the basis of a buyer's description of what the goods are to do, with the seller supplying the goods for that purpose, the goods supplied must be adequate to do the job. This warranty is defeated if the buyer orders goods according to a trade name or specification. Where this is done it makes no difference that the seller knows of the purpose intended and believes that the goods will not fit the purpose. Black requires a punch press for a blanking operation on a production line which he is setting up. His calculations (in error) show a requirement of a 40-ton press. White, with full knowledge of the purpose intended, is called upon to supply the press and does so. On the first day of operation the punch press crank breaks and Black brings an action on the implied warranty of suitability for purpose. Since Black specified the press, he would not be allowed to recover. If, on the other hand, Black had asked White to supply a press for the blanking operation, allowing White to determine the required press size, suitability would have been warranted.

MERCHANTABILITY.   The implied warranty of merchantability is somewhat akin to suitability for a described purpose. The distinction is in degree and in the manner in which the warranties arise. All goods sold are subject to the warranty of merchantability. To be merchantable, goods must be of the usual quality sold in the market; they must be sound and undamaged, free from hidden defects; they must be fit for the general purpose for which such goods are sold. In the above example if it could be shown that the punch press crankshaft had not been properly heat-treated and, therefore, would not withstand a 40-ton force, Black might recover under merchantability.

EXPRESS NON WARRANTY.   Parties to a sales contract are free to contract in any lawful manner they choose. Frequently, sales contracts contain disclaimer clauses—clauses which, in effect, state that the buyer takes the goods at his own risk. As long as public policy is not seriously involved the courts usually uphold such clauses as representing the will of the parties at the time of the agreement. The provision that the buyer takes the goods "as is" will be held to relieve the seller of many of his usual warranties. Of course, even in an "as is" sale the merchandise sold must be what it is purported to be. That is, sale of a vertical milling machine indicates that what is bought will constitute a vertical milling machine even though the term "as is" is used in the sale. The "as is" pertains only to the condition of the subject matter, not to its existence.

BREACH

Breach of Warranty

If the goods received by the buyer are not as warranted by the seller, the buyer has an election of remedies. The buyer may, at his option:

1) keep the goods sent by the seller and deduct from the price the value of the warranty. In the example of the automatic screw machine, for instance, the cost of installing new collets and pushers would be deducted from the purchase price; 2) keep the goods sent and maintain a damage action for breach of warranty; 3) refuse to accept the goods and maintain a damage action for breach of contract; or 4) rescind the contract and recover any of the price paid for the goods (and offer to return the goods to the vendor). Once the buyer has elected a remedy he cannot change his election. Damages are usually limited to the direct and natural costs resulting from the breach of warranty.

Buyer's Rights

DIFFERENT QUANTITY. Differences in quantity are treated under three possibilities—a shortage, an overage, or goods mixed with other goods. Black, a building contractor orders 40,000 board feet of lumber from White. White ships Black 30,000 board feet, a shortage of 10,000 board feet. If Black knows that the 30,000 board feet is all he will get, he may either reject the shipment or accept it and pay for it at the contract rate. If Black accepts the shipment without knowing that 30,000 board feet is all he will get, and uses the lumber, he will be liable for the value of the lumber. Now suppose White ships too much—say 50,000 board feet. Black has three alternatives. He may accept and pay for the 50,000 board feet at the contract rate; he may reject the excess; or he may reject the entire shipment. If Black's lumber comes to him mixed with other lumber, he has the choice of rejecting the entire mass or separating out his lumber and rejecting the remainder. If the buyer rejects either the entire shipment or a portion of it he is under no duty to return it to the seller. The buyer has a duty to inform the seller that the goods were rejected, but it is up to the seller to come and get them.

FAILURE TO DELIVER. Where the seller is to deliver goods to the buyer and fails to do so, the buyer may have one of four courses of action open to him. If title to the goods has passed but the seller fails to deliver, his retention of the goods amounts to the tort of conversion. There are provisions in the local law which will give the buyer an adequate remedy for the tort.

If there is any question as to the buyer's right to the goods he can usually get them under a writ of replevin. Replevin requires the posting of a bond, usually for the value of the goods in question, to be forfeited if the court finds that the other party is entitled to the goods. Such a writ, when issued, directs a sheriff or other law officer to pick up the goods and deliver them to the party bringing the replevin action.

If the buyer does not yet have title to the goods and the seller fails to deliver them, he may maintain a damage action for nondelivery. In such an instance the measure of the buyer's damages is that which directly results from the seller's failure to deliver. If the buyer buys substitute goods in the market, any increase in price would be the damage suffered by him.

Equity remedies were originally meant for unusual cases. However, they have been found to be so convenient that more and more of our present laws dictate their use. The Uniform Sales Act allows the use of specific performance where there is nondelivery by the seller. If damages seem not to be the appropriate remedy, a court having equity jurisdiction may direct the seller to specifically perform his contract.

Seller's Rights

If a sales contract does not specify otherwise, the buyer must accept and pay for the goods when the seller delivers them. Delivery by the seller and payment by the buyer are concurrent conditions—they are to happen at the same time unless the parties have provided otherwise. To bind the buyer to payment, the goods must of course be of the quantity that the buyer asked for. If the buyer fails to take such goods when they are properly delivered to him, the seller has a damage action available to him for profit lost by the refusal to take the goods and the cost of attempted delivery.

UNPAID SELLER'S LIEN.   The seller has a right to be paid for goods sold. If the parties have not made a contrary agreement, the seller may hold the goods in his possession until he is paid. If title to goods (held by the seller to secure payment) has passed to the buyer, the seller is exercising what is known as an unpaid seller's lien. The seller may exercise his lien against the buyer's goods in his possession in two related circumstances: where goods were bought on credit by the buyer and the credit period has expired, and where the buyer has become insolvent (cannot pay his bills as they fall due). The seller, of course, loses his lien right if the buyer is allowed to take the goods. The same is true if he extends the period of credit for the buyer. The lien is not effectively lost, though, when the goods are delivered to a carrier for transportation to the buyer.

STOPPAGE IN TRANSIT.   Stoppage in transit occurs only in rather limited circumstances. For it to occur, the seller must have parted with both possession of and title to the goods. The goods must be in the hands of the carrier. The buyer must be insolvent. If all these conditions are met, the seller has a right to notify the carrier to hold the goods for him. If the buyer gets the goods before the stop notice catches up with them, the seller's right is lost.

RESALE OF GOODS.   If the buyer defaults, the seller in possession of the goods may either resell them or merely rescind the contract and keep them. The buyer must have delayed an unreasonable length of time to give the seller this right.

Resale of the goods may take place without notification to the buyer. The second buyer gets good title to the goods even though title had previously passed to the first buyer. If, on resale, the price that the seller receives is greater than the original sale price, the excess belongs to the seller. If it is less, the seller has an action available against the first buyer for the remainder.

The seller has an option to rescind the contract. To do this, he must notify the buyer of his election of rescission. After rescission the seller has an action available for any damage he has suffered at the hands of the buyer.

If the goods have been delivered to the buyer, the seller's rights are limited to an action for the purchase price. He has lost his right to rescind the contract. Excepting the cases of conditional sales and chattel mortgages, he cannot retake and resell the goods to get his money.

ALLIED STEEL AND CONVEYORS, INC. v. FORD MOTOR COMPANY

277 F. 2d 907, Mich. (May 11, 1960)

WILLIAM E. MILLER, District Judge.

The question presented on this appeal is whether a provision in certain written agreements between appellant and appellee purporting to indemnify appellee against damages resulting from its own acts of negligence was binding upon the parties at the time the damages were sustained.[1]

On August 19, 1955, Ford ordered from Allied numerous items of machinery and equipment. The consideration to be paid was $71,325.00. Under the terms of the order, Allied was to install the machinery and equipment on Ford's premises for an additional consideration of $6,900.00, with a provision that should Ford elect to install the machinery with its own labor, Allied would furnish a supervisor to direct the installation on a per diem basis. The order further provided that "the signing and returning to Buyer by Seller of the Acknowledgment Copy shall constitute acceptance by Seller of this Purchase Order and of all of its terms and conditions." The order was submitted on printed forms regularly used by Ford, and was designated "Purchase Order No. 15145." Item 15 of the printed form provided that if Allied was required to perform work on Ford's premises, Allied would be responsible for all damages or injuries occurring as a result of the fault or negligence of its own employees, including any damages or injuries to Ford's employees and property.

---

[1] Appellant, Allied Steel & Conveyors, Inc., and appellee, Ford Motor Company, will be referred to herein as "Allied" and "Ford."

Attached to the Purchase Order and made a part thereof was a printed form designated Form 3618, which included an indemnity provision broader in scope than Item 15 of the purchase order, requiring the Seller to assume full responsibility not only for the fault or negligence of its own employees but also for the fault or negligence of Ford's employees, arising out of or in connection with Allied's work. This provision in Form 3618, however, was marked "VOID." On December 16, 1955, Ford submitted to Allied its Amendment No. 1 to the purchase order, deleting the item of $6,900.00 for the cost of installation by Allied and providing that the installation would be done by Ford. The original Purchase Order and Amendment No. 1 were both duly accepted by Allied and the agreements were performed.

Subsequently, on July 26, 1956, Ford submitted to Allied Amendment No. 2 to Purchase Order 15145, and it is this Amendment which is the focal point of the present controversy. By the amendment Ford proposed to purchase additional machinery to be installed on Ford's premises by Allied, at a total cost of $173,700.00. Amendment No. 2, as did Amendment No. 1, provided:

> This purchase order agreement is not binding until accepted. Acceptance should be executed on acknowledgment copy which should be returned to buyer.

The copy of Ford's Form 3618 attached to Amendment No. 2 was identical to the printed Form 3618 which was attached to the original Purchase Order, but the broad indemnity provision in Form 3618, making Allied liable for the negligent acts of both its own and Ford's employees, was not marked "VOID." The record makes it clear that the reason for not voiding the broad indemnity provision of Form 3618 attached to Amendment No. 2 was that the installation work on Ford's premises was to be performed by Allied's employees, whereas under the original purchase order as amended by Amendment No. 1 the installation work was to be done by Ford's own employees. Another pertinent provision of Form 3618 was:

> Such of the terms and conditions of Seller's Purchase Order as are inconsistent with the provisions hereinabove set forth are hereby superseded.

The acknowledgment copy of Amendment No. 2 was duly executed by Allied on or about November 10, 1956, and was received by Ford on November 12, 1956. At that time Allied had already begun installation of the machinery on the Ford premises, although the exact date upon which the installation was commenced is not shown in the record. On September 5, 1956, in the course of the installation, one Hankins, an employee of Allied, sustained personal injuries as a result of the negligence of Ford's employees. Hankins later filed an action against Ford in the District Court for the Eastern District of Michigan, Southern Division. After the complaint was filed, Ford added Allied, Hankins' employer, as a third-party defendant, relying upon the indemnity provisions of Form 3618, and demanding judgment against Allied ". . . for all sums that may be adjudged against the defendant, Ford Motor Company, in favor of plaintiff, John T. Hankins." The trial before a jury resulted in verdicts for $12,500.00 in favor of Hankins and against Ford, and in favor of Ford and against Allied for the same amount. This appeal by Allied followed denial by the District Court of its motion for judgment notwith-

standing the verdict of the jury and entry of the judgment against it in favor
of Ford upon the third-party complaint.

It was Allied's insistence at the trial, as it is here, that the agreement evidenced by Amendment No. 2 which was signed and returned to Ford on
November 10, 1956, was not in effect on September 5, 1956, when Hankins
was injured; and further, that, in any event, it was the intention of the parties
to void the broad indemnity provision in Form 3618 attached to Amendment
No. 2, thus leaving in effect Item 15 contained in the original Purchase Order
which made Allied liable only for its own negligence. Although the agreements
contained in Amendment No. 2 were fully performed by the parties and Allied
received full payment for its goods and services, the point made by Allied is
that it did not become bound by the provisions of such amendment until
November 1956, when it actually signed and returned to Ford the acknowledgment copy of Amendment No. 2. It argues that it was under no contractual
obligation on September 5, 1956, the date of Hankins' injury, to indemnify
Ford against Ford's negligent acts.

Allied first says that the contractual provisions evidenced by Amendment
No. 2 were not in effect at the time of the Hankins injury because it had not
been accepted at that time by Allied in the formal manner expressly required
by the amendment itself. It argues that a binding acceptance of the amendment could be effected only by Allied's execution of the acknowledgment copy
of the amendment and its return to Ford.

With this argument we cannot agree. It is true that an offeror may prescribe
the manner in which acceptance of his offer shall be indicated by the offeree,
and an acceptance of the offer in the manner prescribed will bind the offeror.
And it has been held that if the offeror prescribes an exclusive manner of acceptance, an attempt on the part of the offeree to accept the offer in a different
manner does not bind the offeror *in the absence of a meeting of the minds on
the altered type of acceptance.* . . . On the other hand, if an offeror merely sug-
gests a permitted method of acceptance, other methods of acceptance are not
precluded. . . . Moreover, it is equally well settled that if the offer requests
a return promise and the offeree without making the promise actually does or
tenders what he was requested to promise to do, there is a contract if such performance is completed or tendered within the time allowable for accepting by
making a promise. In such a case a tender operates as a promise to render complete performance. . . .

Applying these principles to the case at bar, we reach the conclusion, first,
that execution and return of the acknowledgment copy of Amendment No. 2
was merely a suggested method of acceptance and did not preclude acceptance
by some other method; and, second, that the offer was accepted and a binding
contract effected when Allied, with Ford's knowledge, consent and acquiescence, undertook performance of the work called for by the amendment. The
only significant provision, as we view the amendment, was that it would not be
binding until it was accepted by Allied. This provision was obviously for the
protection of Ford, . . . and its import was that Ford would not be bound by
the amendment unless Allied agreed to all of the conditions specified therein.
The provision for execution and return of the acknowledgment copy, as we
construe the language used, was not to set forth an exclusive method of ac-

ceptance but was merely to provide a simple and convenient method by which the assent of Allied to the contractual provisions of the amendment could be indicated. The primary object of Ford was to have the work performed by Allied upon the terms prescribed in the amendment, and the mere signing and return of an acknowledgment copy of the amendment before actually undertaking the work itself cannot be regarded as an essential condition to completion of a binding contract.

It is well settled that acceptance of an offer by part performance in accordance with the terms of the offer is sufficient to complete the contract. An interesting discussion of the effect of part performance is found in the opinion of the Court of Appeals for the Eighth Circuit in *Durasteel Co. v. Great Lakes Steel Corp.*, 205 F. 2d 438. After citing numerous authorities from various jurisdictions, Chief Judge Gardner, speaking for the Court, quotes the following statement of the Supreme Court of Nebraska in *Sheridan Coal Co. v. C. W. Hull Co.*, 87 Neb. 117, 127 N.W. 218, 220:

> . . . But what will constitute an acceptance depends frequently upon circumstances. A direct, unequivocal, written acceptance of an offer to purchase is satisfactory evidence of the fact, but, if the parties have not stipulated otherwise, the acceptance need not be in any particular form nor evidenced by express words; the delivery by the vendor of a part of the property referred to in the offer to buy, may take the place of words as proof of acceptance.

Other authorities are to the effect that the acceptance of a contract may be implied from acts of the parties . . . and may be shown by proving acts done on the faith of the order, including shipment of the goods ordered, . . . It would seem necessarily to follow that an offeree who has unjustifiably led the offeror to believe that he had acquired a contractural right, should not be allowed to assert an actual intent at variance with the meaning of his acts.

It has been argued on behalf of Allied, by way of analogy, that Ford could have revoked the order when Allied began installing the machinery without first having executed its written acceptance. If this point should be conceded, . . . it would avail Allied nothing. For, after Allied began performance by installing the machinery called for, and Ford acquiesced in the acts of Allied and accepted the benefits of the performance, Ford was estopped to object and could not thereafter be heard to complain that there was no contract. . . .

In *Case Threshing Machine Co. v. Donalson*, 10 Ga. App. 428, 73 S.E. 618, the defendant had signed a written order for the purchase of machinery. The order, which contained warranties as to kind and character of the machinery and other conditions, specifically provided that it must be signed by all parties before delivery of the goods. In an action by the seller to recover the purchase money, Donalson alleged a breach of the warranties. The Georgia Court of Appeals, in its opinion, stated:

> It is insisted that the plaintiff was not bound by the express warranties unless the contract was actually signed by it. We do not concur in this view. When the plaintiff performed the contract according to its terms this was an acceptance, and it followed that the plaintiff was thereupon bound by all the warranties, terms, and conditions contained in the contract, just as the defendant was also bound. . . .

A situation analogous to the one now before us is found in *Columbia Weigh-*

ing Machine Co. v. Vaughan, 123 Kan. 474, 255 P. 973,974. In that case, Vaughan had signed an order for a weighing machine. The order contained this statement:

It is understood you are to supply us with any mechanical parts required for the machine for a period of five years without charge. Whenever we may want a part, we are to inform you by registered mail. . . . All orders are subject to acceptance of the company.

The Columbia Company did not indicate its acceptance in writing, but shipped the machine. When Columbia brought action to recover the purchase price, Vaughan interposed the defense that his offer had not been accepted so as to bind Columbia to also furnish parts for the machine for five years without charge. The Supreme Court of Kansas in deciding the case enunciated the following principles:

Defendant argues that there is a radical distinction, in regard to communications, between offers which ask that the offeree *do* something and offers which ask that the offeree *promise* something, and that in offers of the former kind communication of the acceptance is ordinarily not required, while in offers of the latter kind communication of the acceptance is always essential, citing 13 C. J. 284. The cases cited in support of the text are not offers of the kind we have before us. There may very well be an offer of a promise to do, the acceptance of which does not require, or contemplate, immediate action, but only a promise of future action. Such an offer could be accepted only by the offeror making the promise, since no immediate action is required of him. But this is not the case before us. Here defendant offered to buy a machine, not at some time in the future, but to make a present purchase, with the understanding, which means upon the conditions stated in the order. . . . Plaintiff, by shipping the machine, accepted the offer, and thereby the offer became a contract, the terms and conditions of which became binding on both parties. But, defendant argues, this did not obligate plaintiff to furnish necessary parts for 5 years free of charge. This argument is not sound. The order was not divisible in this respect. When plaintiff accepted the offer, it was accepted in its entirety. It could be accepted in no other way. Both parties became bound by all of its conditions and provisions.

· · · · ·

The contract consists of the offer and its acceptance. The acceptance may be shown by any act or conduct clearly evincing an intention to accept the offer made. . . . The delivery of the merchandise ordered clearly evinces the intention to accept. . . . 'This was the very highest form of acceptance.'

The Supreme Court of Michigan cited and approved the *Columbia Weighing Machine Co. Case,* supra, in *Ludowici-Celadon Co. v. McKinley,* 307 Mich. 149, 11 N.W. 2d 839, 840, in which it appeared that appellant's salesman offered to furnish appellee a quantity of tile at a certain price. The offer contained the following language:

This proposal is good for 30 days. Its acceptance will constitute a contract, subject to the approval of our executive department at Chicago.

The offer which was also signed by appellee was returned to appellant. Appellant thereupon wrote a letter to appellee which read:

We acknowledge, with thanks, receipt of our proposal. . . . We are passing this to our Executive Department for consideration and attention.

Appellee received no further writing from appellant. However, appellant began partial deliveries which were received and paid for by appellee. Appellee thereafter discovered that it could not use all of the tile covered by the proposal, and it refused to accept further deliveries. In reviewing an action brought by the seller to recover the full purchase price, the Court held that the receipt by the appellee of the partial deliveries constituted an acceptance of appellant's offer and consummated the contract so as to bind both parties, stating in its opinion . . . :

Had the plaintiff seller refused to deliver the remainder, the defendant buyer could have recovered damages for the breach of the contract. It must, therefore, follow that the seller is likewise entitled to recover damages because of the buyer's refusal to accept the remainder of the tile.

These authorities, while not in all respects parallel are closely analogous to the present case and we think support our conclusion that Amendment No. 2, with all of its provisions and conditions, became a binding bilateral contract at the time Allied, with Ford's knowledge and consent, began performance by delivery and installation of the machinery upon Ford's premises.

As further grounds for reversal, Allied submits (1) that the parties intended to void the broad indemnity provisions in the copy of Form 3618 which was attached to Amendment No. 2 and thus leave in effect Sec. 15 of the original Purchase Order whereby Allied assumed responsibility only for its own negligence, and (2) that Amendment No. 2 is ambiguous and, under the well-recognized rules of construction, should be construed against Ford who was responsible for its drafting.

As to the intent of the parties, the record discloses that the jury found that there had been a meeting of the minds in regard to the provisions of Amendment No. 2, including Form 3618 which was attached thereto. We think this finding is amply supported in the record, but in any event, Allied is confronted with the cardinal rule that, in the absence of fraud or wilful deceit, one who signs a contract which he has had an opportunity to read and understand, is bound by its provisions. . . . And Allied, having received the purchase order amendment and having undertaken to supply the equipment and to perform the services called for by such amendment, cannot be heard to complain that it did not read the amendment and is not bound by its provisions and conditions.

Finally, we find no merit in Allied's contention that Amendment No. 2 is ambiguous and that its provisions are contradictory. As heretofore stated, the indemnity provision in the copy of Form 3618 which was attached to the original Purchase Order was voided. Page 1 of Amendment No. 2 contained spaces, or boxes, by which it could be indicated whether the original Purchase Order was being amended with respect to "Price", "Terms", "F.O.B.", "Routing", "Quantity", and "Specifications", and only the spaces, or boxes, opposite the words "Price" and "Specifications" were checked. This fact is made the basis of Allied's argument that the contract is at least ambiguous and should be construed against Ford, since the indication was that the amendment was to affect only prices and specifications and not the "terms" of the contract with respect to indemnity or otherwise. But Page 3 of Amendment No. 2, contained a single paragraph which would have attracted attention upon the most casual examination, reading as follows:

Form 3618 Revised June, 1955 attached hereto is made a part of the terms and conditions of this Purchase Order. In those cases where this attachment may be in conflict with the terms and conditions appearing on the reverse side of this order, the form No. 3618 shall apply.

This provision left no doubt that the broad indemnity provision was to govern, and it seems clear to us that if Allied did not know the contents of the amendment, its failure was due simply to the fact that it did not read the amendment in its entirety and not to any ambiguity in the amendment itself. This conclusion is strengthened by the fact that the agreement was subsequently formally executed by Allied and the obligations created thereby were fully performed by both parties.

The judgment of the District Court is Affirmed.

ARCO BAG CO., INC. v. FACINGS, INC.

151 N.E. 2d 438, 18 Ill. App. 2d 110, Illinois, June 9, 1958

JUSTICE ROBSON delivered the opinion of the court.

This is an appeal from a judgment against defendants for breach of contract. Plaintiff and defendant, Facings, Inc., entered into contracts whereby it is purported plaintiff agreed to lease and the defendant to hire, with option to purchase, four lift trucks. Facings, Inc. failed to meet its payments as provided in the contracts and plaintiff repossessed the trucks and brought this action for the balance due under the contracts, a total of $3,000 in attorney's fees, and $133.57, the cost of repossessing the trucks. William E. Decker, who had signed each contract in an individual capacity, was joined as a defendant. The case was tried without a jury and a judgment for $24,283.57 was entered in favor of plaintiff against both defendants. The principal question presented on appeal is whether or not the contracts contain any provision indicating, as part of the agreement, a predetermination of the extent of defendant's liability upon default.

Three of the contracts were executed on April 29, 1955; the fourth is dated June 1, 1955. In substance each provides that the total amount due for the use of each truck shall be $5,400, payable at the rate of $150 per month; that the lessee is given an option to purchase the equipment at the termination of the lease for a price of $400 provided that the total rental has been paid, the option to be exercisable at any time during the term of the lease and no later than ten days after its termination; that in the event of the lessee's default or insolvency the lessor may enter the lessee's premises and repossess the equipment. Other provisions of the contracts relate to repairs, operators, liability for loss or damage, insurance, taxes, title, inspection, nonwarranty of equipment by the lessor, possession, and assignments. The contracts also contain the following two provisions:

Nonwaiver:

Time is of the essence, Lessor's failure at any time to require strict performance by Lessee of any of the provisions hereof shall not waive or diminish Lessor's right thereafter to demand strict compliance therewith or with any other provision. Waiver of any default shall not waive any other default. Lessor's rights hereunder are cumulative and not alternative.

Miscellaneous:

Lessee will not change or remove any insignia or lettering on the equipment. All notices relating hereto shall be mailed registered to Lessor or Lessee at its respective address, above shown or at any later address last known to the sender. In case of any default by Lessee hereunder all sums due and to become due hereunder shall, at the option of Lessor or any assignee of Lessor, become payable forthwith. Lessee waives all rights under all exemption laws. Lessee admits the receipt of a true copy of the Equipment Lease. This lease is irrevocable for the full term hereof and for the aggregate rental herein reserved, and the rent shall not abate by reason of termination of Lessee's right of possession and/or the taking of possession by Lessor or for any other reason, and delinquent installments of rental shall bear interest at the highest lawful rate. In case of any default by Lessee hereunder, Lessor may sell the equipment or may re-lease the equipment for a term and a rental which may be equal to, greater than, or less than the rental and term herein provided. Any proceeds of sale, received within 60 days after repossession, or any rental payments received under a new lease made within such 60 days for the period prior to the expiration of this lease, less Lessor's expenses of taking possession, storage, reconditioning and sale or re-leasing, shall be applied on the Lessee's obligations hereunder, and Lessee shall remain liable for the balance of the unpaid aggregate rental set forth above. Lessee's liability shall not be reduced by reason of any failure of Lessor to sell or re-let within such 60 days.

Defendant, Facings, Inc., paid the amount due under the contracts for the month of May, 1955. The payments for June were not made at the appointed time. The president of plaintiff corporation contacted Facings, Inc. The president of Facings, Inc. promised to make payment, but failed to do so and, in the middle of June, referred plaintiff to defendant Decker. On June 30, 1955, Facings, Inc. sent a check for $600 to plaintiff. The check was returned by the bank for insufficient funds. During June plaintiff contacted Decker's office, although no written demand for payment was ever sent to Decker. Plaintiff's president and secretary, Ben Linderman, testified that he could not specifically recall speaking directly to Decker. Decker testified that he had spoken to Linderman by phone in the middle of June, that this conversation was his first knowledge of any default by Facings, Inc., and that he then told Linderman that he would "do something about it."

On July 27, 1955, plaintiff's attorney, Abe Linderman, who is also an officer of plaintiff, went to the premises occupied by defendant corporation to repossess the trucks. Abe Linderman then called Decker and informed him of the action he was taking. Decker offered to send a check within the hour. Linderman declined the offer and proceeded to repossess the trucks. Subsequently plaintiff filed this action against Facings, Inc. and Decker to recover the balance of the payments on each truck for the entire term of each lease.

Defendants answered alleging that the repossession was wrongful, that Decker was at all times ready, willing, and able to pay the amounts due. Both defendants filed counterclaims for business losses, loss of capital and punitive damages, all of which they alleged became due them as a result of the arbitrary, wrongful, and malicious repossession of the trucks by plaintiff. Plaintiff produced no evidence to establish its damages and the court found all of the issues in favor of plaintiff under the contract provisions related heretofore in this opinion.

(1) The parties have referred to the contracts in question as "sale-lease" or "lease-purchase" agreements. They have characterized the monthly payments to be made under each contract as rent. This terminology is of no significance, for, where the total amount of "rent" payable for goods is substantially equivalent to their value and the "lessee" has the option of purchasing the goods after all rent is paid, the contract is, in all legal effect, a contract of conditional sale and is in fact recognized as such by the plaintiff. . . . This court must determine whether or not the contracts in question specifically provide that upon default by the lessee or purchaser, and repossession by plaintiff, plaintiff is entitled also to recover the total amount of monthly payments designated in each contract, or, in effect, substantially all of the stipulated purchase price for each truck.

The nonwaiver clause in the contracts clearly states that plaintiff's rights are cumulative and not alternative. Plaintiff's right to repossess the trucks is set forth in the provision of the contracts relating to default. That provision also gives plaintiff the right to a reasonable sum as attorney's fees should legal proceedings be necessary to recover any "moneys due and to become due." However, plaintiff's right to recover any money in the event of default and repossession, is covered solely by the last clause of each contract, which is labeled "miscellaneous." That clause states in substance that the contract is irrevocable; that plaintiff's right to the aggregate of the monthly payments for the entire term shall not terminate upon repossession by it of the trucks; that plaintiff may within sixty days after repossession, sell or "re-lease" the trucks as it sees fit; that it shall apply any proceeds from such sale or "releasing" to the "lessee's" obligations under the contract; and, finally, that the liability of the "lessee" shall not be reduced by reason of any failure of plaintiff to sell or "re-let" within the sixty day period. Plaintiff contends that the "miscellaneous" clause in each contract is actually a provision for liquidated damages. We cannot accept plaintiff's contention. In *Giesecke v. Cullerton*, 280 Ill. 510, 513 (1917), our Supreme Court said:

This court has said more than once that no branch of the law is involved in more obscurity by contradictory decisions than whether a sum specified in an agreement to secure performance will be treated as liquidated damages or a penalty and that each case must depend upon its own peculiar and attendant circumstances, and that therefore generally rules of law on this subject are often of very little practical utility. While the intention of the parties must be taken into consideration, the language of the contract is not conclusive. The courts of this State, as well as in other jurisdictions, lean toward a construction which excludes the idea of liquidated damages and permits the parties to recover only the damages actually sustained. . . .

The peculiar and attendant circumstances of the instant case reveal that the construction of the "miscellaneous" clause now advanced by plaintiff would if accepted by this court, place plaintiff in a far more advantageous position than it would have occupied had the contracts been duly performed. Plaintiff has regained possession of its equipment, has reserved the right to re-lease or sell the equipment, and now seeks to hold defendants liable for the full amount of the payments to which the parties initially agreed by abstaining from such re-leasing or resale for a stipulated period after the default.

It is true that there are some authorities holding valid a provision in a conditional sale contract whereby the parties expressly agree that, upon default by the vendee, the vendor would be entitled to repossess the equipment and to recover the unpaid balance of the purchase price as liquidated damages. . . . In each of those cases the term "liquidated damages" was specifically set forth in the contract. In Illinois, even the use of the term "liquidated damages" does not conclusively determine whether a sum stipulated in a contract is actually a provision for liquidated damages or is, in effect, a penalty, which is merely a fixed sum intended by the parties as a security against the actual damages sustained. . . . However, the failure to use such language is a factor in determining whether or not the parties actually intended a liquidated damage provision. The contracts in the instant case are devoid of language even remotely suggesting that liquidated damages were within the contemplation of the parties under the terms of the contracts.

On the other hand, it is evident that the parties contemplated some liability on the part of either Facings, Inc. or Decker in the event of default. The contracts provide for "re-leasing" or sale by the lessor of the repossessed equipment with application of any proceeds so obtained to the liability of the lessee. In some jurisdictions repossession by the conditional vendor terminates the obligations of the vendee under the contract. . . . In others a provision allowing the conditional vendor to recover from the defaulting vendee the amount of any deficiency which may exist after an application of the proceeds of resale to the original debt has been held valid and enforceable. . . . In Illinois, repossession under a contract of conditional sale does not constitute a rescission of the contract. . . . The validity of a provision authorizing resale by the vendor has also been recognized in this State. . . .

We can only conclude that the contracts in the instant case provided for a penalty rather than liquidated damages. It was thus incumbent upon plaintiff to establish its actual damages. In light of the language pertaining to the "re-leasing" or sale of the equipment after repossession, we feel that evidence relating to the ultimate disposition of the trucks would be pertinent in establishing damages, for the plaintiff should stand in no better position as a result of this suit than it would have occupied had the contracts been fulfilled.

Nor do we find any merit in the counterclaims of the defendants. The rights and remedies of the parties must be determined from the terms of the contracts upon which this controversy centers. The record reveals a default in the payments for the month of June, 1955. The contracts provide for repossession by the plaintiff in the event of such default. For this reason alone we cannot probe the motives of the plaintiff in insisting upon the strict enforcement of a provision in the contracts which is clear and unambiguous on its face.

The judgment is reversed and the cause remanded for proceedings consistent with the views herein expressed.

Judgment reversed and cause remanded with directions.

REVIEW QUESTIONS

1. Brown, in Seattle, Washington, ordered a machine from the White Company in Detroit, Michigan. The contract stated that the machine was to be shipped F.O.B. Detroit. At the bottom of the sheet the note "we will deliver the machine to you in Seattle at our cost" was written in longhand and signed by White. En route between Detroit and Seattle the machine was destroyed in a cyclone. Whose machine was lost? Why?

2. Black bought an automatic machine from White to replace a machine which had previously required two men to operate. In selling the machine to Black, White pointed out the saving in the cost of two men's time. He also stated that "productive capacity will be doubled" with the new machine. Hourly production increased even more than double —1,100 pieces per hour against 500 pieces per hour previously. However, there was a problem involved. The machine seldom ran an hour without breaking down. Whenever it broke down, either one or two machine repair men would be called upon to fix it. After a month or so one machine repair man was ordered to stand by for breakdown whenever the machine was scheduled to run. Weekly production on the automatic machine is only slightly greater than previous weekly production on the hand operated machine. Black has charged White with fraud. Can he recover on this basis? Why or why not? Is he stuck with the machine? What defense does White have?

3. Describe four implied warranties.

4. Distinguish between conditional sale and chattel mortgage.

5. In *Arco Bag Co., Inc. v. Facings, Inc.,* why was the contract treated as a conditional sale rather than a lease? What would be the measure of damages consistent with the court's decision?

6. In *Allied Steel and Conveyors, Inc. v. Ford Motor Company,* outline the points made by the court in finding that there was a contract and then affirming the lower court decision.

20 AGENCY

There is a limit to the amount one person can do; he cannot be in two or more places at the same time. When duties and desired objectives become too numerous for a person to handle, they are usually delegated to others. This delegation of duties may take one of three forms: 1) employer-employee (sometimes called master-servant) relationship, 2) owner-independent contractor relationship, or 3) an agency.

In satisfying the normal requirements of his job, the engineer (whether he is a consultant or an employee) must act as agent for his employer at least part of the time. While he is thus engaged, his rights and liabilities are dictated by the law of agency.

The agent replaces his employer in dealing with other persons. Herein lies the distinction between the agency relationship and the employer-employee relationship. The agent is still an employee for many purposes, but special rights and duties are involved in agency. A lathe operator in a plant is an employee. Since he does not deal with other persons as a representative of his employer, he is not an agent.

An independent contractor agrees to produce a result. The intent of the parties and the degree of control exercised by the owner determine whether the relationship is that of owner-independent contractor or employer-employee. The degree of liability of the employer (or owner) is determined by the relationship he has created. He is liable for tortious injuries caused by his employees and for harm to them as such injuries may arise from their employment. On the other hand, his liability for injury to, or injury caused by, an independent contractor is extremely limited. The degree of control exercised by the employer is probably the main criterion in determining the relationship. There are many instances, particularly in workmen's compensation cases, where a supposed owner-independent contractor relationship was held to an employer-employee relationship because of the degree of control exercised by the employer (owner).

Black, a manufacturer, hires White as time-study man in Black's plant. In setting production standards and making methods changes, White is Black's employee. White is soon promoted to process engineer, in which capacity he is in charge of the installation of an automatic machine being purchased from Gray Automation. When White deals with Gray Automation and other outsiders, he becomes Black's agent. He fills a dual role, for while he is agent in dealing with others, he is still Black's employee in some of his duties as process engineer. In installing the machine, Gray Automation is an independent contractor unless an excessive degree of control is exercised by either Black or White.

Agency involves three people. The *principal* is the person who is represented by the agent, and is the source of the agent's authority. The *agent* is the person who represents his principal, acting in his place. *Third parties* are persons with whom the agent deals in the name of his principal.

Creation of Agency

The agency relationship may be created in any of four ways: by agreement, by ratification, by estoppel, or by necessity. The responsibility and authority of the agent is a little different under each circumstance.

AGREEMENT.   In agency by agreement, both parties must intend to create a relationship which amounts to agency. The parties may not consider the relationship to be agency when they enter into it—but if the result amounts to an agency, it will be so construed.

The means used by the parties to express their intentions to form an agency ordinarily is unimportant as long as the ideas are exchanged. An agency contract is much the same as any other contract in this respect. The intent may be either expressed or implied.

The agency agreement is not necessarily a contract, but it usually is. A contract requires consideration, but a simple agreement may create a valid gratuitous agency. Black owns a truck. White does not, Black, without promise of compensation, agrees to transport a machine for White from a freight depot to a machine shop across town. In doing this he must deal with others. Even though Black is to be paid nothing for his efforts, his actions are controlled by White when Black picks up, transports, and unloads the machine. An agency was formed.

An agreement to act as agent for another ordinarily may be either oral or written. However, for certain purposes a written or a sealed instrument may be required. Where the instrument to which the principal is to be bound requires a seal, the agent's authority must be in writing and sealed. Probably the most frequently used form of this is the power of attorney which constitutes the agent an attorney-in-fact for his principal. Where the nature of a transaction is such as to require a public recording of it, any powers of attorney involved are also recorded.

Another form of written agency is the corporate proxy. By the use of a proxy, a stockholder appoints some particular person to act for him in voting his shares of stock in a particular way.

RATIFICATION.   Ratification cures the defect of lack of authority. If a person contracts with another as an agent when he really has no authority to do so, the person for whom he purports to act is not bound to the contract. Much the same is true if an actual agent exceeds the authority given him by his principal. In either of these circumstances the principal may, if he wishes, agree to be bound by the terms of the contract. Such ratification is retroactive—the time of entering into the contract goes back to the time when it was made. The effect of ratification is the same as though the principal had previously retained an agent to act in that particular manner for him. Black hires White as a salesman to sell the company's products. In his travels White finds a buyer, Gray, for a used milling machine which Black has wanted to sell for some time. White, without delay, contracts in Black's name to sell the machine to Gray. If Black no longer wishes to part with the machine or, possibly, has contracted to sell it to another, he will not be bound to the agreement with Gray. If Black does not ratify, White will be personally liable for any harm to Gray resulting from the contract. If he does ratify, Black will be held to the contract just as though White had been given specific orders to sell the machine. The fact that White did not have authority to sell the machine does not allow Black to ratify a portion of the contract. Black must ratify all or nothing. Gray is not bound to the agreement until Black ratifies. If he finds that White acted without authority, he may withdraw before Black's ratification.

There are four requirements for a valid ratification: 1) there must be a principal in existence when the supposed agent acts. A corporation, for instance, cannot make a binding ratification of contracts made in the corporation's name before it was formed. New contracts will be required if the corporation is to be bound; 2) the person acting without authority must act as an agent. If he acts for himself, subsequent ratification by another will not create enforceable obligations between the third party and an outsider. If an agent of an undisclosed principal exceeds his authority, later ratification by his principal will not cure the defect; 3) the principal must be aware of the facts when he ratifies. A principal's actions which would imply ratification have little effect unless the principal knows what he is doing. Of course, if the principal does not investigate the details when he has a duty to do so, his negligence may be interpreted so as to give him implied knowledge; and 4) the principal must intend to ratify. Intent and ratification may be interpreted from the principal's actions after he obtains knowledge of the transaction. If he does nothing after being informed of the transaction, ratification could be implied from his inaction.

ESTOPPEL. Agency by *estoppel* arises where one person appears to have authority to act for another and, despite lack of real authority, does act in the name of the other. Apparent authority is the key to the concept. If the principal acts in such a way that another person appears to be his agent (thus, in effect, deceiving the third party), he is then estopped from denying that the other person is his agent. The third party must, of course, have dealt with the supposed agent because of the principal's actions if he is to prove agency by estoppel.

NECESSITY. Agency by necessity occurs as a result of an emergency. It is a rather rare happening. If, in order to save his employer from a disaster of some sort, an employee must deal with others without an opportunity to obtain authorization, an agency by necessity is created.

Where a wife binds her husband to pay for necessaries (or where a dependent binds his guardian), agency is sometimes said to exist. The more common holding, though, is that the husband (or guardian) has a duty of support, and binding him to such contracts is a result of this duty rather than agency.

Competency of Parties

Since, in agency, the principal is the party to be bound to a third party, he must be competent to contract. The agent may be a gray-haired man of sixty, but if his principal is a minor, the contract is voidable at the minor's option. From this there arises a practical desirability of investigating the principal before contracting with him. Not only could an incompetent principal avoid a contract made by his agent for him, but he might also avoid his contract with his agent.

Though competency of the principal is of major concern to those dealing with him, competency of the agent is not. Almost anyone may be agent; it is the principal who is bound. A minor agent contracting with a third party would bind his adult principal to the contract.

Agent's Authority

The agent's *authority* comes from his principal. It consists of express orders or directions given to him by his principal in addition to authority which may reasonably be implied. Implied authority is based on previous dealings between the parties, or local or trade customs. If none of these control the situation, the extent of implied authority is that which is necessary to accomplish the purpose of the agency.

If the agent contracts beyond his authority, his principal is not bound.

From this there is an obvious burden upon the third party to determine whether the agent has authority to contract. The third party is safe in dealing with the agent if he can obtain evidence of the agent's mission. Implied authority necessary to the accomplishment of the purpose is included despite the principal's instructions to his agent to the contrary. Black is a buyer for the White Manufacturing Company. His present assignment is to buy a six-station automatic indexing table, drive, and base, to be used in machining small die castings. He has been specifically told not to buy any tooling with the machine. Nevertheless, he contracts with Gray for a machine with tooling which, he is told, may be reworked for the die castings. The contract for the machine and the tooling will be binding. Black's specific orders to buy the machine might well be taken to imply that he also had a right to purchase tooling for it. If Gray knew of Black's assignment, he would not have a duty to go further and determine any unusual restrictions which might have been imposed on Black.

A third type of agent's authority is known as *apparent authority*. The reasoning of apparent authority runs so close to that of agency by estoppel as to make the two nearly indistinguishable. By some act or negligence on the part of the principal an agent is either clothed with more authority than he really has been given, or one who is not an agent is made to appear as though he were.

An agent is chosen for his particular capabilities and fidelity. He is the one in whom the principal places his trust. The agent cannot, therefore, by his act alone delegate his authority to another. If the agent hires a sub-agent, the principal has no liability to the sub-agent for wages or other benefits and is not liable for the sub-agent's acts. The rule is not without exception; if part of the agent's express or implied task is hiring others for his principal, those so hired work for the principal.

Agent's Duties

Agency is a fiduciary relationship—the principal's trust and the loyalty of the agent are implied. The law enforces these qualities in the relationship; breach of them is a cause of action. The agent is personally liable for the results of his disloyalty.

OBEDIENCE.   An agent owes his principal a duty of strict obedience in all ordinary circumstances. Disobedience is a breach of the agency agreement. It is not the agent's function to question or judge the wisdom of his principal's orders—it is his function to do everything in his power to obey them. Of course, when the principal outlines to his agent a general purpose to be accomplished, the agent may be required to use judgment and discretion in working out the details. Still, the purpose to be accomplished is not open to question. Direction by the principal is implicit even in a gratuitous agency, once the agent has begun his performance.

Strict obedience is limited to lawful and reasonable possibility. The agent need not, of course, follow instructions of an unlawful nature. Neither would he be expected to accomplish an impossibility. In an emergency situation an agent may have the right to fail to obey instructions strictly. The reasoning here is the same as that in authority of necessity; if the agent's failure to follow instructions will save his principal from disaster, his right to disobey is apparent.

CARE AND SKILL. The agency relationship normally implies that the agent will use ordinary care and skill in carrying out his duties. The test of whether or not he has done so is the test of the reasonably prudent man. Has the agent acted as a reasonably prudent person would be expected to act in like circumstances? Negligence in following the principal's orders may make the agent liable for payments to him; in addition, he may have to pay for losses suffered by the principal which could be reasonably anticipated from failure to follow the instructions properly.

If the agent professes to be a specialist, e.g., a consultant in some professional field, the standard of skill expected of him is that which is normally attributed to such a person. The standard is the same whether the person really is such a specialist or not; failure to perform as a specialist would be expected to perform makes the agent liable. Black, a manufacturer, hires White—an engineering consultant on conveyors—to design, recommend, and oversee the installation of a monorail conveyor system in his plant. If, because of very poor planning and design, the conveyor must be removed shortly after its installation, Black may have an action available against White. If Black's action is to be successful, he *must* prove (usually by expert testimony) that anyone possessing the knowledge and skill normally possessed by an engineering consultant specializing in conveyors would have made a more effective design. Damages could run as high as the total of the consultant's fee plus the cost of the improper installation and the cost of its removal.

TO ACT FOR ONE PRINCIPAL. An agent has a duty to act for and accept compensation from only one principal. He could not, for instance, reasonably represent both buyer and seller in a sales contract. The buyer's interest and the seller's interest are at opposite poles—each desires to get the best possible deal for himself. If the agent represents more than one party to a contract, the transaction is voidable at the option of either principal.

The agent is relieved of his responsibility to act for only one party if the parties are told of the multiple relationships and acquiesce. An agent's interest which is adverse to his principal's interests is allowable if the principal knows of the interest and continues the relationship in spite of it.

Kickbacks or secret commissions from third parties are against public policy. The agent's compensation should come from his principal.

If the agent acquires in his own name property which should go to his principal, the agent will be deemed to be holding the property as bailee. Similarly, the agent cannot contract with himself as the third party without his principal's consent. To do so gives the principal the right to avoid the transaction at his option.

ACCOUNTING.   The agent has a duty to account for all money or property involved in agency transactions. Further, the principal's property must be kept separate from the agent's property. If commingled money or property belonging to both principal and agent, is lost, the agent must make good the principal's loss. If the property were kept separate and the loss occurred through no fault of the agent, only the principal would lose.

The agent has no right to use the principal's property as his own without consent to do so. Using property of another without his consent is the same in agency as elsewhere—it is conversion.

Closely akin to the agent's duty to account to his principal for money or property is the agent's duty to report information to his principal. Generally, notification to an agent has the same effect as notice to his principal. In either case the principal is charged with possession of the knowledge.

LOYALTY.   The essence of agency is the identity of the agent with his principal's purpose. The agent is often in position to gain personally from information acquired by him. To use the information so as to add to the agent's personal fortune is an act of disloyalty. Recovery by the principal for such misuse of information is possible.

Principal's Duties

Most agency agreements are contractual in nature, and both parties have a duty to live up to their agreement. The principal does not, however, have to pay for disloyal service. Neither will he have to pay if payment is made contingent upon the agent's success (as commissions for sales) unless the agent's efforts meet with success.

PAYMENT.   In the usual agency contract the means and amount of payment are stipulated. If such a stipulation is not made, though, the agent is entitled to reasonable payment for his services. If principal and agent are not close friends or relatives and there is no other reason to assume that the agent acted for nothing, an unliquidated obligation of payment by the principal to the agent exists. A gratuitous agency is, of course, an exception to this.

Payment of an agent on a commission basis presents some special problems. When has the agent earned his commission? Does the principal have to pay if he deals directly with the third party? What happens if the principal accepts an order through his agent to sell to a third party and then principal and third party agree to disagree? Such problems arise not only in agencies to sell a company's products; they are also common in real estate and other agencies.

Generally, barring agreement to the contrary, the agent has performed and is entitled to his commission when he has found a buyer and has contracted with him for the principal. A real estate agent (or broker) ordinarily does not have the power to contract for his principal. Therefore, it is only necessary that the real estate agent find a buyer ready, willing, and able to buy the property to be sold at the owner's price. With these conditions satisfied, the principal has an obligation to pay the agent his agreed commission.

If, after the agent has performed his obligation, the principal and the third party do not complete the transaction, the principal is still bound to pay his agent. It matters not that the principal will no longer profit by the transaction.

The agency agreement will often state whether a commission is to be paid to the agent if principal and third party deal directly. An *exclusive agency* for the sale of real estate, for instance, requires that the real estate agent be paid his commission regardless of who sells the realty. Without the exclusive agency feature, the owner's sale of the realty to another would create no obligation to pay the agent. The same is generally true of an agent who sells a product. If the sale is made without his services he has done nothing to earn a commission and is not entitled to it.

EXPENSES.   The principal is legally bound to pay his agent's expenses. To constitute an obligation of the principal the expenses must, of course, be connected to the purpose of the agency. Thus, cost of travel, meals, and overnight hotel or motel accommodations connected with an agent's trip to sell his principal's product should be paid by the principal. Similar costs incurred by the agent on a pleasure trip with his family ordinarily would not be covered by the principal.

INDEMNITY.   While the agent has a duty to follow his principal's orders, the principal also has a duty to indemnify the agent if the result injures someone and the agent has to pay for the injury. Of course, the agent is not required to perform unlawful acts; he is prohibited in the same manner as anyone else from committing a crime. If, though, a tort or crime is committed by the agent innocently following his principal's instructions, the principal is liable for the result. Both principal and agent are liable to the third party for acts committed out of and in the course of the agent's employment; but if the agent has to pay, he can recover from his principal. The agent alone is responsible for acts which are not connected with his employment.

Black is an agent of the White Machinery Company. His function is to answer customers' complaints and thus make the sales of the machines permanent. He is a trouble-shooter. As such, he is entitled to compensation according to his agreement with the White Machinery Company. He is also entitled to payment for legitimate expenses in connection with his job. If, while instructing someone in the proper use of a machine, an injury should occur, White Machinery Company would be liable.

Third Party Rights and Duties

So far we have considered the rights and liabilities of two of the agency parties—the principal and the agent. But there is another party from whose standpoint agency should be considered. The third party has a stake in the relationship. Normally, an agent's transactions bind his principal and a third party—but are there instances when one or neither party would be bound? Must the third party rely on all that the agent tells him? These and other questions concern the third party.

DUTY TO QUESTION AGENT'S AUTHORITY.   We have noted that the agent has the authority given him by his principal. He also has authority common to other agencies of a similar nature. The third party is safe in relying upon the agent's authority to this extent once he has established that he is dealing with an agent of an existing principal. If the third party knows nothing of either principal or agent from previous contacts, he is well advised to determine by some objective means if the principal and the agency relationship actually exist. Obviously, if the principal is non-existent or the principal exists but there is no agency, the third party may part with something of value in good faith and get nothing for it; a person cannot be bound by someone's merely claiming to be his agent. Under such circumstances the third party would be left with an action against the agent only and it is likely that he would be hard to find.

AGENT'S RIGHT TO COLLECT.   Does the agent have the right to collect from a third party? Usually he does not, barring specific authority, or trade or local practice to the contrary. Ordinarily, the third party must give his consideration directly to the principal. Black represents the White Manufacturing Company. He obtains an order from Gray for a quantity of his principal's product and receives part payment for the goods. Black is not seen again locally. The one who is to stand the loss of the part payment depends upon whether Black had express or implied authority to receive payment. If no such authority can be found, Gray is the loser to the extent of the payment. The situation would be different if Black had brought the goods along with him—under this circumstance the right to collect can be implied.

Somewhat akin to the agent's authority to receive payment is his authority to sign a negotiable instrument in his principal's name. Authority to do this must be expressly given to have binding effect.

TRANSACTIONS BINDING AGENT.   In the normal course of affairs the third party has no action available against the agent in a transaction. If the agent has acted within the scope of his express and implied authority, it is the principal and the third party who are bound. It is possible, though, for an agent to act as surety for his principal; or he may contract with the third party in such a way that it is he, rather than his principal, who is to be bound. Ordinarily an agent will agree in a transaction in such a manner that he indicates his principal and the fact that he is agent for the principal. If the agent however, merely agrees in his own name or signs as "Black, agent," indicating no principal, he may be held personally liable.

TORT. If, while in the course of his principal's business, the agent commits a tort against the third party, the third party may charge either the agent or principal with the act. Successful action against the agent then gives the agent a right to recover from his principal. An exception to this appears to exist where the principal is a minor and the agent an adult—here the agent must stand the loss.

If the third party, without cause, brings about the discharge of the agent, he has committed a tort. In fact, the rule is more general than this—anyone who maliciously causes another to lose an employment relationship has committed a tort and an action will lie against him.

Undisclosed Principal

Normally the third party is aware that he is dealing with an agent of a known principal. Such is not always the case, though. The agent may not reveal that he is working for any principal, thus allowing the third party to assume that he is dealing directly with the party to be bound. Or the agent may reveal that he represents another without naming his principal (partially disclosed principal).

In either case where the principal has not been disclosed to the third party, the third party may elect to hold either principal or agent to the contract. If the third party elects to hold the agent, and the agent has acted within the scope of his authority, the agent has a right to be indemnified by his principal. Either the principal or the agent may hold the third party to the transaction, but the principal's right to do so is superior to the agent's.

The enforceability of undisclosed principal transactions appears to be counter to the concept that a contract must be entered into voluntarily and intentionally by the parties. However, the legality and enforceability of such contracts is well established. It is, in effect, an exception to the general rule of contracts.

An undisclosed principal contract will not be enforced where the third party, either expressly or by implication, makes clear his intent to deal exclusively with the agent. White Manufacturing Company wishes to expand its operation into another section of the country. It retains Black to purchase land for the expansion without revealing the company's name. (Such purchases are sometimes undertaken to keep local land prices from soaring.) Black contracts with Gray to buy 200 acres of suitable land. Gray can elect to hold Black to the contract or, when the principal is revealed, hold the White Manufacturing Company. Gray is bound to the contract unless he has either expressed or implied his intent to deal exclusively with Black. If Black, under questioning by Gray, had denied the existence of a principal, this would be grounds for fraud, making the contract voidable at Gray's election.

Termination

The rules for winding up an agency agreement are about the same as those for winding up any employment agreement, except that a third party must be considered. The usual contract of employment of a so-called white-collar employee is oral and terminable at the option of either employer or employee. If an engineer or a sales agent or an accountant engaged in such employment decides to leave, it is only necessary to so inform the employer, settle the accounts, and leave. The employer's right to terminate such an agreement is similar. Not all agency contracts are of this simple form, though, and they are not always terminated in this fashion.

BY LAW. Death, insanity, or bankruptcy of either principal or agent automatically terminates an agency relationship. Death or insanity of the principal is effective even though the agent is not aware of the event—that is, if the agent deals with another following the death or insanity of his principal, but before the agent is informed, the transaction is not binding.

If the agency has been created for a specific purpose, destruction of an essential to the accomplishment of the purpose ends the agency. Similarly, passage of a law which makes the purpose of the agency unlawful terminates the agency.

BY ACTS OF THE PARTIES. Agencies created to accomplish a specific purpose or to last for a stated time are generally not terminable at the option of the parties without possible repercussions. If an agency is created to accomplish a particular purpose, it ends when the purpose is accomplished. If a time limit for the agency is set, it ends when the time runs out.

Where an agency has been created for a purpose or to last a certain time, neither the principal nor the agent may unilaterally terminate the agency without giving the other a right of legal action. Both parties may, of course, agree to disagree before the contract is finished. Revocation of the agency by the principal terminates the agency; but if it is done without just cause or agreement, the principal is likely to be held liable for payment to his former agent for the remainder of the term for which the agency was to run. Similarly, renunciation of the principal by the agent ends the agency, but may allow recovery by the principal. As indicated earlier, disloyalty by the agent would be just cause for early termination by the principal. In any case, termination by a unilateral act of either principal or agent does not become effective until the other party is informed of it.

AGENCY WITH AN INTEREST.   If the agent has an interest in the subject matter of the agency, the relationship cannot be terminated by an act of the principal. More is meant by the term *interest* than just the agreed compensation for the agent's services. Essentially, it means part ownership or an equity in the subject matter. The result here is more in the form of a partnership venture in most instances; one partner could not very well fire another.

NOTICE.   When an agency is terminated, third parties should be notified. If the agency is terminated by law, notification is considered to have taken place, since death, insanity, or bankruptcy would be a matter of public record. When termination takes place by acts of the parties, though, there is a particular necessity to inform those who have dealt with the agent. If, in ignorance of the dissolution of the agency, a third party deals with an agent as he has dealt with him before, the principal will be bound. The reason for this is the agent's apparent authority to act for the principal. Notification to those who have previously dealt with the agent prevents this, but such notification is not effective until the third persons receive it. Thus, a notice in a newspaper or trade journal would not be effective notification to third persons in previous dealings.

Partnerships

Each partner in an enterprise is an agent for it. Generally, the rules of agency apply to partnerships. As long as the transaction involved is in the normal course of business of the partnership, agreement by one partner binds all partners to the contract. Transactions beyond the normal scope of the partnership require approval of all the partners. Just as notice given to an agent is the virtual equivalent of notice given to the principal, notice given to any partner is also notice to the partnership.

VAUX v. HAMILTON

103 NW 2d 291 North Dakota (May 26, 1960)

STRUTZ, Judge.

The two actions involved in this litigation arose out of a collision of an automobile driven by the plaintiff Vaux, in which the plaintiff Nixon was a passenger, and a Cadillac automobile driven by the defendant Dorothy Hamilton which carried the dealer's license of the defendant Day's Auto Brokers, Inc. The accident occurred just west of Jamestown, North Dakota, on U. S. Highway No. 10.

Both actions are against the same defendants and involve the same facts. The cases were consolidated for trial in the district court of Stutsman County, and both cases were argued together on appeal. Both appeals will be considered in one opinion.

The defendant Day's Auto Brokers, Inc., is a foreign corporation engaged in the business of selling used cars in the city of Seattle, Washington. Through its agent, DeLain Belch, the defendant purchased the Cadillac automobile involved in this litigation in the Detroit area. The employee purchasing the car attached the defendant's dealer's license to the car after its purchase and then left it with the Midwest Auto Delivery for delivery to the defendant's place of business in Seattle. The delivery service advertised for a driver to deliver the automobile to Seattle, and the advertisement was answered by the defendant Ruby Cuthbert. The agreement under which she was to drive the car to the defendant's place of business in Seattle provided that all gas and oil and other expenses be paid by the driver. While the car was being so driven to Seattle, it was involved in a collision just west of Jamestown resulting in the litigation now before the court.

The plaintiffs alleged in their respective complaints that the defendant Cuthbert was the agent of the defendant Day's Auto Brokers, Inc., in delivering the car. This was denied by the defendant Day's Auto Brokers, Inc. Verdicts were returned by the jury in favor of both of the plaintiffs and against the defendant Day's Auto Brokers, Inc., and the defendant Dorothy Hamilton, who was driving the car at the time of the collision. The defendant Day's Auto Brokers, Inc., has appealed from the judgments and from orders denying its motion for judgment notwithstanding the verdict or, in the alternative, for a new trial.

The burden of establishing agency rests on the party alleging it, as respects the master's liability for negligence of the alleged servant. . . .

Thus, where existence of agency is denied, the burden of proving agency is on the party asserting its existence.

The evidence as to the existence of agency in this case, relied on by the plaintiffs, consists of the deposition of Henry Freymueller, the president of defendant Day's Auto Brokers, Inc. He testified, on cross-examination by the plaintiffs, that the defendant company obtained the automobile in question by having its employee, DeLain Belch, purchase it and then deliver it to the drive-away firm for shipment after attaching defendant's "in-transit" dealer's license; that the defendant was to pay to Midwest Auto Delivery a flat fee to deliver the said automobile. Freymueller further testified:

Well, we pay them to get the car out here. The discretion of how they deliver it is up to them.

There was the further evidence of the defendant Ruby Cuthbert, the girl who answered an ad of Midwest Auto Delivery, advertising for a driver to deliver a car to Seattle. She stated that she had seen the advertisement of Midwest Auto Delivery in her local paper; that she answered the advertisement and agreed to drive the car in question to Seattle; that she did not know who owned the automobile but that it had a Washington dealer's license on it. She then said:

It is quite the thing, they advertise in newspapers in Ontario anyone who wants to go to the West Coast, it is not employment, it is a case if you go to the West Coast it is a cheap way to go, and they—. . . .

She further stated that she and her two companions, the defendants Dorothy Hamilton and Margaret Jack, were to pay the oil and gas and their own expenses incurred while taking the automobile to Seattle.

On this evidence the jury found the defendant Hamilton to be the agent of defendant Day's Auto Brokers, Inc.

In reviewing the sufficiency of the evidence on appeal from the judgment and from an order denying motion for judgment notwithstanding the verdict or for a new trial, this court will view the evidence in the light most favorable to the verdict. . . .

The record is silent as to whether this was the first occasion on which the defendant Day's Auto Brokers, Inc., had had the Midwest Auto Delivery deliver an automobile for it. While there is evidence that the defendant Day's Auto Brokers, Inc., was in fact the owner of the automobile involved in the collision, ownership of the automobile alone does not establish or prove agency. Neither is ownership alone sufficient to impose liability upon the owner of a car because of the negligence of another who is permitted to use it. . . .

It is true that defendant Cuthbert was performing an act in the interest of defendant Day's Auto Brokers, Inc., but acts of the alleged agent cannot establish agency without evidence showing that the alleged master had knowledge thereof or assented thereto. . . .

In this case, the testimony was undisputed that the defendant Day's Auto Brokers, Inc., did not even know of the existence of the three girls who were delivering the automobile until after the accident had occurred.

The limited evidence presented to the jury on this question is more indicative of a relationship of independent contractor than of master and servant. Here, Midwest Auto Delivery was hired for one purpose, namely, to deliver the car to Seattle, and was responsible only for that result; it could accomplish that result in its own way. The record fails to disclose any right of control by defendant Day's Auto Brokers, Inc., over details as to how that result was to be accomplished. Such evidence may be available, however, on a new trial. While, under the present state of the record, on appeal from the judgment and from the order denying the motion for judgment notwithstanding the verdict or for a new trial, there is a failure to sustain the allegations of the complaints as to agency, this court need not order judgment for the defendant but will order a new trial when it appears that the defects may be remedied upon a new trial. . . .

Other specifications of error alleged by the defendant relate largely to instructions given by the court, or instructions refused by the court, relating to matters of agency, independent contractors, and liability of the owner of a vehicle for negligence of one permitted to use it for the user's own purposes. Since a new trial in these cases must be granted and, in view of what we have said above, it is unlikely that these questions will arise upon a new trial, we do not now consider them.

However, one specification of error deals with a matter which may well arise on the retrial of these actions. The trial court overruled an objection by the defendant to the following question put by the plaintiffs to a medical expert, testifying on behalf of the plaintiffs, as to the future pain and suffering of one of the plaintiffs:

> Doctor, can you state with a reasonable degree of medical certainty that there is a distinct possibility that this might happen?

An objection that the question was leading, suggestive, speculative, and conjectural was overruled.

The question in the form in which it was asked was clearly objectionable. While there are exceptions to the general rule that an opinion of a witness may not be received in evidence and although, under certain circumstances, the opinion of an expert is admissible, testimony which consists of no more than a mere guess of the witness is not admissible. Such testimony must be as to a definite probability and must not involve, to an excessive degree, the element of speculation or conjecture. The question directed to the medical expert in this case was calling for a mere guess on the part of the doctor "that there is a distinct possibility that this might happen."

Webster defines "possibility" as "the character, state, or fact of being possible, or that which may be conceivable." Thus, even if an event might occur only once in ten thousand times, it still is within the realm of possibility, though very improbable.

A medical expert is qualified to express an opinion to a medical certainty, or based on medical probabilities only, but not an opinion based on mere possibilities. . . .

For the reasons stated, the orders denying motion for new trial in the above actions are reversed, and new trials are granted.

IDZIK v. REDDICK

103 NW 2d 300 Wisconsin (June 7, 1960)

DIETERICH, Justice.

On or about February 19, 1954, the plaintiff answered the following ad contained in the Portage Daily Register and Democrat under the heading of "business opportunity;"

> Man & Wife desiring to increase their income. You can own a non-competitive spare-time business with a small investment—then with the assistance of a substantial national organization, expand to a full-time, permanent, dignified business within one year.
>
> You will operate this business from your home without employees or office expense.
>
> The couple selected in your area would perform an important function in the rapidly growing national program of this company. To qualify you must have a character and credit reputation that bears rigid investigation and be willing to make

a fully-secured investment of $1,250 to $4,000. This is not a vending operation, but a good sound business that is going nationally. In reply please state address and phone number. Write P.O. Box 11, Zone 13, Wauwatosa, Wisconsin.

The ad was placed in the paper by Reddick with the knowledge and consent of Hastings. The ad was paid for by Hastings.

The defendant Reddick personally called upon the plaintiff at his home and presented his business card upon which was printed "Hastings Distributing Company, 6100 West Bluemound Road, Milwaukee, Wisconsin . . . E. Lyle Reddick, state supervisor. . . ." The testimony discloses that Reddick stated that he represented Hastings Distributing Company.

On March 15, 1954, Reddick repeated in substance the representations contained in the newspaper ad,—if the plaintiff purchased the "Minut-Bun Machines," Reddick would see to it that all of the machines were placed in retail establishments; the business operation was to be nationally advertised; the plaintiff's investment was secured by money back guarantee; the plaintiff was to be given an exclusive area franchise, this agreement to be subsequently reduced to writing by an attorney. None of the machines were placed in retail establishments by or through either of the defendants. There was no advertising of the business operation whatever, and no written exclusive area franchise was ever given to the plaintiff. The plaintiff's source of profit was the difference between his cost of the sandwich materials and the retail selling price to establishments in which the machines were placed.

On March 15, 1954, the defendant Reddick wrote up the order for five Minut-Bun Machines. This was a printed order entitled "Hastings Distributing Company since 1932," order No. 3665, and disclosed that the price was $497.50 upon which there was paid $150, leaving a balance of $347.50 due to be paid on delivery of the machines.

The down payment in the amount of $150 under purchase order No. 3665 was by check dated March 15, 1954, made payable to E. Lyle Reddick and cashed on March 16, 1954, by Reddick.

Plaintiff received a letter dated March 16, 1954, from defendant S. J. Hastings, which reads as follows:

Thank you for your order of five Minut-Bun Machines and the deposit of $150, paid to our independent distributor Mr. Reddick. He informs me that he will deliver the machines and collect the balance due of $347.50 within the next few days.

We welcome you in the happy Minut-Bun products family and wish you much success. You are now a Minut-Bun distributor and will be entitled to buy your meats direct from the packer at wholesale prices. Minut-Bun meats products is a national operation. You will secure the highest quality prepared meats ready to serve at the lowest possible prices. I could go on and on explaining the advantages of being associated with a nation wide operation of this kind but space is limited.

Thank you again for the confidence you have placed in our products, and assuring you with some effort on your part you will be very successful.

On March 29, 1954, plaintiff purchased five more Minut-Bun Machines at the same price and gave Reddick another check for $150. Plaintiff made out a check to Hastings Distributing Company dated March 30, 1954, in the sum of $413.30. This check was cashed by Hastings on April 5, 1954.

Plaintiff received the following letter from S. J. Hastings dated May 14, 1954:

Thank you for the order given our independent distributor, Mr. Reddick for five more Minut-Bun Bars.

Please advise by return mail if we should ship these machines C.O.D. or if you are mailing us a check for the balance of $347.50.

I wish you much success in your Minut-Bun operations and if we can be of any assistance to you, please write.

On May 19, 1954, plaintiff made out another check to Hastings Distributing Company in the sum of $347.50, and it was cashed by Hastings on May 24, 1954. On the same date plaintiff sent the following letter to Mr. Hastings:

Enclosed find check for $347.50, representing balance of payment for five Minut-Bun Bars.

Please note my address is now 1119 West Wisconsin street, Portage. . . .

Please advise Mr. Reddick of this shipment as I would like these machines and those previously purchased to be located as soon as possible.

The record discloses that the defendant Hastings testified that he had not used the order blank for a number of years; and that the order blank exhibited by the plaintiff was used only as scratch pads and had not been used in his business at any time during February, March and April, 1954. He also testified on direct examination that he was sure the defendant Reddick used a standard sales order book which could be secured at any stationery house. However, on an adverse examination in another action pending in the civil court, the defendant Hastings testified that an order blank identical to plaintiff's order No. 3665, dated March 15, 1954, was a regular purchase order form used by the Hastings Distributing Company. This was order No. 3670 and was introduced into evidence in this case.

The record further discloses that the plaintiff made numerous telephone calls to the Hastings Distributing Company, asked for and spoke to the defendant Reddick; and although the defendant Hastings denied that defendant Reddick had his office at the Hastings Distributing Company, he admitted that defendant Reddick received telephone calls there.

In July, 1954, Idzik telephoned the defendant Hastings and demanded that the sales of the ten machines be rescinded and his money returned to him in accordance with the money back guarantee. The defendant Hastings denied responsibility for the sales, representations or guarantee and refused to accede to the plaintiff's demand.

The sole issue in this case resolves itself into not one of agency, but one of apparent authority of the agent.

In *McDermott v. Jackson*, 1897, 97 Wis. 64, 72, 72 NW 375, 378, this court said:

If a principal so conducts his business, either through negligence or otherwise, as to lead the public to believe that his agent possesses authority to contract in the name of the principal, such principal is bound by the acts of such agent, within the scope of his apparent authority, in so contracting with any person who, upon the faith of such holding out, believes, and has reasonable ground to believe, that the agent has such authority, and in good faith deals with him, even though such agent have express secret instructions to the contrary. . . . Did the third person, because of appearances for which the principal was responsible, believe, and have reasonable ground to believe, that the agent possessed power to act for the principal in the

articular transaction? If such third person was, in the exercise of reasonable pru-
ence, justified in believing that the agent possessed the necessary authority, then
he principal is responsible to such third person the same as if the agent possessed all
he power he assumed to possess. . . .

The contention of the defendant Hastings is that Reddick was not his agent,
hat Reddick had no authority to hold himself out as an agent or a representa-
ive of the Hastings Company, and that Hastings did not commit any act which
vould lead a reasonable man to believe that Reddick was his agent.

In this case Hastings offered as proof an unexecuted contract dated April 12,
954, which reads in part as follows:

It is understood that you are to make all your contracts with your customers
nd distributors and that all such contracts are to be made upon your own responsi-
)ility and that I am in no way to be responsible for performance of any contract
nade between you and any of your customers or distributors.

It is agreed that you are to pay for all machines upon delivery to your customers
nd that the proceeds received from sale of machines is to be my property and is to
)e paid to me within twenty-four hours after date of delivery to your customer.

We agree with the trial court's determination that this document dated after
he transaction for Minut-Bun Machines is not relevant to establish an inde-
)endent contractor relationship in March of 1954.

The evidence in this case establishes that S. J. Hastings d/b/a/ Hastings
Distributing Company conducted his business in such a manner that the plain-
:iff, Donald Idzik, in the exercise of reasonable prudence was justified in be-
.ieving and had reasonable ground to believe that Reddick possessed the necessary power and authority as agent of the Hastings Distributing Company to
enter into the oral contract.

Every writing incidental to the transaction had the name of Hastings Distributing Company imprinted thereon. The business card of the defendant
Reddick identified him as a state supervisor for Hastings Distributing Company.
This card was the same in color, design, and format as the business cards used
by the defendant Hastings. All of the invoices and orders were the printed
forms of Hastings Distributing Company. All of the shipping invoices designated
Hastings Distributing Company as the shipper. Two payments were made by
check directly to the defendant Hastings Distributing Company, a second one
only after a written demand for payment had been made on the plaintiff by
the defendant Hastings. The telephone calls had been made direct to Hastings
Distributing Company and the plaintiff spoke to Reddick at the Hastings Distributing Company and Hastings admitted that Reddick received the telephone
calls at his company.

There was no attempt on the part of Hastings to inform the plaintiff that the
defendant Reddick was not his authorized agent except in two letters directed
to the plaintiff wherein the defendant Hastings referred to the defendant Reddick as an independent distributor. In one letter the defendant Hastings referred to the defendant Reddick as an independent distributor, but in the same
letter and on the same letterhead demanded that the plaintiff make payment
of the balance due directly to Hastings Distributing Company.

The judgment of the trial court is affirmed.

Judgment affirmed.

REVIEW QUESTIONS

1. Identify the following persons as agents, employees, or independent contractors according to the usual duties involved in their work:
   a. Research chemist working for chemical company.
   b. Free-lance consulting engineer in the labor relations field.
   c. T.V. repair man for local department store—on house call.
   d. Trouble-shooter for steel company (keeps steel sold to customers by recommending proper treatment of a particular heat of steel).
   e. Engineering vice-president for local company.
   f. Dentist.

2. How may the agency relationship be created?

3. Brown is a process engineer for White Manufacturing Company and is about to recommend the purchase of certain machinery and equipment. The Green Equipment Company is one prospective supplier. On a recent trip to the Green Company, Green offered Brown a new station wagon if Green was chosen as the equipment supplier. Brown has always considered himself to be quite ethical, but he is also human and the station wagon sounds tempting. Neglecting the ethical aspects of the situation, Brown is still faced with certain legal problems. What are Brown's rights if, after recommending Green as supplier, Green fails to produce the station wagon? What can happen to Brown if White Manufacturing Co. finds out about the deal?

4. Gray, engineer for Black, White and Company, was sent to observe an automation installation at a plant some 50 miles away. On the return trip he approached an intersection and applied his brakes. His car hit a patch of ice; as a result, he hit another car, injuring its occupants, both cars, and himself. Who is liable for injuries to the other car and its occupants? Who is liable for injury to Gray and Gray's car?

5. In the case of *Vaux v. Hamilton,* what is the relationship between Hamilton and Midwest Auto Delivery? What is the relationship between Midwest Auto Delivery and Day's Auto Brokers, Inc.? Could Midwest Auto Delivery be held liable for the injuries? Give your reasoning.

6. In *Idzik v. Reddick,* what evidence convinced the court of the existence of the agency relationship between Reddick and Hastings?

21
PATENTS

Everything we have in our civilization which distinguishes us from other forms of life results from man's creative efforts. Some of the most commonplace objects were marvels of invention only a few years back; and inventions keep coming at an ever-increasing pace.

Engineers often find themselves in fortunate positions to invent something or to improve upon inventions. They are particularly favored by training in science, natural selection, general temperament, and by the nature of engineering jobs for this endeavor. Inventions generally involve the application of scientific principles to practical problems with a practical solution as the objective. The similarity between invention and the training offered by engineering curricula seems quite obvious. Because of the engineer's training and talents he should be alert to the possibilities of making inventions, of patenting them, and of exploiting them.

Suppose that Mr. Black, an engineer, has just invented an entirely new type of internal combustion engine after many months of effort. The engine will run on the most inexpensive petroleum products and promises to have a longer life than even the best competitors. What should Black do to secure to himself the fruits of his creative efforts? Probably the best advice would be to direct Black to an expert on patents—a patent attorney or a patent agent. But even though the task of obtaining a patent is delegated to another, there is still considerable information which Black may find beneficial. What, for instance, may be patented? What is the nature of a patent? Who is entitled to it? What protection is afforded? What could prevent an inventor from getting a patent? How long will it take—what delays can be anticipated? This chapter represents an effort to answer these and a host of other questions which are likely to arise.

The Patent Right

One meaning of the word "patent" is open or disclosed, obvious or manifest. In a sense these terms could be applied to the right issued to

329

an inventor by the Patent Office. To obtain the protection afforded by a patent, the inventor must make a full and complete disclosure of hi invention. No material feature or component may be withheld. The revela tions must be such that a person skilled in the field could, by use of the patent, duplicate the thing patented.

The patent right is often called a contract between the government and the inventor. In consideration for complete revelation of the invention the government gives the inventor the right to *exclude others from* mak ing, using, or selling his invention. The right extends for seventeen years from the date of issue, after which the content of the patent becomes public property. It is worth noting that the patent right is the right to exclude others from making, using, or selling the invention—it is not the right to make, use, or sell it. The reason for this is to avoid conflict with state or other federal laws which might prohibit making, using, or selling such things as those covered in the patent; or a statute might prohibit making, using, or selling things in a particular *manner* proposed by the inventor. Also, the inventor should not be able to impose upon the prior rights of another or of the public in general merely because he has ob tained a patent for his invention. For instance, if use of the invention injures another, the presence of the patent should not allow the injury to continue.

The patent right is usually considered to be a unique kind of personal property. It may be bought or sold, mortgaged, licensed, or given or willed to another nearly as easily as any other personal property.

History of Patents

Concerted efforts by a government to recognize and reward an in- ventor by giving him a protected monopoly in his invention began during the 15th century in the Republic of Venice. In England the practice began as a grant of monopoly from the sovereign. But not only grants of monopolies to inventors took place; there were also grants of trade monopolies of various types. Abuses of these grants led to the passage in 1624 of the Statute of Monopolies, terminating the right of the sovereign to create monopolies. However, the granting to its inventor of a monopoly in an invention was preserved in the sixth section of the act, which provided for letters patent to be issued. Letters patent were provided for in the Statute of Monopolies, but no formal procedure for granting patents was set up in England until 1850.

The United States colonists brought the idea of patenting inventions to the new world. Prior to the adoption of the U.S. Constitution, patents were issued by the individual colonies, but there was at least one glaring defect in this system. A patent issued by a colony secured the patent rights in only that colony. If someone in another colony could obtain the essence of the patent, he was free to make any use of it that he might desire. It is for this reason, among others, that the U.S. Constitution provides that Congress shall have the power "to promote the progress of science and useful arts, by securing for limited times to authors and inventors the exclusive right to their respective writings and discoveries."

The first United States patent law was enacted in 1790. Since then there have been numerous changes of the law and of the governmental department in which it is to operate. The Patent Office is now headed by a commissioner of patents and is part of the Department of Commerce. A 1952 Act of Congress (effective Jan. 1, 1953) revised the law and brought it up to date.

THE RIGHT TO PATENT

The right to patent was neatly summarized in section 31 of the old U.S. Patent Act (35 USCA). It stated that: "Any *person* who has *invented* or *discovered* any *new* and *useful art, machine, manufacture,* or *composition of matter,* or any new and useful *improvements* thereof, or who has invented or discovered and asexually reproduced any distinct and new variety of *plant,* other than a tuber-propagated *plant,* not known or used by others in this country, before his invention or discovery thereof, and not patented or described in any printed publication in this or any foreign country, before his invention or discovery thereof, or more than one year prior to his application, and not in public use or on sale in this country for more than one year prior to his application, unless the same is proved to have been abandoned, may, upon payment of the fees required by law, and other due proceeding had, obtain a patent therefor." The present act broke this summary into separate elements intended to be more convenient for court use. However, the meaning expressed is virtually unchanged. The only major change concerns foreign patents as a bar to patentability; foreign patents now act as bars to patentability only if they were granted before filing of an application for a similar patent in the United States.

Certain rules of practice have had to be developed in the Patent Office to aid in interpreting the patent law. Congress has declared in the legislation the right of the Patent Office to set up and maintain such rules; there are now some 350 of them.

Any person (other than Patent Office employees) may be granted a patent if he meets the patent law requirements. A corporation is a legal person, but it cannot effectively apply for a United States patent. The corporation could acquire patent rights from another and exploit those rights, but the patent must first be applied for by a "natural" person. Natural persons include those of foreign nationality as well as United States citizens.

A patent may be applied for by someone other than the inventor under two circumstances. If the inventor is deceased, the executor or administrator of his estate may apply for a patent in his place. If the inventor is insane, his guardian may apply for him.

A patent may be issued to two or more persons as joint inventors. However, under this circumstance it must be shown that all the joint owners had a hand in creating the invention. Mere partnership in an enterprise or financial assistance does not make one a joint inventor.

ASSIGNMENT.   Since a United States patent has the attributes of personal property, it may be assigned to another person. Assignment of the rights may take place either before or after the inventor obtains his patent, but it requires a sworn, written notification to the Patent Office to be effective. Notification of the Patent Office completes the assignment of an existing patent. If the office is not informed within three months and the patent is subsequently assigned to another, the first assignee to record the transaction will be the new owner of the right.

A patent may be issued directly to the assignee. When this is done it is the patent application which is assigned by the inventor. The inventor must still swear to the specification, but any patent resulting from the application will be granted to the assignee.

It is, of course, possible to assign a portion of the rights acquired in a patent. But the interest assigned must be specified in the assignment. That is, assignment of a half interest in the royalties resulting from a patent could be determined and upheld in court. However, if the assignment is of, say, 10 per cent of *the patent* to another, the assignee would be likely to be held to have a share in the patent equal to that of the inventor. It is improbable that the court would endeavor to determine what portion of the entire patent would constitute 10 per cent of its value.

SHOP RIGHTS AND CONTRACTS TO ASSIGN.   As a general rule the patent rights to an invention belong to the inventor. But if the inventor used his employer's time and equipment in his creative activities, then certainly it seems only right that the employer should have some benefit from the result. The employer's right to benefit under these circumstances is well established in the law. Some difficult questions arise in this connection, though, in regard to contracts made in anticipation of invention, and inventions created wholly or partly on the employee's own time.

A shop right is a non-exclusive, non-assignable license to use an employee's invention. It is limited to the particular employer involved and does not imply that compensation or royalties will be paid to the inventor. It arises from implications of the employment rather than from an express agreement to assign patent rights. Both the inventor and the employer have rights arising from the patent grant and neither can exclude the other.

An employer's shop right to inventions created by his employees on company time and with the employer's facilities is an implied right; or, in some cases, the right may be based on estoppel. However, the duty to assign patent rights may be made the subject matter of a contract. The employee agrees that as consideration for his continued employment he will assign any patents obtained by him to his employer. The duration of the agreement may even be made to run for a period beyond termination of the employee's services. And the scope of the agreement may be made to go well beyond things which the employee might invent which would immediately benefit his employer. There is a limit, though, to the all-encompassing extent to which such agreements may be taken. It is considered against public policy for the length of time to be excessive, thus practically forcing a scientist or engineer to be tied to one employer or else change his profession. It is often the practice for such agreements to run for a year beyond termination of the employee's services. In essence, though, the question of an employer's rights in a patent obtained by a former employee is determined by when the creative work was done. If the work on which the patent was based was done for the former employer and if he had a right to the assignment of patents obtained by the employee, he may maintain an action for assignment of the patent.

It has become almost standard practice to require new engineers and scientists to agree to assign patent rights. Some companies even include an agreement to assign patent rights in their application forms. In many instances this is merely an added precaution taken by the company. If an employee has been specially hired and retained to do research aimed toward obtaining patents, the patents so obtained must be assigned to the employer, even without an agreement to assign. On the other hand, the right of an employer to patents obtained by someone not hired to invent is a matter of shop rights, unless there exists a contract to assign. Since companies frequently move their technical personnel into and out of research as occasions demand, the precaution of an agreement as to patents seems well founded.

Consider Mr. Black and his engine. Assume him to be an engineer for the White Mfg. Company. If the engine was developed as a result of research and development endeavors for which the White Company paid Black a monthly salary, Black's patent must be assigned to the White Company. If Black was hired as a manufacturing engineer, but spent part of his time developing the engine with company facilities, the company is entitled to at least shop rights in the engine. With shop rights the White Company could still make, use, and sell the engine even though the patent was granted to Black.

Mr. Black may have used his own facilities in developing his engine at home in the evenings. Does the White Company have a right to his invention? Yes, they do if Black was hired to invent or if he had agreed to assign patents to the White Company as a condition of his employment. Incidentally, an oral contract to assign future patent rights is quite enforceable if the contract terms can be proved.

INVENTION OR DISCOVERY. One of the fundamental requirements of the subject matter of a patent is that it constitute an invention or discovery. These two terms, "invention" and "discovery," are often used synonymously, despite differences in meanings. Discovery refers to the recognition of something which is in existence but which has never before been recognized, whereas invention refers to the production of something which did not exist before.

To be patentable, an invention or discovery must not only be new or previously unrecognized; it must also be something extraordinary. An obvious or normally predictable result is not patentable. That which an ordinary skilled person in the field involved could reasonably be expected to do may not be patented.

There is no fixed yardstick of patentability in law. Each case is judged on its own merits in the light of similar cases and the present state of the art in the field of the subject matter of the proposed patent. The standard is more strict now than it was fifty years ago and it was tighter then than it was in the early 1800's. But this only reflects progress in the various fields of learning. That which might have been patentable at the turn of the century is now commonplace to the journeyman in the field involved. In the final analysis, it is the judgment of the court that determines whether true invention or discovery is present. Since the judgment is a human opinion, it is open to the criticism that it could be fallible and must, in some instances, be arbitrary. True though this may be, no adequate substitute for human judgment on the question has yet been found.

NEW AND USEFUL. A patentable invention cannot be something which is already known and used by others in the art involved. This rule is tempered with reason, though, as are most rules of law. For instance, an invention which duplicates something discovered and used by an ancient Egyptian civilization and then lost to the intervening posterity might be patentable even though it was known at one time.

Description of the invention or discovery in a printed publication can be a bar to obtaining a patent. Certainly, if the subject of the invention was published by another prior to the "inventor" conceiving it, it cannot be said to be new. Publication by the inventor more than a year prior to his application will also prevent him from getting his patent rights. In this connection the courts have found it necessary to determine what is meant by the term "publication." Publication is held to consist of making information available to the general public. It is not held to occur if the information is given to a restricted group of persons with the express or implied condition that the information is not to become public knowledge. Probably one of the best examples of a publication is a patent; copies of patents issued in the United States are available to anyone at a price of $.25 each ($.10 for a design patent).

For a publication to be a bar to patenting an invention it must contain more than a mere reference to a new idea. Sufficient details must be present to enable the reader to make practical use of the idea. Black, for instance, might safely refer in a published article to a new internal combustion engine in very general terms. As long as he did not reveal the essence of his secret he would not start time running toward the year's limitation.

Public use or sale of the invention more than a year prior to filing the patent application also defeats patentability. If Black started manufacturing his engines for public sale, time would start to run against the year from the date of his first sale. Of course, there are many shades of gray between black and white. For instance, manufacture of a limited number of the machines for experimental use by certain persons would be unlikely to be held "public use." This is especially true where the inventor has told the users of the need for secrecy regarding the invention. Court cases have even held that it is still experimental use even though the inventor may have made some profit in the transactions. "Experimental use" is essentially determined by the intent of the inventor and the nature of the invention. Some things must be tried publicly. Experimental use of a new road surfacing material, for example, would almost necessarily require public use in a street or highway if truly typical conditions are to be encountered.

The invention must be useful as well as new. In court the word "useful" is given a rather broad interpretation; essentially, it is required that no harmful effect on society would result from the invention. The primary purpose of the entire patent system is to benefit the public. It follows, then, that the inventor of something which has no benefit to offer the public or is harmful or immoral should not be entitled to a patent.

An invention must be operable or capable of being used if it is to satisfy the test of useful purpose. If there is any question of the ability of the invention to perform as claimed, the Patent Office may require a model to be built for demonstration purposes. Thus, if the examiner had difficulty understanding Mr. Black's use of internal combustion, he might demand a model from Black. However, the requirement of a model is exceedingly rare. It is much more likely that the examiner would require an affidavit from someone who had actually seen the engine in operation.

Patentable inventions extend to ornamental designs and curiosities. But there is one type of invention which the patent office refuses to accept as patentable—any "perpetual motion" machine. It is held that such machines are obviously inoperable and will continue to be until the law regarding conservation of energy is repealed.

The Atomic Energy Act of 1954 rather severely restricts the right to obtain a patent on any invention to be used in the production or utilization of fissionable materials. Under this act no patent for an invention or discovery of this nature may be issued without approval of the Atomic Energy Commission.

WHAT IS PATENTABLE. An idea is not patentable; but the machine or process or thing into which it has been incorporated may be. That is, a physical law or principle, no matter how beneficial it is likely to be to mankind, is not patentable as long as it remains an idea. Its physical embodiment might be patented, though, if the other tests of patentability are met.

There are seven categories of inventions or discoveries which may be patented:

1. An *art* or a *process* or *method* of doing something—for instance, a new type of heat treatment of steel alloys to obtain certain physical properties.

2. A *machine*. By this term is meant an inanimate mechanism for transforming or applying energy, such as Black's newly conceived internal combustion engine.

3. A manufacture—anything (other than a machine) made from raw material by hand, machine, and/or art. Many manufactured products would serve as examples—a golf club, ash tray, paper clip, and paper pulp.

4. A *composition of matter,* such as a new dental filling material to be used in place of dental amalgam or gold, or a new drug, or an insecticide.

5. A new and useful *improvement* of any of the above. Original patents in a field are often followed by numerous improvement patents. For instance, Morse's original telegraph patent was followed by over 5000 improvements. Similarly, the basic patents on radio receivers, the automobile, and plastics each began a long parade of patented improvements.

6. A new variety of *plant*—roses, camellias, hybrid corn, etc.

7. A *design*. A particular pattern, form, or contour of a product may be patented. Cloth, door chimes, soft drink bottles, and packages for goods have been subjects of design patents. Design patents run for shorter periods of time than other patents. The prospective patentee may apply for a design patent to run 3½, 7, or 14 years at his option. There is only a slight additional cost to apply for the longer-term design patents.

PATENT PROCEDURE

The patent procedure is set up in such a manner that an inventor can obtain a patent on his invention without outside help. Why, then, should a prospective patentee spend money to obtain the services of a patent attorney or a patent agent? There are two main reasons for the expenditure: First, although the procedure as outlined here may appear fairly simple, technicalities and complications may arise requiring knowledge which only a person who has studied patent procedure could possess. Second, unless the patent is properly drawn up and presented, the patentee is likely to find the wording he used (which was so clear to him) to be worthless.

Usually the motive for getting a patent on something is a practical one. The patentee hopes to make money on his patent by selling or licensing it to another, or by using the product, or by manufacturing and selling it himself. An application for a patent, then, is usually based on economic reasoning. If an invention is worth patenting at all, the inventor should try to get the greatest possible coverage in the rights to be protected. The extent of coverage is largely determined by the wording of the claims. An experienced patent attorney or agent can word the claims in such a manner that the broadest possible coverage is obtained.

There is another prominent motive for obtaining patents—one in which the profit resulting from the patent is not quite so apparent. It stems from the fact that realistic limitations must be imposed upon the claims in any patent—that is, the coverage in the claims can extend only as far as they can be justified by the nature of the invention and its novelty. To prevent others from entering the field of the patent by patenting something close to what is already covered, the holder of a patent may attempt to "fence in" his invention. This is done by obtaining patents which are not necessarily profitable by themselves, but which serve as protection for a profitable patent. This practice, often known as "blocking," is in common use by many large enterprises. Since the practice causes frustration to outsiders, many criticisms have been leveled against it. It is, however, lawful unless the result would tend to give the patent holder a monopoly over an entire industry.

PRELIMINARY SEARCH.   It is often stated that "there is nothing new under the sun." Certainly, it is improper to assume that because something is not being manufactured and sold commercially it is not covered by a patent claim. Somewhere in the over three million United States patents, or in the multitude of foreign patents, there is quite likely to be something similar to the subject matter under consideration. The purpose of a patent search is to ferret out any similar patents to find out if a patent can be obtained on the new "invention," and, if a patent can be obtained, the limits of the claims to be made. The preliminary search is not a legal requirement; it is, rather, a practical expedient. It is quite possible to apply for a patent without a preliminary search, but it is not advisable unless the applicant or his attorney is completely familiar with the state of the art involved.

Application

There are three main components of a patent application: 1) the petition, 2) the specification (including claims and possible drawings or a model), and 3) the oath. In addition to these requirements the proper fee must accompany the application. The fee for all patents other than design patents is $30.00 plus $1.00 for each claim in excess of 20. The fee for design patents depends upon the length of time for which the patent is expected to be issued. A 3½-year design patent requires a $10.00 filing fee; a 7-year patent, $15.00; and a 14-year patent, $30.00.

PETITION.   The petition is addressed to the Commissioner of Patents and is essentially a request for a grant of letters patent to be issued to the applicant. It may also include an assignment of the power of attorney to the applicant's attorney or agent, although the power of attorney may be attached on a separate sheet.

SPECIFICATION.   The purpose of a patent specification is to clearly describe the invention. The clarity of description must be such that any skilled person in the field to which it pertains could, by using the specification, reproduce the invention and use it. One or more drawings or, possibly a model may be required to make the invention clear. Models, however, are not permitted as substitutes for drawings unless they are specifically requested by the Patent Office.

Drawings are required in all cases in which drawings will be meaningful. This includes almost every type of invention except compositions of matter and processes. There are special rules pertaining to patent drawings and, for this reason, most applicants hire specialists to make them. However, almost any engineer with the required drawing courses and a little experience could make an acceptable patent drawing by following the Patent Office rules. In addition to being technically acceptable, the drawings must meet the following requirements: 1) they must be made with India ink on heavy, high quality paper which is calendared and smooth; 2) the sheets must measure 10 inches wide by 15 inches high, with a marginal line 1 inch inside each edge; 3) a 1¼-inch space must be left under the top margin as a title block; 4) for shading, the light must come from the upper left-hand corner at a 45° angle. Shading lines cannot be less than one-twentieth of an inch apart; 5) clear and careful lettering is required with a minimum height of one-eighth inch; 6) each sheet should be signed by the applicant or his attorney in the lower right hand corner, either just above or just below the lower marginal line. Actually, signature of the drawings is not a legal requirement if reference to the drawings is made in other signed papers; but the practice is to sign the drawings as well.

A substantial portion of the body of a specification is usually devoted to describing the various views shown in the drawing and the functions of the components. Prior to the explanation of the drawing details, though, there should be a brief summary of the substance and nature of the invention and, possibly, its purpose. The claims usually follow the detailed description of the invention.

CLAIMS. The claims are the operative part of a patent. They are essentially statements of what is considered to have been invented and, therefore, preserved to the patent holder. From the applicant's point of view, the broader the coverage in the claims, the greater the rights he will have in his patent. Others may legally encroach upon his invention to the point where they will enter the area set aside in the claims. It would be to Black's advantage, for instance, to claim "an internal combustion engine." Of course, such a claim would not be allowed; but if it were, he could force manufacturers of any kind of internal combustion engines to cease manufacturing or pay him royalties. The natural end result would be payment to Black to use the right he reserved in his claim. The principles of internal combustion engines are well within the public domain, however, so Black's claim would have to be restricted to a particular kind of engine. His claim might read "an internal combustion engine comprising . . . ," the remainder restricting the claim to what is new in his invention.

Patents are available to the public. If a particular patent appears highly profitable economically, it is likely to attract many people, who will try to approach the invention as closely as possible without infringement. It is here that patent claims are really tested. Prospective producers of patented things may go to great lengths to avoid the payment of royalties; and, if they can find a way around the claims in a patent, there is no reason why they should not use it.

Since it is difficult to tell in advance just what portion of an invention will come to be most important in the next seventeen years, a considerable amount of imagination must be used in making the claims. Sometimes an apparently insignificant component of a device becomes more lucrative than the invention itself.

The original claims in a patent application should be as broad as the preliminary investigation will allow them to be. If they are too broad, the patent examiner who investigates the application will require them to be narrowed down. If they are too narrow in the beginning, however, they cannot be broadened without giving up the original patent application date—and there may be good reason for desiring to retain that date. The time lost in making a new start is by itself reason enough.

OATH. The third essential component of every patent application is an oath taken by the applicant that he believes himself to be the originator of the thing for which he requests a patent. The oath may be taken before any person authorized by law to administer oaths, either in the United States or in the appropriate foreign country (if the applicant is not a citizen of the United States). A statement of citizenship (e.g., "citizen of Great Britain") is required in the oath.

Examination

When the patent application has been prepared it is submitted to the Patent Office for examination and the hoped-for approval. There, the application will be sent to one of the examining divisions (specializing in particular types of subject matter) and will be assigned to a patent examiner. Actual examination takes place according to filing dates on the applications. An application may wait for six months or even a year before the examiner gets to it.

The application is examined to determine whether it complies with the law and whether it is truly something new. If the form and content of the application comply with the law, the examiner turns next to the question of novelty. The search undertaken by the patent examiner is likely to be considerably more extensive than the preliminary search. This is particularly true if the patent is allowed.

To determine if the proposed invention is really something new, the patent examiner does not confine his examination merely to old patents. His search is likely to take him far afield. Not only will he compare what is proposed with what has been patented—he is likely to examine trade publications, newspaper articles, even mail order catalog descriptions and goods for sale in local stores.

The result of the examiner's work is communicated to the applicant or his attorney in a letter known as an "Office Action." If the examiner has found reason to quarrel with the novelty of the proposed invention, the entire application will be rejected.

The Office Action may show that some or all the claims have been allowed. If all claims are allowed, the patent will be issued promptly. If some claims are allowed and others rejected, the applicant may obtain a patent including the approved claims. Or he may reword or further restrict the rejected claims to resolve the conflict between them and the claims on a previous patent (as cited in the Office Action). Or he may, as some do, just quit in disgust.

AMENDMENT.   Amendment of an application that has been wholly or partly rejected as a result of its first examination is nearly always complex and legally technical. Sometimes a visit to the examiner by the applicant's attorney can clear up misunderstandings or indicate rewording of certain claims to make them satisfactory. Much of the attorney's time will be spent in studying the claims in the application and comparing them with other patents and publications with which the examiner has noted a conflict. Amendments to the application are then made. It may be noted that making changes in a patent application requires considerable care as well as knowledge of Patent Office rules. Generally, nothing may be deleted or replaced by the applicant or his attorney. Rather, a separate paper must be drawn, answering all the examiner's objections and recommending deletions or substitutions to cure the defects. The examiner will then make the corrections upon resubmission of the application. The original numbering of the claims is retained, although some of the claims may have been deleted. That is, if there were twelve claims in the original application and Number 11 were to be eliminated, the last claim would still be numbered "12."

RESPONSE.   Response to an Office Action (submission of the amended application) must take place within six months. If no response is made within the time limit, the application is considered to be abandoned.

Re-examination of the altered application may require another waiting period of from six months to a year. And these rounds of Office Action followed by response may continue indefinitely. If a year per round may be assumed, considerable time may elapse between the original application and the final outcome. If the applicant persists in his pursuit of a patent, the rounds of Office Action and response will end with either attorney and examiner finally agreeing on the claims and issuing a patent, or the applicant's receiving a "final rejection."

Appeal

In the Patent Office the "final rejection" is not always final. There is still the possibility of appeal of the examiner's decision to a higher tribunal. Relatively few applications are finally rejected by the examiner and then appealed by the applicant. Generally, the attorney and the examiner can find common ground before appeal is necessary. Nevertheless, an appeal procedure exists as a final recourse in patent law.

There exists within the Patent Office itself a Board of Appeals to which a finally rejected application may be taken. Although the Board of Appeals is a part of the Patent Office, there is no apparent tendency in it to support the examiner's position. Frequently the Board will overrule the examiner and allow claims which were previously rejected.

If the Board of Appeals maintains the examiner's position, a further appeal is still possible. The applicant may take his case to the United

States Court of Customs and Patent Appeals, or he may file a civil action against the Commissioner of Patents in a United States District Court. If either action is successful the court will order the patent to be issued. However, just as with court actions involving administrative boards, the Patent Office must be shown to be clearly wrong for the court to overrule its decision.

Interferences

Less than 1 per cent of the patent applications filed in the United States Patent Office become involved in interference proceedings. Nevertheless, the possibility does exist, and the cost involved is sufficient to make consideration of it worth while.

An interference arises when two patent applications claim the same thing or nearly the same thing. It may also arise as a conflict between an application and a patent which has been issued for less than a year. As the result of either conflict, one adversary wins and holds the disputed claim or claims and the other has nothing but experience as a reward for his trouble.

In an interference, just as in any other court case, the winner is determined by the evidence he can present to the court. Records of the conception and pursuit of the invention must have been made and kept if a contestant is to have a chance of winning. This is one reason why nearly all companies require research staff members to keep notebooks of activities (with pages serially numbered and with dated entries), and why periodic witnessing of the contents is necessary. Anyone capable of understanding the contents, by the way, may act as witness to research notes.

Interference actions are taken first to the Patent Office Board of Patent Interferences. Appeal may be taken to the Court of Customs and Patent Appeals or to a United States District Court.

The purpose of an interference proceeding is to discover which of two adversaries actually was the first inventor. Two dates become important: the date of conception of the invention, and the date of reduction to practice. If one party to an interference action can prove that he was first to conceive of the invention and first to reduce it to practice, he is entitled to the patent protection.

Proof by one party of his first conception is not enough. He may also be called upon to prove that he pursued the idea with reasonable diligence. If the other party was not first to conceive of the invention, but was first to reduce it to practice he may obtain the desired patent by proving that his adversary temporarily abandoned the idea.

Inventions are often developed in secrecy. But too much secrecy can be fatal to the patent. Proof of reduction to practice requires testimony of someone who actually saw the invention in operation.

Assume that Mr. Black's claims in his application for his engine are met with an interference. That is, one Mr. White has made application to patent a similar engine and has posed claims which conflict with Black's. The case is tried before the Board of Interferences. White proves by records that he has the earlier date of conception of the invention. If White can now prove an earlier date of reduction to practice, the patent will issue to him. It may be noted that his patent application will serve as constructive reduction to practice. However, Black built and ran his engine before witnesses while White was still at the drawing board. At this point White may still get the patent if he pursued his invention with reasonable diligence since he first conceived of it. Black's hope for the patent rests on his ability to prove that White temporarily abandoned his endeavor for a substantial period—even four or five weeks might be enough. Here, White's records (if he has made and kept them) will protect his rights; without records he may lose what is rightfully his.

Allowance and Issue

Few patent applications become involved in appeals; fewer yet in interferences. Most patent issues between applicant and examiner are settled satisfactorily in the early stages, and either a patent results or the application is abandoned.

If the patent is allowed, the applicant is sent a notice of allowance. Usually the patent will be issued on the fifth Tuesday following the date of allowance.

INFRINGEMENT AND REMEDIES

The grantee of a patent has a lawful monopoly. His monopoly right would be virtually worthless, though, if he could not resort to court action to enforce it. It must be, and is, possible to prevent others from encroaching upon the area of activity reserved to the patentee. He should be compensated if another enters the field reserved to him and benefits because the patent exists, and such compensation is available to him.

Action for patent infringement may be brought in any Federal District Court. The nature of the action and procedural rules are those of equity jurisdiction; as you recall from Chapter 2, actions at law and in equity are merged in the federal courts. Thus the action may be taken for damages alone or for an injunction with or without damages.

In a patent infringement action the defendant is charged with having made, used, or sold the subject matter in violation of the protected monopoly created by the patent. The essence of such actions is the test of extent of coverage in the claims compared with the alleged violation. It is here that unnecessary restrictions in claims are likely to prove costly, for the court will interpret the claims literally. What the patentee has given up in the Patent Office he cannot get back in court; he has only the claims allowed. For instance, the claims in one patent referred to "wide, thin members" in a structure. When a competitor used cylindrical members to accomplish the same purpose he was sued for infringement. The court held that this was not infringement. Where another patent claim referred to a semi-circular connector, use of a different connector or none at all did not infringe.

Defense

The defendant in an infringement action has essentially two defenses available to him. He may either seek to prove that the patent or the claims in it are invalid or that his action did not amount to infringement.

To support an infringement action the claim must be restricted to the disclosure in the patent. That is, if the patentee has gone ahead and made so many changes in his invention that the claims no longer cover it, he is no longer protected. The reasoning seems obvious, but cases on this point indicate that to some patent holders the discovery of lack of protection came as a shock.

All patents are presumed in court to be valid. It may be possible, though, for the defendant to attack the validity of the patent by quarreling with some fact of the application, e.g., the statement in the oath that the applicant believes himself to be the first inventor of the subject matter. Successful attack voids the patent, and the defendant is free to continue his acts.

The defendant may claim noninfringement. He may admit the acts complained of and then show that the claims are not sufficiently broad to cover these acts.

Remedies

Patent infringement usually gives the patent holder a right to a damage action. And from this arises the cause for injunction in such cases. If the defendant were not to be prohibited from continuing to infringe, the right to damage action could be repeated throughout the life of the patent.

The present patent law provides for either an injunction, or damages, or both in patent infringement cases. In addition, the law allows the court to go beyond mere compensatory damages and assess up to triple damages against the defendant if the case appears to warrant it. In exceptional cases the court may even assess a reasonable amount for plaintiff's attorney's fees.

The measure of compensatory damages in an infringement case is the cost to the plaintiff. However, the statute requires that he be compensated at least in the amount that he lost or would have lost in royalties because of the infringement. A question may arise as to the amount of royalties to be assessed if the plaintiff has not made previous royalty arrangements with others. If such is the case, the question is settled either by a jury or by the court with or without the aid of an expert witness.

There is a time limitation on infringement damages. Assessment of damages may not cover a period of more than six years of past infringement.

Patent Markings

If the plaintiff in an infringement case is to get any damages for the injury to him, he must have informed the defendant of his patent. Marking patented goods with the patent number serves this purpose. If he has not so marked the goods, the plaintiff must prove that he informed the defendant of the existence of the patent and that the infringement continued.

Goods sold are often marked "Patent Pending" or "Patent Applied For." These terms have no legal force as far as infringement is concerned. However, if they are used when, in fact, no application has been filed, it may be assumed that the purpose of their use was to defraud the public. The current statute provides for a $500 maximum fine for each such unlawful use of the term. Half the fine assessed goes to the member of the public who brings the charge.

COMMENTS AND CRITICISMS

Our patent law is not perfect; very few man-made laws are. But despite its imperfections, the present law seems to accomplish the objectives stated by the framers of our Constitution reasonably well.

One common criticism is directed toward the time and money required to obtain a patent. At first, the criticism seems well-founded. As to time, few patents are issued in much less than a year after the application is begun; some have required twenty years or more. This sounds like a long time to wait for patent protection but, as a practical matter, the delay is seldom a hardship and may be of benefit to the applicant. The greater the delay in issuing the patent, the greater will be his time of practical patent protection. Theoretically, the applicant is not protected while his application is being processed. However, should he be threatened with an "infringement," the patent office will usually expedite issuance of the patent to permit legal action for the infringement. Thus, practically, the applicant has a large measure of protection during the application processing period. The monetary outlay required is extremely variable, depending upon the complications which may arise. It is possible for the patent to cost only very nominal fees. However, it is more likely to cost somewhere from $100 to several thousand dollars. But a patent is somewhat like other business ventures. The probable cost in time and money should be weighed against the expected results. If economic analysis shows that the venture is likely to be profitable, it should be undertaken. If the likelihood of profit is remote, perhaps it is better kept and used as a trade secret. Many large corporations require that a patent be able to pay for all the expenditures required in a certain length of time, or recover a given profit on the investment, to justify the cost of the patent and the cost of setting up to produce the patented item. A pay-off period of two or three years is not uncommon; neither is a 20% or a 25% profit margin.

Occasionally the objection is heard that the small inventor has no fair chance to compete with the research staffs of big business. It is true that research staffs are brought together to make a talented team and that in many things teamwork pays off. But even in a research team the best ideas often flow from one individual or a small nucleus of people. Once the idea occurs it is often pursued more rapidly by teamwork, but if a "free lance" inventor has the first date of conception and has pursued it diligently, speed by a corporate research team is to no avail.

Members of industrial research staffs sometimes complain that they are not adequately compensated for patents which they obtain and then must assign to their employers. Perhaps the criticism is valid, for many receive only a dollar or five dollars for the assignment. However, the opposite argument is that the staff member is paid not only for the time during which he has produced something worthwhile, but also for other time which was not so productive. It is also argued that the research job, considering only the activities involved, is more enjoyable to many people than the alternatives. The employer also has an investment in research facilities which must return a profit if he is to survive.

Corporations are often criticized because with large funds available, they can indulge in long legal battles to win infringement or interference suits from less fortunate competitors. Sometimes the mere threat of a long legal battle is sufficient. While this criticism has merit, there is still an end of the road for all legal battles. If the small inventor is legally right and has chosen his attorney well, the mere preponderance of legal counsel on the other side is not sufficient to win. There is another aspect.

to this particular problem. Because of the large costs involved and the unpredictability of the outcome of such cases, large concerns will frequently pay out of court rather than undertake a court defense. That is, if an inventor claims that a manufactured product infringes his patent and demands a small royalty, the manufacturer may purchase the patent or pay the royalty rather than go to court, even though the particular patent might be only remotely related to his product. The legal cost to the patent holder could be quite small, since he can usually find an attorney willing to work on a contingency basis.

One criticism which seems to have greater validity than most is concerned with the public welfare. Suppose someone invents something of great public benefit—perhaps a cure for cancer. Under present law it would be possible for him to obtain a patent monopoly on his invention, make very limited amounts of the cure, and sell it at enormous prices. All but wealthy people would be deprived of the cure—a rather appalling prospect.

Other criticisms are directed at the extension of the scope of patent monopolies by pooling arrangements, tying clauses, marketing agreements, and the like. Some of these arrangements are lawful; others are not. Most of the criticisms have some merit.

Despite shortcomings in the patent law, protection is afforded to the inventor, and the rate of technological advance of our economy is testimony to its success. Imperfect though it is, it is successful.

APPLICATION OF CAVALLITO

282 F. 2d 363 (July 6, 1960)

Smith, Judge.

The issue in the present appeal arises from the affirmance by the Board of Appeals of the examiner's rejection of claim 1 of appellants' application Serial No. 344,677 filed March 25, 1953, for Bis (N-Heterocarbocyclic) Alkanes.
Appealed claim 1 reads as follows:

An organic compound selected from the group consisting of (A) those comprising two N-heterocarbocyclic radicals, each radical containing between three and five fused rings joined by an alkylene bridge attached to a nitrogen of each of said radicals, at least three of said rings being composed solely of carbon and nitrogen in the ring, said alkylene bridge containing three to ten carbon atoms, inclusive, and (B) acid addition and quaternary ammonium salts of the foregoing compounds.

Six claims have been allowed. No prior art has been cited and no question is raised as to novelty, utility or unobviousness of the invention.

As described in the specification, the compounds embodying the invention claimed in rejected claim 1 have the general formula $R-C_nH_{2n}-R'$ wherein R and R' are N-heterocarbocyclic radicals each of which contains between three and five fused rings, at least three of said rings being composed solely of carbon and nitrogen as ring-forming atoms. . . ." The alkylene bridge $(-C_nH_{2n}-)$ of the molecule is attached to the N-heterocyclic radicals through a ring of nitrogen. R and R' may be the same radical or may be different radicals. However, appellants specify that the "heterocyclic moiety of the present invention must contain in at least three of the rings, carbon and nitrogen as the only ring-forming components." There must also be three to five of the fused rings which "must be attached to the alkylene chain to form the compound of the present invention through a nitrogen of the ring radical."

The invention also contemplates the acid addition salts and the quaternary ammonium salts of compounds having the general formula but only "where such compounds are possible because of the structure of the rings."

The specification describes processes for producing the compounds having the chemical structure claimed in appealed claim 1 and discloses what are termed "representative" dihaloalkanes and "representative" N-heterocarbocyclic substances containing the required three to five fused rings which contain carbon and nitrogen as the ring-forming components in at least three of the rings.

The specification contains 19 examples of illustrative procedures for producing compounds which it is asserted have the claimed chemical structure. The examiner has allowed claims to the specific compounds of certain of those examples and to the quaternary ammonium salts of compounds having the general formula $R-C_nH_{2n}-R$ and in which the N-heterocarbocyclic radical (R) is selected from a group of specified "unsubstituted carbolines, yohimbines, berberine, and hydrogenated and lower-alkyl-substituted carbolines, yohimbines and berberines."

The position of the examiner which was affirmed by the Board of Appeals was that the specification "adequately supports claims to compounds having the carboline, yohimbine or berberine ring structure." He rejected claim 1 as drawn to "a broad elastic formula" which he states was not supported by the specification.

The examiner and the Board of Appeals appear to have given great weight to the large number of possible compounds which would be embraced within the scope of claim 1. Testing this claim as to but one field of the asserted utility, the examiner and the Board of Appeals have rejected the claim as covering inoperative embodiments. In support of this ground of rejection, the Board of Appeals said:

A chemist will readily recognize that claim 1 is broad enough to cover at least several hundred thousand compounds. Measured against this are the nineteen compounds actually prepared. In our opinion this is insufficient to support such a claim. . . .

There are at least two grounds upon which this rejection is improper and cannot be sustained. (1) Appellant's disclosure is not properly limited to the nineteen specific examples referred to and (2) it is the nature of the disclosure rather than the number of examples given which determines the sufficiency of the disclosure to support the appealed claim.

Appellants have disclosed, in addition to the nineteen illustrative examples referred to by the board, a large group of what are said to be representative dihaloalkanes and N-heterocarbocyclic substances which are suitable for use in the general process disclosed for producing compounds within the scope of claim 1. We think the proper evaluation of the disclosed support for claim 1 must be made with respect to the entire disclosure, and this is not limited to the nineteen specific examples.

The examiner and the board appear to have considered only the nineteen specific examples for the reason that these examples are "tangible" disclosures of compounds having therapeutic properties. It is the position of the board that when the subject matter lies in the field of therapeutics, in which prediction is very limited, ". . . the scope of the claims should conform rather closely to the tangible disclosure."

These observations of the board are not determinative of the issue here. Appellants disclosed as their invention chemical compounds having a novel structural configuration. These compounds as disclosed are asserted to be useful not only as "hypotensive agents" but also "as intermediates in the preparation of more complex organic compounds."

Neither the examiner nor the board has raised any issue as to the sufficiency of these disclosures, so for purposes of this appeal, we are assuming, without passing upon the issue, that appellants' disclosures when read by one of ordinary skill in this art would teach him how to use the claimed compounds either as the disclosed "hypotensive agents" or as the disclosed "intermediates."

Under these circumstances, the examiner and the board should have considered appellants' entire disclosure rather than just the nineteen specific examples to which reference is made in the board's opinion.

The examiner and the Board of Appeals also rejected the appealed claim as "too broad in the definition of the heterocyclic radical since the definition leaves open to speculation the nature of the other two rings and the skeletal structure of the first three rings." We do not agree with this rejection. The claimed invention resides in a compound which results from the hooking together of known kinds of N-heterocyclic radicals in a particular way. That way, as specified in claim 1, is by use of an alkylene bridge "attached to the nitrogen of each of said radicals." While the claim is broad in specifying the two N-heterocyclic radicals it is not indefinite in that it claims them in such a manner that an organic chemist having the ordinary skills of this phase of the chemical art, can tell whether any given compound is within or without the scope of the claim. Thus, the claimed limitations require that the N-heterocyclic radical must be:

1. N-heterocarbocyclic;

2. Contain 3, 4, or 5 fused rings;

3. At least 3 of the rings must have ring atoms solely of carbon and nitrogen; and

4. Be joined to the alkylene bridge through a ring nitrogen.

It is our opinion that claim 1 covers appellants' inventive concept, and that this inventive concept is not limited to the use of any particular kind of N-heterocyclic radicals so long as they have the general structure and chemical characteristics claimed. The invention is disclosed as a novel, useful, and unobvious chemical structure responding to the general formula $R-C_nH_{2n}-R'$ and in which the R and R' radicals must possess a given structure as recited in the claim and be joined to the alkylene bridge in the particular manner recited therein. While such a claim is broad it does set forth specifically the radicals from which the selection of particular radicals must be made. This claim is therefore a proper claim.

Viewed in its entirety, the decision of the Board of Appeals relied upon grounds of rejection for which there is no express statutory basis. The nearest to a possible statutory basis we can find would be predicated upon the provisions of 35 U.S.C. sec. 112 which require an applicant to "particularly point out and distinctly claim" his invention. It is our opinion that appellants' appealed claim 1 meets this requirement, and, since the board did not spell out this ground of rejection, we are left with a rejection which appears to be based on the opinion of the board as to what constitutes proper public policy in granting a claim which is as broad in its scope as is claim 1.

We have pointed out primarily the features of appellants' invention which are claimed in claim 1 and for which we have found a basis in the specification. We believe it is as incumbent upon this court as it is upon the Patent Office to consider carefully the entire disclosure of an applicant and to evaluate the breadth of the claim against the disclosure.

The sole issue for determination in any case such as the present is whether there has been a legally sufficient disclosure of the invention to support a claim having the breadth here contended for.

This clear issue has been obscured by the actions below in which both the board and the examiner have judged the adequacy of only one part of the disclosure while ignoring other parts and failing to consider all the asserted fields of utility.

The appealed claim covers a very large number of chemical compounds which may be developed in the future and which will possess the structure which applicants assert and the Patent Office admits is a novel structure. Due to the nature of chemical compounds and chemical processes it is conceivable that an almost infinite number of compounds may be developed by chemists if they have before them the teachings which appellants assert to be new in this field, namely, the particular structure and molecular arrangement of their new compounds. It seems to us that it is proper for the Patent Office to examine such assertions of patentability with great care but, when that has been done, the standards by which the ultimate determination of patentability or unpatentability should be made are those standards which Congress has provided in the patent statutes.

In the final analysis the board's holding appears to be that as a matter of law nineteen examples are not enough to support a claim embracing many thousands of compounds. We are unable to agree to that proposition. The sufficiency of a disclosure depends not on the number but rather on the nature of the claimed compounds *per se* and the nature of the supporting disclosures. If a claim covers compounds which are closely related, a comparatively limited disclosure may be sufficient to support it. If, however, the claim covers compounds which are related only in some structural respects, a more extensive supporting disclosure may be necessary to support it. Moreover, the selection of the examples and other exemplary material used as the disclosure to support a claim must be adequately representative of the area covered by it. In some instances a limited disclosure which is typical of various areas covered by a claim may be of greater value in determining the patentable characteristics of the claimed compounds than a more extensive disclosure would be if related only to a limited portion of the area.

At the oral argument, appellants' counsel stated that the disclosure of appellants' invention should be likened unto the discovery of an island which could be located after its discovery by the reference or bearing points given by the discoverer. The impression he sought to convey by this analogy was that the disclosures in this application provided reference or bearing points which adequately mark out and establish the area of the invention and that claim 1, while admittedly broad, was no broader than the invention so disclosed.

In the instant case neither the examiner nor the board has undertaken to consider specifically the nature of the claimed compounds with respect to the adequacy of all the disclosures to support the appealed claim. For that reason, we are unable to determine from the present record whether the analogy to reference or bearing points is accurate. We are, therefore, of the opinion that the alleged insufficiency of appellants' disclosure is not clearly established by the facts stated in the board's opinion. For this reason we hold that on the record as now presented, the rejection of claim 1 is not properly supported.

We do not think that we should attempt to determine from the present record whether in fact the disclosure of this application is sufficient to support a claim of the breadth of claim 1. The examiner should have made this determination and a definite finding on the matter. In the absence of such a finding, both the board and this court are left without the benefit of his expert technical view on this important aspect of the case.

For the foregoing reasons, the decision of the Board of Appeals is reversed and remanded for further proceedings consistent with this opinion.

Reversed and remanded.

WORLEY, *Chief Judge, concurs in the result.*

GREPKE v. GENERAL ELECTRIC COMPANY

280 F. 2d 508 (July 1, 1960, Indiana)

SCHNACKENBERG, Circuit Judge.

This action was brought by plaintiff, Henry D. Grepke, an employee of defendant, General Electric Company, a corporation, to recover damages for its alleged appropriation of property rights he claimed to have in a novel method for inserting the balancing weights in the armatures of electric motors. After trial before a jury, a verdict for plaintiff for $5,000 damages was returned. Judgment on the verdict was entered and defendant has appealed. Defendant relies for reversal on the failure of the trial court to grant its motions to direct a verdict, one such motion having been made at the conclusion of the plaintiff's case and another at the conclusion of all of the evidence. Defendant also moved unsuccessfully for a judgment notwithstanding the verdict.

There is competent evidence in the record tending to prove, *inter alia*, the facts which we now set forth.

Plaintiff had been employed by defendant for over 33 years, including 1940 to 1959, when he worked as an armature balancer in the Finishing Armature Section of the Series or Specialties Motors Department 401, in Division 1, Building 4, on the third floor of defendant's Fort Wayne, Indiana, plant. In 1940, William Wickliffe was a supervisor or foreman in said Division 1.

In 1940 plaintiff conceived what he believed to be a new and novel method for balancing an armature by the way he inserted balancing weights therein, which idea he submitted to defendant in accordance with a suggestion system which it maintained, while a confidential relationship existed between them.

The operation of the suggestion system was as follows: Ideas received found their way to a suggestion office where they were typed up, assigned a number and "acknowledged." That office filed the original typed copy and a duplicate typewritten copy was sent to a secretary of a subcommittee within a particular section or department where the suggestion would be expected to be used. This subcommittee normally consisted of men similar to a cost reduction man, a cost accountant, or a cost man, a time study man, generally a general foreman and an engineer or a planning engineer. The subcommittee in the department normally passed on whether the idea would be used and made the reward or referred the matter to a "central committee" composed of three or four additional men. If the subcommittee did not return the typed duplicate copy to the suggestion office within some several weeks, it was notified, but there were no regulations that prevented the subcommittee from creating its own files or records of ideas. If any "problems" arose, or if the person originating the idea requested it, the invention would then be reviewed by the secretary and a central committee. In some instances inventions would be referred to an "overall committee" at Schenectady, New York, or to a planning engineer or planning people employed in the Fort Wayne plant to improve motors, but no record was kept when that was done. Such planning people would also have access to the original ideas on file upon request, and they sometimes kept a separate file or group of ideas for future reference and no record was kept when this was done. In 1953 all suggestion records were turned over to and kept by the department to which they would have been referred. However, since 1947 it was customary to destroy after six years the suggestion records except a log book.

Plaintiff submitted his idea to the foreman and, under date of November 19, 1940, the committee on suggestions acknowledged receipt thereof and assigned a number to the suggestion. Defendant rejected plaintiff's idea and notified him accordingly. His idea was to insert balancing weights from the top of armatures. Under the old method, balancing weights were inserted from the end of armatures and this method continued until 1953. In that year, foreman Wickliffe determined that a large number of armatures were damaged and rejected as a result of the use of the old method. Wickliffe then assigned the task of finding a different way to balance armatures to one John

Pugh, who had been a foreman in training under Wickliffe for some six months in the same Department 401, in Division 1, and later became a "motion time survey specialist."

In April 1953, Pugh submitted a "cost improvement project," consisting of a method of balancing armatures, which was placed in production in 1954.

Pugh, as a witness for defendant, testified that in 1953 he independently invented the method now employed by defendant, that it consisted in inserting the balancing weights from the top instead of the ends of armatures, and that he was unacquainted with Grepke at the time and had no access to or knowledge of Grepke's earlier 1940 suggestion.

Defendant's instruction No. 1, which was given by the court to the jury, reads:

The Plaintiff Henry Grepke's complaint alleges that in 1954, the Defendant General Electric Company in effect utilized a novel method for inserting balancing weights in the armatures of electric motors that was identical to the method previously suggested to it by the Plaintiff in 1940. By its answer, the Defendant General Electric Company denies that the methods are similar, but, on the contrary, claims that its present method of so inserting such balancing weights is entirely dissimilar and different from that suggested by the plaintiff. You are instructed that the burden of proving such methods are substantially equivalent or similar is upon the Plaintiff, and if you find from a fair preponderance of the evidence that such methods are not substantially equivalent or similar and that the Defendant's present method differs in material respects from that suggested by the Plaintiff, you should find against the Plantiff and for the Defendant, General Electric Company.

1. Was Pugh's alleged invention in 1953 an appropriation of plaintiff's suggestion to defendant in 1940? Under proper instructions, to which no objection by either party was made, the jury in effect answered this controlling question in the affirmative. Defendant focused the attention of the jury upon the issue between the parties as to whether plaintiff's method and Pugh's method were substantially similar or equivalent, by defendant's instruction No. 1, and the jury by its verdict for plaintiff thereby found that issue against defendant.

We might add that this court in Smith v. Dravo Corp., 203 F. 2d 369, 377, said:

As a general rule the similarity standing alone is an adequate basis upon which to find misappropriation. Thus, in Hoeltke v. C. M. Kemp Mfg. Co., 4 Cir., 80 F.2d 912, 924, the court said:
'The similarity of defendant's device to that of complainant is strong proof that one was copied from the other.'

It is important to note that there is no question raised on this appeal as to the new and novel nature of plaintiff's idea or as to the existence of a confidential relationship between plaintiff and defendant. Plaintiff's idea was at all times in possession of defendant from and after 1940. Moreover, Pugh worked for plaintiff's foreman, Wickliffe, he had conversation with that foreman concerning the balancing of armatures, he had access to the files, and he worked in the same building, division and department as plaintiff.

As the court said in *Golding v. R.K.O. Pictures*, 1950, 35 Cal. 2d 690, 221 P. 2d 95, 98:

. . . Was the plaintiff's material copied by the defendant? There will seldom be direct evidence of plagiarism, and necessarily the trier of fact must rely upon circumstantial evidence and the reasonable inferences which may be drawn from it to determine the issue. An inference of copying may arise when there is proof of access coupled with a showing of similarity. . . . Where there is strong evidence of access, less proof of similarity may suffice. . . .

In *Bowles v. Zimmer Mfg. Co.*, 277 F. 2d 868, 875, we said, in discussing the defendant's motion for a directed verdict:

On such a motion, it is the duty of the court to consider the evidence in the light most favorable to plaintiff and to consider as proven facts those which the evidence tends to prove, drawing against the party requesting a directed verdict such inferences as the jury might reasonably draw from the evidence. . . .

Defendant argues:

The only way the jury could possibly fix liability on the defendant for the misappropriating and stealing of Grepke's suggestion would be to speculate that Pugh somehow and in some manner was told about the Grepke suggestion and utilized the same rather than that he developed his method by his own inventive efforts. Under the established rules of law, such conjecture and speculation cannot be indulged in and in the face of the positive denial of such fact by unchallenged evidence, the Trial Court should have accepted its responsibility and directed a verdict for the defendant as a matter of law.

However, in *Lavender v. Kurn*, 327 U.S. 645, 66 S.Ct. 740, 90 L.Ed., 916, the court made it clear that a jury may draw inferences from the evidence. The court, 327 U.S. at page 653, 66 S.Ct. at page 744, said:

It is no answer to say that the jury's verdict involved speculation and conjecture. Whenever facts are in dispute or the evidence is such that fair-minded men may draw different inferences, a measure of speculation and conjecture is required on the part of those whose duty it is to settle the dispute by choosing what seems to them to be the most reasonable inference. Only when there is a complete absence of probative facts to support the conclusion reached does a reversible error appear. But where, as here, there is an evidentiary basis for the jury's verdict, the jury is free to discard or disbelieve whatever facts are inconsistent with its conclusion. And the appellate court's function is exhausted when that evidentiary basis becomes apparent, it being immaterial that the court might draw a contrary inference or feel that another conclusion is more reasonable.

Moreover, the credibility of Pugh and the weight to be given to his testimony were questions for the jury. We are not impressed with the contention of defendant that Pugh was a disinterested witness. His relation to a defendant and the effect of the outcome of this case upon his claim that he was the inventor of a valuable method cast considerable doubt upon any contention that he lacked interest in this litigation. Nor was the jury required to believe Pugh's testimony which was to the effect that he had no knowledge of plaintiff's method, especially as there was evidence that he had opportunities for access to the suggestion which plaintiff in confidence had given to defendant.

We do not consider fatal to plaintiff's case that the period from 1940 to 1953 elapsed before defendant openly appropriated plaintiff's idea. It is common knowledge that, during most of that period, the United States was engaged in wars and that manufacturers such as defendant were preoccupied in assisting the government in its war effort, leaving little opportunity for development of new ideas.

We cannot say that on the entire record the court had a duty to direct a verdict in favor of defendant or to enter judgment notwithstanding the jury's verdict.

2. Defendant argues that the evidence shows that in 1954 the method of inserting balancing weights from the top of armatures instead of from the end was well-known in the industry. It therefore concludes that the alleged misappropriation by defendant of plaintiff's suggestion, disclosed in confidence and in which he had a property right, disappeared as a matter of law.

This position is unsound. If, as the jury evidently believed from the evidence, defendant in 1940 solicited and obtained in confidence plaintiff's idea and in 1953 Pugh appropriated that idea for defendant's benefit, we consider irrelevant the alleged fact that in 1954, or even before then, from sources other than plaintiff, a similar method had been adopted in the industry. Certainly defendant does not contend that Pugh resorted to general knowledge in the industry in reaching the result which he claimed to have achieved in 1953.

In *Smith v. Dravo Corp.*, 203 F. 2d 369, 375, we said, quoting from Nims, Unfair Competition and Trade Marks, sec. 148:

> The fact that a trade secret is of such a nature that it can be discovered by experimentation or other fair and lawful means does not deprive its owner of the right to protection from those who would secure possession of it by unfair means.

3. Defendant contends that "there was a complete absence of credible evidence to sustain a verdict for $5,000 in damages." We note the obvious ambiguousness of this language. While defendant in the district court attacked the verdict by a motion for a new trial, which was overruled, no reversal is sought in this court upon the overruling of that motion. It is upon a motion for a new trial that defendant might have properly made its argument that the amount of the verdict was excessive or that the evidence of damages was not credible. But no ruling upon defendant's motion for a new trial is before us now. As we have pointed out, in this court defendant relies for reversal on the trial court's failure to grant its motions to direct a verdict in its favor. On such motions the credibility of evidence and the effect or weight thereof cannot be decided. . . . On the record before us we would be limited to the question (if raised by defendant) of whether there is a failure of *any* evidence that plaintiff was damaged. Only if defendant raised that question and if we find in defendant's favor on that question, can we say that the district court erred as a matter of law in overruling defendant's motions for a directed verdict and for judgment notwithstanding the verdict.

On behalf of himself, plaintiff testified to facts which we now summarize.

In the Fort Wayne plant in 1954, 1955, 1956, and 1957, an estimated 10,000 armatures per week were processed, of which 30% utilized the plaintiff's idea. Two thirds as many per week were produced in 1958 of which 40% utilized that method. Cost and time studies of the new method showed a savings of 2.28 minutes for each 5 armatures on one model, and a time savings of 1.13 minutes for armatures of another model, and a time savings of .86 minute per armature on another model. Rates paid to employees for this work were reduced accordingly. The motions savings represented by the invention amounted to 12 seconds per weight used in an armature, premised upon the elimination of at least 6 motions by the new invention. During the time involved, an average of some six to eight weights were inserted in each armature and persons doing this work were paid $2.60 to $2.85 per hour.

The attorney for defendant told the court that the defendant ". . . knew perfectly and accurately . . . how much was paid on each one of these armatures . . ." what the hourly rates were and presumably therefore the exact savings, which information was not in the possession of plaintiff. The record also shows that he stated ". . . that the defendant, in the absence of a jury, certainly could have proved the value of the idea to the defendant. . . ." Defendant, however, chose to rely entirely on the testimony of plaintiff and offered nothing to that effect.

In *A. C. Becken Co. v. Gemex Corporation*, 272 F. 2d 1, 5, we said:

We do not consider that the proof of damages offered by plaintiff was speculative in nature and that it is impossible to contend that plaintiff has been damaged by the action taken by defendant, as the latter contends. Rather, we think, that there was no speculation as to the fact of actual damage and that plaintiff's business was seriously curtailed by the cutoff by defendant. It is not the law that the defendant who caused the damage can be permitted to escape liability because it is difficult for plaintiff to express in terms of dollars the damages it has suffered. *William H. Rankin Co. v. Associated Bill Posters*, 2 Cir., 42 F.2d 152, at page 155, where the court said:

'. . . This evidence, while purely an estimate and introduced as such, was proof of a kind as definite and certain as the subject-matter admitted. It had to do with what was never actually earned because of the defendants' wrongdoing. The witness testified from his knowledge of the business history, made his calculations upon what appears to be a reasonable basis, and the defendants had ample opportunity by cross-examination or the offer of their own evidence on the subject to discredit him and show any fallacy in his reasoning or testimony. . . .

The district court was led into error in finding as a fact and concluding as a matter of law that plaintiff was not damaged as a result of defendant's conduct. Damage was proved. . . .

In the case at bar the evidence proves that plaintiff was damaged by defendant's appropriation of his idea. The action of the district court in overruling defendant's motion for a new trial is not before us for review. No error was committed in the denial of defendant's motions now under review.

We find no error in this record and the judgment of the district court is affirmed.

Affirmed.

DUFFY, Circuit Judge, *dissenting*.

The burden was upon the plaintiff to prove that the adoption by defendant in 1954 of the method of inserting balancing weights was the result of copying plaintiff's suggestion made some thirteen years prior thereto. In my judgment, there was a complete failure on plaintiff's part to meet the burden which was upon him.

If other employees of defendant, without knowledge of plaintiff's earlier suggestion, hit upon the same idea, and defendant adopted same, there would be no liability on the part of the defendant. Also, if defendant adopted in 1954 an idea from a practice then well established in the industry, again there would be no liability. It seems clear that for liability to attach, defendant must have knowingly misappropriated plaintiff's suggestion made thirteen years earlier. In my view, the motion for a directed verdict should have been granted.

REVIEW QUESTIONS

1. Why is the patent right the right to exclude others from making, using, or selling the invention rather than the right to make, use, or sell it?

2. White, an electrical engineer, goes to work for the ABC Company to design automation circuitry. No patent agreement is required of him. Using company time and facilities (in part), he develops a new product and makes application for a patent on it. If he obtains a patent, what rights, if any, will the ABC Company have in the product?

3. In Example 2, assume that White had signed an agreement to assign patent rights to the ABC Company, but had developed the product at home, using only his own time and facilities. What rights, if any, will the ABC Company have in the patent?

4. Outline the steps followed in patent procedure.

5. Why are records of invention development necessary?

6. In Grepke v. General Electric Company, why would the improved method of inserting balancing weights not be patentable?

APPENDIX

Job No. 5006

Sealed bids will be received by the Board of Control until 11:00 A.M., Tuesday, October 28, 1958, in the Budget Commission Room, Second Floor, Hillsborough County Courthouse, Tampa, Florida, at which time and place all bids received will be publicly opened and read aloud for furnishing all labor and materials for the following:

PROJECT	AMOUNT OF CERTIFIED, CASHIER'S OR TREASURER'S CHECK, OR BANK DRAFT WITH BID	DEPOSIT FOR DRAWINGS AND SPECIFICATIONS
CLASSROOM-ADMINISTRATION-OFFICE BLDG. University of South Florida, Tampa, Fla.	$71,250.00	$50.00

All work shall be done in accordance with the drawings and specifications prepared by Pullara, Bowen and Watson, Architects and Engineers, in association with Guy C. Fulton, Architect to the Board of Control. Work shall be done in accordance with Instructions to Bidders and Contract Documents pertaining thereto, which drawings and specifications, instructions, contract documents and form of contract may be secured or examined at the office of the Architect to the Board of Control, East Entrance, Building E, University of Florida, Gainesville, Florida.

Contractors may secure drawings and specifications from the office of the Architect to the Board of Control for a deposit of $50.00 per set, with a limit of two sets per contractor. The cost of each set will be refunded to the bidder upon his return of the sets to the Architect to the Board of Control, Gainesville, Fla., in consideration of the bidder's agreement hereinafter referred to.

IF ANY GENERAL CONTRACTOR FAILS TO SUBMIT A BONA FIDE BID, HIS DEPOSIT CHECK SHALL BE FORFEITED.

Contractors, subcontractors, material dealers and other interested parties may secure full or partial sets of drawings by paying the printing and handling costs at the rate of 75¢ per sheet, COST NOT REFUNDABLE, and by depositing the sum of $5.00 for a specification, which cost is refundable upon return of the specification in good condition WITHIN 14 DAYS AFTER BID DATE.

Each bid must be submitted in strict accordance with the Proposal Form, fully completed, which Proposal Form will be shown in the specifications.

Each bid must be accompanied by a Certified, Cashier's or Treasurer's Check, or a Bank Draft, made payable to BOARD OF CONTROL, in the amount of $71,250.00, as a guarantee and with an agreement that the bidder will not revoke or cancel his bid, or withdraw from the competition for a period of 30 days after the opening of bids, and that in the event the contract is awarded to the bidder, he will, within 10 consecutive calendar days after it is awarded, enter into written contract with the Board of Control in accordance with the accepted bid, and give the Board of Control a contract performance and payment surety bond with good and sufficient sureties satisfactory to the Board of Control, in the amount of 100% of the accepted bid. The bidder's said agreement is incorporated in the Proposal Form. The cost of the bond shall be included as a part of the bidder's base bid proposal.

Bidder's qualifications must be satisfactory to the Board of Control. The Board of Control reserves the right to waive informalities in any bid and to reject any and all bids, or to accept any bid.

Each bid shall be accompanied by a Certified, Cashier's or Treasurer's Check, or Bank Draft on any National or State Bank. All Certified Checks shall have State Documentary Stamps attached.

BOARD OF CONTROL
By: J. B. Culpepper, Executive Director

INSTRUCTIONS TO BIDDERS

Part I, General

1. Definition of Terms: Whenever in these specifications the following terms or pronouns in place of them are used, their intent and meaning shall be interpreted as follows:

Owner: Board of Control, State of Florida.

Contractor: Any individual, firm, partnership or corporation entering into an agreement to perform the work specified herein.

Architect: The Architect to the Board of Control acting directly or through a duly authorized representative unless otherwise specifically stated in the contract.

Inspector: An authorized representative of the Architect or Owner assigned to inspect any of the materials, workmanship or completed work entering into the work.

Bidder: Any individual, firm, partnership or corporation, submitting a proposal for the work contemplated.

Surety: The corporate body which is bound with and for the Contractor, who is primarily liable, and which guarantees the faithful performance of the contract.

Proposal: The approved forms on which the Bidder has submitted his proposal for the work contemplated.

Plans: The official plans, and other drawings or reproductions thereof, pertaining to the work to be done.

Specifications: The Instructions to Bidders, General Conditions, Supplementary General Conditions, Special Provisions, Detailed Technical Specifications and such other documents as are set forth in any of the contract documents.

Contract: The Agreement evidenced by the contract documents, which are: Agreement next preceding the signatures of the parties, the specifications, the drawings, and performance and payment bond in 100% of the contract sum, with surety satisfactory to the Owner.

2. Procurement of Drawings and Specifications: General Contractors may secure drawings and specifications from the Office of the Architect to the Board of Control, East Entrance, Building E, University of Florida, Gainesville, Florida, at the cost which is set forth in the Call for Bids with a limit of two sets per contractor. The cost of each set will be refunded to the bidder upon the return of the set to the Architect to the Board of Control, in consideration of the bidder's agreement not to cancel his bid or withdraw from the competition and to enter into the contract and supply performance bond in the time limit and as set out hereinafter.

3. Examination of Plans, Specifications and Site of Work: The bidder is required, before submitting his proposal, to visit the site of the proposed work and familiarize himself with the nature and extent of the work and any local conditions, that may in any manner affect the work to be done and the equipment, materials and labor required. The fact that he submits a bid shall be an acknowledgement by the bidder that he has satisfied himself as to the nature and location of the work, the general and local conditions, particularly those bearing upon transportation, disposal, handling and storage of materials, availability of labor, water, electric power, roads and uncertainties of weather, of similar physical conditions at the site, the conformation and conditions of the ground, the character of equipment and facilities needed preliminary to and during the prosecution of the work and all other matters upon which information is reasonably obtainable and which can in any way affect the work or the cost thereof under this contract. The Contractor further acknowledges that he has satisfied himself as to the character, quality, and quantity of surface and sub-surface materials to be encountered insofar as this information is reasonably ascertainable from an inspection of the site, including all exploratory work done by the Owner, as well as from information presented by the drawings and specifications made a part of this contract. Any failure by the Contractor to acquaint himself with all the available information will not relieve him from responsibility for estimating properly the difficulty or cost of successfully performing the work. The Owner assumes no responsibility for any understanding or representations made by any of its officers or agents during or prior to the execution of the contract, unless (1) such understanding or representations are expressly stated in the contract and (2) the contract expressly provides that the responsibility therefor is assumed by the Owner.

4. *Explanation to Bidders:* No oral explanation in regard to the meaning of drawings and specifications will be made and no oral instructions will be given before the award of contract. Discrepancies, omissions or doubts as to the meaning of the drawings and specifications should be communicated in writing to the Architect or Engineer for interpretation. Bidders should act promptly and allow sufficient time for a reply to reach them before the submission of their bids. Any interpretation made will be in the form of an addendum to the specifications which will be forwarded to all bidders and its receipt by the bidder should be acknowledged on the Bid Form.

5. *Familiarity with Laws:* The bidder is assumed to be familiar with all Federal, State and local laws, ordinances, rules and regulations, that in any manner affect the work. Ignorance on the part of the Bidder will in no way relieve him from responsibility.

6. *Preparation and Submission of Bids:*

(a) Each bidder shall copy the Proposal Form on his own letterhead, IN DUPLICATE, indicate his bid prices thereon in proper spaces, for the entire work and for the alternates on which he bids. Any erasures or other corrections in the proposal must be explained or noted over the signature of the bidder. Proposals containing any conditions, omissions, unexplained erasures, alterations, items not called for or irregularities of any kind may be rejected by the owner.

(c) Each bid must give the full business address of the bidder, state whether he is an individual, corporation or partnership. Proposals by a corporation must be signed with the legal name and seal of the corporation followed by the name of the state of its incorporation and by the manual signature and designation of an officer, agent or other person authorized to bind the corporation, and if the person signing is not the president, be accompanied by a duly authenticated document evidencing the authority to the officer or agent. Proposals by partnerships shall show the names of all partners and must be signed in the partnership name by one of the partners. The partnership signature shall be followed by the manual signature of the partner signing. In every case, the name of the person signing, and his designation shall be typed or printed below his signature. A bid by a person who affixes to his signature the word "President," "Secretary," "Agent," or other designation without disclosing his principal may be held to be the bid of the individual so signing. Satisfactory evidence of the authority of an officer, agent, attorney or other person signing for a corporation and for an agent, attorney, etc., signing for a partnership or an individual shall be furnished.

(c) Proposals with the bid guarantee shall be enclosed in a sealed envelope which shall be marked:

"Sealed bid for LABOR AND MATERIALS FOR CLASSROOM-AD-

MINISTRATION-OFFICE BUILDING for the University of South Florida, State Project No. 603.2," addressed as indicated by the advertisement. That sealed envelope shall then be placed within a mailing envelope, sealed, marked and addressed as above and delivered or mailed.

7. *Qualifications of Bidders:* The Contract will be awarded only to responsible contractors, qualified by experience and in a financial position to do the work specified. In order to facilitate prompt award of the contract, the Bidder may submit with his proposal:

(a) Experience record showing the Bidder's training and experience in similar work.

(b) List and brief description of similar work satisfactorily completed, with location, date of contracts, together with names and addresses of owners.

8. *Disqualification of Bidder:* More than one bid from an individual, firm, partnership, corporation or association under the same or different names will not be considered. Reasonable grounds for believing that a Bidder is interested in more than one proposal for the same work will cause the rejection of all proposals in which such Bidders are believed to be interested. Any or all proposals will be rejected if there is reason to believe that collusion exists among the Bidders and no participants in such collusion will be considered in future proposals for the same work. Proposals in which the prices obviously are unbalanced will be rejected.

9. *Bid Guarantee:* Bids shall be accompanied by a bid guarantee in the amount of $71,250.00 which shall be a certified check or cashier's check, or a bank draft made payable to the Owner. Such check shall be submitted with the understanding that it shall guarantee that the bidder will not withdraw his bid for a period of thirty (30) days after the scheduled closing time for the receipt of bids; that if his bid is accepted, he will enter into a formal contract with the Owner in accordance with the form of agreement included as a part of the Contract Documents, and that the required Bond will be given; and that in the event of the withdrawal of said bid within said period, or failure to enter into said contract and give said bond within ten (10) days after he has received notice of acceptance of his bid, the bidder shall be liable to the Owner for the full amount of the bid guarantee as representing the damage to the Owner on account of the default of the Bidder in any particular thereof. The checks shall be returned to all except the three lowest bidders after the formal opening of bids. The Board reserves the right to hold the bid guarantee of the three lowest bidders until after the Owner and the accepted bidder have executed the Contract and the Performance and Payment bond has been approved by the Owner. If the required contract and bond have not been executed within thirty (30) days after the date of the opening of the bids, then the check of any bidder will be returned upon his request, provided he has not been notified of the acceptance of his bid prior to the date of such request. Certified checks offered as his guarantees must have Florida Documentary stamps attached.

10. Receipt and Opening of Bids:

(a) Bids will be opened publicly at the time and place stated in the invitation. The officer whose duty it is to open them will decide when the specified time has arrived and no bids received thereafter will be considered. No responsibility will be attached to any officer for the premature opening of a bid not properly addressed and identified.

(b) At the time fixed for the opening of bids, their contents will be made public for the information of bidders and others interested who may be present either in person or by representative.

11. Bid Modification: Bid modification will be accepted from bidders if addressed as indicated in part 6 (c) hereof, at the place where bids are to be received and if received prior to the opening of bids. Modifications may be telegraphic or in other written or printed form. Modifications will be read by Owner or Architect prior to opening formal bids.

12. Withdrawal of Bids: Bids may be withdrawn on written or telegraphic request received from bidders prior to the time fixed for opening. Negligence on the part of the bidder in preparing the bid confers no right for the withdrawal of the bid after it has been opened.

13. Award of Contract:

(a) The contract will be awarded as soon as possible to the lowest responsible bidder; provided his bid is reasonable and it is to the interest of the Owner to accept it.

(b) The Owner reserves the right to waive any informality in bids received when such waiver is in the interest of the Owner.

(c) Each bidder shall, if so requested by the Owner, present evidence of his experience, qualifications and ability to carry out the terms of the contract, including a financial statement.

14. Rejection of Bids: The Owner reserves the right to reject any and all bids when such rejection is in the interest of the Owner, and to reject the bid of a bidder who is not in a position to perform the contract.

15. Alternates: Alternates may be included in the specifications, whereby the bidder shall indicate the sum he will deduct from or add to his base bid. Such alternates may or may not be accepted, but if so, it is the intention of the Owner to accept alternates in the sequence named in the Proposal Form unless the Board finds it distinctly advantageous to the State to do otherwise.

16. Assessments and Taxes: The Owner is exempt from the Florida Sales Tax. The Owner is exempt from all Federal excise taxes on materials, appliances, etc., which are incorporated into and become a part of the finished improvement. The Owner is not required to pay for any municipal building permit. The bidder shall take this into consideration in preparing his proposal.

Part II, Contract Documents

The contract documents consist of the Agreement (Form A-1, Sixth Edition, of the American Institute of Architects) as changed or modified; the General Conditions of the Contract (Form A-2, Sixth Edition, of the American Institute of Architects, Pages 1-10) as changed or modified by any of the contract documents, the Supplementary General Conditions, the Instructions to Bidders, the Specifications and Drawings, and the Bond.

Copies of Forms A-1, Sixth Edition, and A-2, Sixth Edition, American Institute of Architects are on file with the specifications and drawings in the office of the Architect and may be had upon application.

Modification of Agreement

The agreement, Form A-1, Sixth Edition, A.I.A., shall be modified as follows:

1. Page 1, Article 1, at the end, after words "the Specifications and Drawings" add "and other contract documents."

2. A provision will be added to Article 2 of Form A-1, Standard form of Agreement, A.I.A., 6th Edition, to provide liquidated damages. "Inasmuch as failure to complete the project within the time herein fixed will result in substantial injury to the Owner, and, as damages arising from such failure cannot be calculated with any degree of certainty, it is hereby agreed that if such work is not substantially completed as herein defined within the time fixed herein, or within such further time, if any, as in accordance with the provisions of this agreement shall be allowed for such performance or completion, the Contractor shall pay the Owner as liquidated damages for such delay, and not as a penalty, $225.00 for each and every calendar day after the date fixed for such substantial completion, until such substantial completion shall have been fully accomplished. This provision for liquidated damages for delay shall in no manner affect the Owner's rights to terminate the contract as provided in Article 22 of the General Conditions or elsewhere in the contract documents; and the Owner's exercise of right to terminate shall not release the Contractor from his obligation to pay said liquidated damages in the amounts hereinafter set out. Said liquidated damages shall be payable in addition to any excess expenses or costs payable by the contractor under said Article 22 of the General Conditions, and shall not exclude the recovery of damages by the Owner under other provisions of the contract except for Contractor's delays."

3. Page 3, Article 4. Substantial completion will here be defined to mean that all materials required by the drawings and specifications are incorporated in the building, that all labor has been performed and that the work is ready for a final check of inspection by the Architect. It shall not mean the inclusion of such minor alterations and patching as the final inspection shall disclose.

4. Under Article 6, add: "The General Conditions of the contract, referred to above for the contract documents, and except as to any of said General Con-

ditions which may be eliminated by any of the said contract documents. Supplementary or other General Conditions, if any, which may be added shall also be a part of the contract documents and of this contract."

5. As Article 7 of the contract add, "The Board of Control is a public agency of the State of Florida, and the work to be performed under the terms of this contract is a public work within the meaning of Section 215.19, Florida Statutes (Chapter 29782, Acts of 1955, as amended by Chapter 57-755, Laws of Florida); the requirements of such law as to wage rates, and the method provided therein for the settlement of disputes thereof, shall be applicable to both parties to this contract.

In case of any dispute regarding payment of the prevailing rate of wages of employees in any of the several classifications which the contracting authority is unable to settle, the matter shall be referred to the Florida Industrial Commission for determination.

Upon receipt of the affidavit contemplated in Section 215.19 (3) (a), Florida Statutes (Chapter 57-755, Laws of Florida), the contracting authority herein shall withhold from the contractor, until final determination of the claim, an amount of money equal to the amount claimed in such affidavit to be due and unpaid."

Note: The contractor's attention is directed to the fact that the latest amendment makes the stipulation that contracting authority must withhold claim until final determination of claim as above stated.

6. As Article 8 of the Contract add: "Article 40 of the General Conditions of the contract, standard form of the American Institute of Architects, is eliminated and shall not be a part of this contract; and any claim, matter, dispute or controversy otherwise subject to arbitration under this contract shall be determined and settled as follows: Except where under the terms of this contract the Architect's determination is final and except as otherwise specifically provided in this contract, all disputes arising under this contract, including claim by Owner for damages for delay in completion of the construction within the time agreed upon in Article 2 of the contract, shall be decided by the Architect, subject to written appeal within 30 days to the Secretary of the State of Florida, whose decision shall be final and conclusive upon the parties thereto as to such disputes. In the meantime, the Contractor shall diligently proceed with the work as directed. In the determination and settlement of any such dispute, the said Secretary of State shall assess the costs and charges of the proceeding upon either or both parties, as he may deem equitable under the circumstances, which costs and charges may include, but shall not be limited to any professional, legal or technical advice and counsel he may require; and, if he deems it equitable, he may award to the successful party in any dispute damages for delays, or for necessary costs and expenses caused by the proceeding, if he finds that the appeal or refusal to accept the Architect's determination was without reasonable cause. The determination of all such matters in the manner provided in this Article shall be a condition precedent to any right to legal action of either party against the other or any matter of dispute arising under his contract.

In the event of the refusal or inability of the Secretary of State of the State of Florida to act in any of said cases, all such disputes, or other matters herein required to be determined by the Secretary of State, including assessments or awards hereinabove authorized, shall be determined by the Board of Commissioners of State Institutions of the State of Florida or its duly authorized representative; and, in that event the decision, assessment or award of said Board of Commissioners, or its duly authorized representative, shall be final and conclusive upon the parties thereto."

7. Article 9 will be inserted, eliminating the last sentence of Article 31, of the General Conditions, and making it the duty of the contractor to comply with the terms and conditions of the contract without exception.

8. Article 10 will be added cancelling Article 40 of the General Conditions, Standard Form A-2 and providing that any claim, matter, dispute or controversy otherwise subject to arbitration under the contract shall be determined and settled as provided in Article 8 of the Agreement.

Liquidated Damages When Owner Terminates Contract

The owner is entitled to completion of the project within the time originally agreed or within such further time, if any, as may be allowed for completion in accordance with the provisions of this contract. In the event of termination of the contract by the Owner prior to completion as provided in Article 22 of the General Conditions or elsewhere in this contract, the contractor shall be liable to the Owner for the amount set out in said Article 22 and for the per diem liquidated damages herein agreed upon:

1. For each day he is in arrears in his work at said termination, as determined by the Architect, and
2. For each of thirty additional days hereby stipulated and agreed to be the time it will require the Owner to effect another contract for completion of the project and for active resumption of work thereon, provided, however, that the sum of (1) and (2) shall not exceed the number of days beyond the original agreed completion date, or any extension thereof as herein provided, reasonably required for completion of the project.

Part III, Bond

The requirements are that the Bond shall be accompanied by a duly authenticated or certified document, in duplicate, evidencing that the person executing the Bond in behalf of the Surety had the authority to do so on the date of the Bond. In the usual case the conferring of that authority has occurred prior to the date of the Bond and the document showing the date of appointment and enumeration of powers of the person executing the Bond is accompanied by a certification that the appointment and powers have not been revoked and remain in effect. *The date of that certification cannot be earlier than the date of the Bond.* The Bond shall be dated not earlier than the Agreement.

Part IV, Instructions re Execution of Contracts and Bonds

Contracts

If the contractor be an individual, the contract shall be signed with his manual signature.

If the contractor be a firm or company owned by an individual, the contract shall be executed in the name of the firm or company by the manual signature of the owner.

If the contractor be a partnership, the contract shall be executed in the name of the partnership by the manual signature of a partner or partners.

If the contractor be a corporation, the contract shall be executed in the name of the corporation and shall bear the corporate seal. It may be signed for the corporation by the president and attested by the secretary; if signed for the corporation by any other officer than the president, the signature of such officer signing shall be attested by the secretary, and the executed contract shall be accompanied by a duly authenticated document, bearing the seal of the corporation, quoting the section of the by-laws of the corporation authorizing the officer so signing to execute contracts on behalf of the corporation, or if authorized by resolution of the board of Directors, the section of the by-laws authorizing the Board of Directors to designate such officer *and* copy of the resolution designating and authorizing him to execute on behalf of the corporation. That document must contain a statement that the authority is in effect on the date of the execution of the contract, and may not be dated earlier than the date of the execution of the contract. The same officer may not execute the contract and authenticate the document of authority.

Bonds

The contract bond: Shall be executed on behalf of the contractor in the same manner and by the same person who executed the contract.

Part V, Requirements of Certificates of Insurance, Public Liability, Workmen's Compensation

Certificates shall be dated, addressed to the Board of Control, State of Florida, Education Building, Florida State University, Tallahassee, Florida, and shall contain:

The name of the insured contractor, the specific job by name and job number, the name of the insurer, the number of the policy, its effective date, its termination date, and;

A statement that the policy protects the contractor and all subcontractors performing work under the contract for the job mentioned above, against all claims for damages for personal injury, including death, resulting from accident and for damage to property, which may arise from operations under the contract, whether such operations be by the contractor, any subcontractor, or anyone directly employed by either of them, and;

A statement of the maximum amount of insurance against injuries, including death resulting from accident to one person, the maximum for each accident, against injuries, including death resulting from accident to two or more persons, and;

A statement of the maximum amount of insurance against damage to property of others resulting from any one accident, and;

A statement that the Insurer will mail notice to the Board of Control at least ten (10) days prior to any material change in provisions or cancellation of the policy, and;

Shall be signed in the name of the Insurer by its authorized resident agent, giving his address.

Certificates need not be on printed forms. A simple statement covering the requirements enumerated herein is sufficient.

Workmen's Compensation insurance certificates shall contain a statement that the policy meets all requirements of the Florida Workmen's Compensation Law.

Part VI, Basis for Bidding

1. Materials: For convenience of description and as a standard of comparison, certain equipment, materials, etc., have been specified by name or manufacturer.

To insure a uniform basis for bidding, the contractor shall base his proposal on the particular system, equipment or material specified. After the contract is let, other equipment, materials, etc., as manufactured by other manufacturers may be accepted only if, in the opinion of the Architect, same is equivalent in quality and workmanship and will perform satisfactorily its intended purpose.

2. Time for Completion: The work must be completed within 510 calendar days after receipt of NOTICE TO PROCEED from the Architect or receipt of the signed contract.

PROPOSAL FORM

(To be copied on Business Letterhead and submitted in Duplicate)

Honorable J. B. Culpepper, Executive Director
Board of Control
Board's Conference Room
Administration Building, University of Florida

Dear Sir:

The Undersigned, hereinafter called the "Bidder," having visited the site of the proposed project, familiarized himself with the local conditions, nature and extent of the work, the drawings, specifications and contract and bond requirements, proposes to furnish all labor, material and equipment necessary, and to construct the CLASSROOM-ADMINISTRATION-OFFICE BUILD-ING, University of South Florida, Tampa, Florida, State Project No. 603.2, in full accordance with the drawings and specifications for said structure as prepared by Pullara, Bowen and Watson, Architects and Engineers, in association with Guy C. Fulton, Architect to the Board of Control, and in full accordance with your Call for Bids, Instructions to Bidders, Contract and Contract Documents relating thereto on file in the office of said Architect to the Board of Control, for the following bid prices:

BASE BID PRICE .... Dollars ($_____)

Alternate No. 1 Shall be for the net amount to be added to the base bid for the furnishing and installation of one Night Depository money chest, including all materials and labor incidental thereto .... $_____

Alternate No. 2 Shall be for the net amount to be added to the base bid for the furnishing and installation of one Burglary Resistive Money Chest, including all materials and labor incidental thereto .... $_____

Alternate No. 3 Shall be for the net amount to be added to the base bid for Landscaping as indicated on the drawings and/or as specified, including all materials and labor incidental thereto .... $_____

There is enclosed a check (Cashier's, Certified, or Bank Draft) in the amount of $71,250.00 payable to BOARD OF CONTROL, the required bid deposit, as a guarantee and for the purposes set out in the Call for Bids and Instructions to Bidders.

In consideration of the agreement by the Board of Control to refund the cost of each set of plans purchased by the Bidder upon their return to the Board's Architect, and other valuable considerations, receipt whereof is hereby acknowledged, the Bidder has agreed and does hereby agree, (1) that the above proposal shall remain in full force and effect for a period of 30 days after the time of the opening of this proposal, and that the Bidder will not revoke or cancel this proposal or withdraw from the competition within said 30 day period, (2) that in the event the contract is awarded to this Bidder, he will within 10 consecutive calendar days after it is submitted, enter into written contract with the Board of Control in accordance with the accepted bid, and to give the Board of Control a contract performance surety bond, with good and sufficient sureties, satisfactory to the Board of Control, in the amount of 100% of the accepted bid, and (3) that in the event of bidder's default or breach of any of said agreements, said bid deposit shall be forfeited to the Board of Control as liquidated damages.

Acknowledgement is hereby made of receipt of the following Addenda issued during the bidding period:

Addendum No. _____Dated_____

Addendum No. _____Dated_____

Addendum No. _____Dated_____

If awarded this contract, the Bidder agrees to complete the work within 510 calendar days after receipt of "Notice to Proceed" from the Architect or the receipt of the signed contract, and to pay liquidated damages as set forth in the "Instructions to Bidders" for failure to complete the project within the stated time.

In Witness Whereof, the Bidder has hereunto set his signature and affixed his seal this _____ day of _____, A.D., 1958.

_____(SEAL)

By _____

_____
Title

THE STANDARD FORM OF AGREEMENT
BETWEEN CONTRACTOR AND OWNER
FOR CONSTRUCTION OF BUILDINGS*

Issued by The American Institute of Architects
for use when a Stipulated Sum Forms the Basis of Payment

Approved by THE ASSOCIATED GENERAL CONTRACTORS OF AMERICA; THE CONTRACTING PLASTERERS' AND LATHERS' INTERNA-
TIONAL ASSOCIATION; COUNCIL OF MECHANICAL SPECIALTY CONTRACTING INDUSTRIES, INC.; THE NATIONAL BUILDING GRANITE
QUARRIES ASSOCIATION, INC.; THE NATIONAL ELECTRICAL CONTRACTORS ASSOCIATION; THE PAINTING AND DECORATING CON-
TRACTORS OF AMERICA, AND THE PRODUCERS' COUNCIL, INC.°

Copyright 1915-1918-1925-1937 © 1958 by The American Institute of Architects. the Octagon, Washington. D. C. Reproduc-
tion of the material herein or substantial quotation of its provisions without permission of The American Institute of
Architects violates the copyright laws of the United States and will be subject to legal prosecution.

This form is to be used only with the standard general conditions of the contract for construction of buildings.

THIS AGREEMENT made the ....

day of .... in the year Nineteen Hundred and ....

by and between ....

.... hereinafter called the Contractor, and ....

.... hereinafter called the Owner,

WITNESSETH, that the Contractor and the Owner for the considerations hereinafter named agree
as follows:

ARTICLE 1. SCOPE OF THE WORK

The Contractor shall furnish all of the materials and perform all of the work shown on the Drawings and de-

scribed in the Specifications entitled ....

....
(Here insert the caption descriptive of the work as used on the Drawings and in the other Contract Documents)

prepared by ....
acting as and in these Contract Documents entitled the Architect; and shall do everything required by this
Agreement, the General Conditions of the Contract, the Specifications and the Drawings.

* Formal approval, which has been given previous editions, has not yet been received from all of these organizations.
AGREEMENT BETWEEN CONTRACTOR AND OWNER
1958 Edition / Five pages / Page 1.

ARTICLE 2. TIME OF COMPLETION

The work to be performed under this Contract shall be commenced ....

and shall be substantially completed ....
(Here insert stipulation as to liquidated damages, if any.)

ARTICLE 3. THE CONTRACT SUM

The Owner shall pay the Contractor for the performance of the Contract, subject to additions and deduc-

tions provided therein, in current funds as follows: ....
(State here the lump sum amount, unit prices, or both, as desired in individual cases.)

....

Where the quantities originally contemplated are so changed that application of the agreed unit price to the quantity of work performed is shown to create a hardship to the Owner or the Contractor, there shall be an equitable adjustment of the Contract to prevent such hardship.

AGREEMENT BETWEEN CONTRACTOR AND OWNER.
1958 Edition / Five pages / Page 2.

ARTICLE 4. PROGRESS PAYMENTS

The Owner shall make payments on account of the Contract as provided therein, as follows:

On or about the .... day of each month .... per cent of the value, based on the Contract prices of labor and materials incorporated in the work and of materials suitably stored at the site thereof up to the .... day of that month, as estimated by the Architect, less the aggregate of previous payments; and upon substantial completion of the entire work, a sum sufficient to increase the total payments to .... per cent of the Contract price ....

(Insert here any provision made for limiting or reducing the amount retained after the work reaches a certain stage of completion.)

ARTICLE 5. ACCEPTANCE AND FINAL PAYMENT

Final payment shall be due .... days after substantial completion of the work provided the work be then fully completed and the contract fully performed.

Upon receipt of written notice that the work is ready for final inspection and acceptance, the Architect shall promptly make such inspection, and when he finds the work acceptable under the Contract and the Contract fully performed he shall promptly issue a final certificate, over his own signature, stating that the work provided for in this Contract has been completed and is accepted by him under the terms and conditions thereof, and that the entire balance found to be due the Contractor, and noted in said final certificate, is due and payable.

Before issuance of final certificate the Contractor shall submit evidence satisfactory to the Architect that all payrolls, material bills, and other indebtedness connected with the work have been paid.

If after the work has been substantially completed, full completion thereof is delayed through no fault of the Contractor, and the Architect so certifies, the Owner shall, upon certificate of the Architect, and without terminating the Contract, make payment of the balance due for that portion of the work fully completed and accepted. Such payment shall be made under the terms and conditions governing final payment, except that it shall not constitute a waiver of claims.

ARTICLE 6. THE CONTRACT DOCUMENTS

The General Conditions of the Contract, the Supplementary General Conditions, the Specifications and the Drawings, together with this Agreement, form the Contract, and they are as fully a part of the Contract as if hereto attached or herein repeated. The following is an enumeration of the Specifications and Drawings:

IN WITNESS WHEREOF the parties hereto have executed this Agreement, the day and year first above written.

Bond No.

BID BOND

Approved by The American Institute of Architects,
A.I.A. Document No. A-310 (1958 Edition)

KNOW ALL MEN BY THESE PRESENTS,

That we, _____

_____ (hereinafter called the "Principal"),

as Principal, and the_____.

_____, of_____,

a corporation duly organized under the laws of the State of_____,

(Hereinafter called the "Surety"), as Surety, are held and firmly bound unto _____

_____

_____ (Hereinafter called the "Obligee"),

in the sum of_____ Dollars

($), for the payment of which sum well and truly to be made, the said Principal and the said Surety, bind ourselves, our heirs, executors, administrators, successors and assigns, jointly and severally, firmly by these presents.

WHEREAS, the Principal has submitted a bid for_____

_____

_____

NOW, THEREFORE, if the Obligee shall accept the bid of the Principal and the Principal shall enter into a contract with the Obligee in accordance with the terms of such bid, and give such bond or bonds as may be specified in the bidding or contract documents with good and sufficient surety for the faithful performance of such contract and for the prompt payment of labor and material furnished in the prosecution thereof, or in the event of the failure of the Principal to enter such contract and give such bond or bonds, if the Principal shall pay to the Obligee the difference not to exceed the penalty hereof between the amount specified in said bid and such larger amount for which the Obligee may in good faith contract with another party to perform the work covered by said bid, then this obligation shall be null and void, otherwise to remain in full force and effect.

Signed and sealed this_____day of_____A. D. 19____.

In the presence of:

_____(Seal)
{ _____
(Principal)

_____
(Title)

_____(Seal)
{ _____
(Surety)

_____
(Title)

Revised to April, 1959.
SB 5714 Printed in U.S.A.

Bond No.

PERFORMANCE BOND
Approved by The American Institute of Architects,
A.I.A. Document No. A-311 (Formerly Form 107) 1958 Edition

KNOW ALL MEN BY THESE PRESENTS:

That _____,
(Here insert the name and address or legal title of the Contractor)

_____

as Principal, hereinafter called Contractor, and_____

_____,
(Here insert the legal title of Surety)

_____

as Surety, hereinafter called Surety, are held and firmly bound unto_____

_____
(Here insert the name and address or legal title of the Owner)

as Obligee, hereinafter called Owner, in the amount of_____

_____Dollars ($_____),
for the payment whereof Contractor and Surety bind themselves, their heirs, executors, administrators, successors and assigns, jointly and severally, firmly by these presents.

WHEREAS, Contractor has by written agreement dated _____
entered into a contract with Owner for_____

in accordance with drawings and specifications prepared by_____

_____
(Here insert full name and title)
which contract is by reference made a part hereof, and is hereinafter referred to as the Contract.

NOW, THEREFORE, THE CONDITION OF THIS OBLIGATION is such that, if Contractor shall promptly and faithfully perform said contract, then this obligation shall be null and void; otherwise it shall remain in full force and effect.

The Surety hereby waives notice of any alteration or extension of time made by the Owner.

Whenever Contractor shall be, and declared by Owner to be in default under the Contract, the Owner having performed Owner's obligations thereunder, the Surety may promptly remedy the default, or shall promptly

1) Complete the Contract in accordance with its terms and conditions, or

2) Obtain a bid or bids for submission to Owner for completing the Contract in accordance with its terms and conditions, and upon determination by Owner and Surety of the lowest responsible bidder, arrange for a contract between such bidder and Owner, and make available as work progresses (even though there should be a default or a succession of defaults under the contract or contracts of completion arranged under this paragraph) sufficient funds to pay the cost of completion less the balance of the contract price; but not exceeding, including other costs and damages for which the Surety may be liable hereunder, the amount set forth in the first paragraph hereof. The term "balance of the contract price," as used in this paragraph, shall mean the total amount payable by Owner to Contractor under the Contract and any amendments thereto, less the amount properly paid by Owner to Contractor.

Any suit under this bond must be instituted before the expiration of two (2) years from the date on which final payment under the contract falls due.

No right of action shall accrue on this bond to or for the use of any person or corporation other than the Owner named herein or the heirs, executors, administrators or successors of Owner.

Signed and sealed this_____day of_____A. D. 19____.

In the presence of:

_____ (Seal)
(Principal)

_____
(Title)

_____ (Seal)
(Surety)

_____
(Title)

Performance Bond
for General Contractors.
Revised to April, 1959
SB 5715 (1)   Printed in U.S.A.

Bond No.

LABOR AND MATERIAL PAYMENT BOND
Approved by The American Institute of Architects

Note: This bond is issued simultaneously with another bond in favor of the owner conditioned for the full and faithful performance of the contract.

✦ KNOW ALL MEN BY THESE PRESENTS:

That _____,
(Here insert the name and address or legal title of the Contractor)

as Principal, hereinafter called Principal, and_____

_____,
(Here insert the legal title of Surety)

as Surety, hereinafter called Surety, are held and firmly bound unto_____

_____,
(Here insert the name and address or legal title of the Owner)

as Obligee, hereinafter called Owner, for the use and benefit of claimants as hereinbelow defined, in the amount of

_____Dollars ($_____),
(Here insert a sum equal to at least one-half of the contract price)

for the payment whereof Principal and Surety bind themselves, their heirs, executors, administrators, successors and assigns, jointly and severally, firmly by these presents.

WHEREAS, Principal has by written agreement dated_____

entered into a contract with Owner for_____

in accordance with drawings and specifications prepared by_____

(Here insert full name and title)

which contract is by reference made a part hereof, and is hereinafter referred to as the Contract.

NOW, THEREFORE, THE CONDITION OF THIS OBLIGATION is such that if the Principal shall promptly make payment to all claimants as hereinafter defined, for all labor and material used or reasonably required for use in the performance of the Contract, then this obligation shall be void; otherwise it shall remain in full force and effect, subject, however, to the following conditions:

1. A claimant is defined as one having a direct contract with the Principal or with a subcontractor of the Principal for labor, material, or both, used or reasonably required for use in the performance of the contract, labor and material being construed to include that part of water, gas, power, light, heat, oil, gasoline, telephone service or rental of equipment directly applicable to the Contract.

2. The above named Principal and Surety hereby jointly and severally agree with the Owner that every claimant as herein defined, who has not been paid in full before the expiration of a period of ninety (90) days after the date on which the last of such claimant's work or labor was done or performed, or materials were furnished by such claimant, may sue on this bond for the use of such claimant, prosecute the suit to final judgment for such sum or sums as may be justly due claimant, and have execution thereon. The Owner shall not be liable for the payment of any costs or expenses of any such suit.

3. No suit or action shall be commenced hereunder by any claimant,
a) Unless claimant, other than one having a direct contract with the Principal, shall have given written notice to any two of the following: The Principal, the Owner, or the Surety above named, within ninety (90) days after such claimant did or performed the last of the work or labor, or furnished the last of the materials for which said claim is made, stating with substantial accuracy the amount claimed and the name of the party to whom the materials were furnished, or for whom the work or labor was done or performed. Such notice shall be served by mailing the same by registered mail or certified mail, postage prepaid, in an envelope addressed to the Principal, Owner or Surety, at any place where an office is regularly maintained for the transaction of business, or served in any manner in which legal process may be served in the state in which the aforesaid project is located, save that such service need not be made by a public officer.

b) After the expiration of one (1) year following the date on which Principal ceased work on said Contract, it being understood, however, that if any limitation embodied in this bond is prohibited by any law controlling the construction hereof such limitation shall be deemed to be amended so as to be equal to the minimum period of limitation permitted by such law.

c) Other than in a state court of competent jurisdiction in and for the county or other political subdivision of the state in which the project, or any part thereof, is situated, or in the United States District Court for the district in which the project, or any part thereof, is situated, and not elsewhere.

4. The amount of this bond shall be reduced by and to the extent of any payment or payments made in good faith hereunder, inclusive of the payment by Surety of mechanics' liens which may be filed of record against said improvement, whether or not claim for the amount of such lien be presented under and against this bond.

Signed and sealed this_____day of_____A. D. 19____.

In the presence of:

_____(Seal)
{
_____
(Principal)

_____
(Title)

_____(Seal)
{
_____
(Surety)

_____
(Title)

Revised to April, 1959
SB 5715 (2)   Printed in U.S.A.

THE AMERICAN INSTITUTE OF ARCHITECTS

THE GENERAL CONDITIONS OF THE CONTRACT FOR THE CONSTRUCTION OF BUILDINGS *

The Standard Form of General Conditions, 1958 Edition, has received the approval of THE ASSOCIATED GENERAL CONTRACTORS OF AMERICA; THE CONTRACTING PLASTERERS' AND LATHERS' INTERNATIONAL ASSOCIATION; COUNCIL OF MECHANICAL SPECIALTY CONTRACTING INDUSTRIES, INC.; THE NATIONAL BUILDING GRANITE QUARRIES ASSOCIATION, INC.; THE NATIONAL ELECTRICAL CONTRACTORS ASSOCIATION; THE PAINTING AND DECORATING CONTRACTORS OF AMERICA; AND THE PRODUCERS' COUNCIL, INC.*

INDEX TO THE ARTICLES

* Formal approval, which has been given previous editions, has not yet been received from all of these organizations.

GENERAL CONDITIONS. 1958 EDITION.
Ten pages / Page 1

ARTICLE 1

DEFINITIONS

a) The Contract Documents consist of the Agreement, the General Conditions of the Contract, the Supplementary General Conditions, the Drawings and Specifications, including all modifications thereof incorporated in the documents before their execution. These form the Contract.

b) The Owner, the Contractor and the Architect are those mentioned as such in the Agreement. They are treated throughout the Contract Documents as if each were of the singular number and masculine gender.

c) The term Subcontractor, as employed herein, includes only those having a direct contract with the Contractor and it includes one who furnishes material worked to a special design according to the plans or specifications of this work, but does not include one who merely furnishes material not so worked.

d) Written notice shall be deemed to have been duly served if delivered in person to the individual or to a member of the firm or to an officer of the corporation for whom it is intended, or if delivered at or sent by registered mail to the last business address known to him who gives the notice.

e) The term "work" of the Contractor or Subcontractor includes labor or materials or both.

f) All time limits stated in the Contract Documents are of the essence of the Contract.

g) The law of the place of building shall govern the construction of this Contract.

ARTICLE 2

EXECUTION, CORRELATION AND INTENT OF DOCUMENTS

The Contract Documents shall be signed in duplicate by the Owner and the Contractor. In case either the Owner or Contractor or both fail to sign the General Conditions, Drawings or Specifications, the Architect shall identify them.

The Contract Documents are complementary, and what is called for by any one shall be as binding as if called for by all. The intention of the documents is to include all labor and materials, equipment and transportation necessary for the proper execution of the work. Materials or work described in words which so applied have a well-known technical or trade meaning shall be held to refer to such recognized standards.

It is not intended, that work not covered under any heading, section, branch, class or trade of the specifications, shall be supplied unless it is shown on drawings or is reasonably inferable therefrom as being necessary to produce the intended results.

ARTICLE 3

DETAIL DRAWINGS AND INSTRUCTIONS

The Architect shall furnish with reasonable promptness, additional instructions by means of drawings or other-

GENERAL CONDITIONS. 1958 EDITION.
Ten pages / Page 2

wise, necessary for the proper execution of the work. All such drawings and instructions shall be consistent with the Contract Documents, true developments thereof, and reasonably inferable therefrom.

The work shall be executed in conformity therewith and the Contractor shall do no work without proper drawings and instructions.

Immediately after being awarded the contract the Contractor shall prepare a estimated Progress Schedule and submit same for Architect's approval. It shall indicate the dates for the starting and completion of the various stages of construction.

ARTICLE 4

COPIES FURNISHED

Unless otherwise provided in the Contract Documents the Contractor will be furnished, free of charge, all copies of drawings and specifications reasonably necessary for the execution of the work.

ARTICLE 5

SHOP DRAWINGS

The Contractor shall check and verify all field measurements and shall submit with such promptness as to cause no delay in his own work or in that of any other Contractor, three copies, checked and approved by him, of all shop or setting drawings and schedules required for the work of the various trades, and the Architect shall pass upon them with reasonable promptness, making desired corrections, including all necessary corrections relating to design and artistic effect. The Contractor shall make any corrections required by the Architect, file with him two corrected copies and furnish such other copies as may be needed. The Architect's approval of such drawings or schedules shall not relieve the Contractor from responsibility for deviations from drawings or specifications, unless he has in writing called the Architect's attention to such deviations at the time of submission, and secured his written approval, nor shall it relieve him from responsibility for errors in shop drawings or schedules.

ARTICLE 6

DRAWINGS AND SPECIFICATIONS ON THE WORK

The Contractor shall keep one copy of all drawings and specifications on the work, in good order, available to the Architect and to his representative.

ARTICLE 7

OWNERSHIP OF DRAWINGS

All drawings, specifications and copies thereof furnished by the Architect are his property. They are not to be used on other work, and, with the exception of the signed Contract set, are to be returned to him on request, at the completion of the work.

379

SAMPLES

The Contractor shall furnish for approval all samples as directed. The work shall be in accordance with approved samples.

ARTICLE 9

MATERIALS, APPLIANCES, EMPLOYEES

Unless otherwise stipulated, the Contractor shall provide and pay for all materials, labor, water, tools, equipment, light, power, transportation and other facilities necessary for the execution and completion of the work.

Unless otherwise specified all materials shall be new and both workmanship and materials shall be of good quality. The Contractor shall, if required, furnish satisfactory evidence as to the kind and quality of materials.

The Contractor shall at all times enforce strict discipline and good order among his employees, and shall not employ on the work any unfit person or anyone not skilled in the work assigned to him.

ARTICLE 10

ROYALTIES AND PATENTS

The Contractor shall pay all royalties and license fees. He shall defend all suits or claims for infringement of any patent rights and shall save the Owner harmless from loss on account thereof, except that the Owner shall be responsible for all such loss when a particular process or the product of a particular manufacturer or manufacturers is specified, but if the Contractor has information that the process or article specified is an infringement of a patent, he shall be responsible for such loss unless he promptly gives such information to the Architect or Owner.

ARTICLE 11

SURVEYS, PERMITS, LAWS AND REGULATIONS

The Owner shall furnish all surveys unless otherwise specified.

Permits and licenses necessary for the prosecution of the work shall be secured and paid for by the Contractor. Easements for permanent structures or permanent changes in existing facilities shall be secured and paid for by the Owner, unless otherwise specified.

The Contractor shall give all notices and comply with all laws, ordinances, rules and regulations bearing on the conduct of the work as drawn and specified. If the Contractor observes that the drawings and specifications are at variance therewith, he shall promptly notify the Architect in writing and any necessary changes shall be adjusted as provided in the Contract for changes in the work. If the Contractor performs any work knowing it

to be contrary to such laws, ordinances, rules and regulations, and without such notice to the Architect, he shall bear all costs arising therefrom.

Wherever the law of the place of building requires a sales, consumer, use, or other similar tax, the Contractor shall pay such tax.

ARTICLE 12

PROTECTION OF WORK AND PROPERTY

The Contractor shall continuously maintain adequate protection of all his work from damage and shall protect the Owner's property from injury or loss arising in connection with this Contract. He shall make good any such damage, injury or loss, except such as may be directly due to errors in the Contract Documents or caused by agents or employees of the Owner, or due to causes beyond the Contractor's control and not to his fault or negligence. He shall adequately protect adjacent property as provided by law and the Contract Documents.

The Contractor shall take all necessary precautions for the safety of employees on the work, and shall comply with all applicable provisions of Federal, State, and Municipal safety laws and building codes to prevent accidents or injury to persons on, about or adjacent to the premises where the work is being performed. He shall erect and properly maintain at all times, as required by the conditions and progress of the work, all necessary safeguards for the protection of workmen and the public and shall post danger signs warning against the hazards created by such features of construction as protruding nails, hoists, well holes, elevator hatchways, scaffolding, window openings, stairways and falling materials; and he shall designate a responsible member of his organization on the work, whose duty shall be the prevention of accidents. The name and position of any person so designated shall be reported to the Architect by the Contractor.

In an emergency affecting the safety of life or of the work or of adjoining property, the Contractor, without special instruction or authorization from the Architect or Owner, is hereby permitted to act, at his discretion, to prevent such threatened loss or injury, and he shall so act, without appeal, if so authorized or instructed. Any compensation, claimed by the Contractor on account of emergency work, shall be determined by agreement or Arbitration.

ARTICLE 13

INSPECTION OF WORK

The Architect and his representatives shall at all times have access to the work wherever it is in preparation or progress and the Contractor shall provide proper facilities for such access and for inspection.

If the specifications, the Architect's instructions, laws, ordinances or any public authority require any work to be specially tested or approved. the Contractor shall give the Architect timely notice of its readiness for inspection, and if the inspection is by another authority than

380

the Architect, of the date fixed for such inspection, required certificates of inspection being secured by the Contractor. Inspections by the Architect shall be promptly made, and where practicable at the source of supply. If any work should be covered up without approval or consent of the Architect, it must, if required by the Architect, be uncovered for examination at the Contractor's expense.

Re-examination of questioned work may be ordered by the Architect and if so ordered the work must be uncovered by the Contractor. If such work be found in accordance with the Contract Documents the Owner shall pay the cost of re-examination and replacement. If such work be found not in accordance with the Contract Documents the Contractor shall pay such cost, unless it be found that the defect in the work was caused by a Contractor employed as provided in Article 35, and in that event the Owner shall pay such cost.

ARTICLE 14

SUPERINTENDENCE: SUPERVISION

The Contractor shall keep on his work, during its progress, a competent superintendent and any necessary assistants, all satisfactory to the Architect. The superintendent shall not be changed except with the consent of the Architect, unless the superintendent proves to be unsatisfactory to the Contractor and ceases to be in his employ. The superintendent shall represent the Contractor in his absence and all directions given to him shall be as binding as if given to the Contractor. Important directions shall be confirmed in writing to the Contractor. Other directions shall be so confirmed on written request in each case.

The Contractor shall give efficient supervision to the work, using his best skill and attention. He shall carefully study and compare all drawings, specifications and other instructions and shall at once report to the Architect any error, inconsistency or omission which he may discover, but he shall not be liable to the Owner for any damage resulting from any errors or deficiencies in the contract documents or other instructions by the architect.

ARTICLE 15

CHANGES IN THE WORK

The Owner, without invalidating the Contract, may order extra work or make changes by altering, adding to or deducting from the work, the Contract Sum being adjusted accordingly. All such work shall be executed under the conditions of the original contract except that any claim for extension of time caused thereby shall be adjusted at the time of ordering such change.

In giving instructions, the Architect shall have authority to make minor changes in the work, not involving extra cost, and not inconsistent with the purposes of the building, but otherwise, except in an emergency endangering life or property, no extra work or change shall be made unless in pursuance of a written order from the Owner signed or countersigned by the Architect, or a written order from the Architect stating that the Owner has authorized the extra work or change, and

no claim for an addition to the contract sum shall be valid unless so ordered.

The value of any such extra work or change shall be determined in one or more of the following ways:

a) By estimate and acceptance in a lump sum.

b) By unit prices named in the contract or subsequently agreed upon.

c) By cost and percentage or by cost and a fixed fee.

If none of the above methods is agreed upon, the Contractor, provided he receives an order as above, shall proceed with the work. In such case and also under case (c), he shall keep and present in such form as the Architect may direct, a correct account of the cost, together with vouchers. In any case, the Architect shall certify to the amount, including reasonable allowance for overhead and profit, due to the Contractor. Pending final determination of value, payments on account of changes shall be made on the Architect's certificate.

Should conditions encountered below the surface of the ground be at variance with the conditions indicated by the drawings and specifications the contract sum shall be equitably adjusted upon claim by either party made within a reasonable time after the first observance of the conditions.

ARTICLE 16

CLAIMS FOR EXTRA COST

If the Contractor claims that any instructions by drawings or otherwise involve extra cost under this contract, he shall give the Architect written notice thereof within a reasonable time after the receipt of such instructions, and in any event before proceeding to execute the work, except in emergency endangering life or property, and the procedure shall then be as provided for changes in the work. No such claim shall be valid unless so made.

ARTICLE 17

DEDUCTIONS FOR UNCORRECTED WORK

If the Architect and Owner deem it inexpedient to correct work injured or done not in accordance with the Contract, an equitable deduction from the contract price shall be made therefor.

ARTICLE 18

DELAYS AND EXTENSION OF TIME

If the Contractor be delayed at any time in the progress of the work by any act or neglect of the Owner or the Architect, or of any employee of either, or by any separate Contractor employed by the Owner, or by changes ordered in the work, or by strikes, lockouts, fire, unusual delay in transportation, unavoidable casualties or any causes beyond the Contractor's control, or by delay authorized by the Architect pending arbitration, or by any cause which the Architect shall decide to justify the delay, then the time of completion shall be extended for such reasonable time as the Architect may decide.

No such extension shall be made for delay occurring more than seven days before claim therefor is made in writing to the Architect. In the case of a continuing cause of delay, only one claim is necessary.

If no schedule or agreement stating the dates upon which drawings shall be furnished is made, then no claim for delay shall be allowed on account of failure to furnish drawings until two weeks after demand for such drawings and not then unless such claim be reasonable.

This article does not exclude the recovery of damages for delay by either party under other provisions in the contract documents.

ARTICLE 19

CORRECTION OF WORK BEFORE FINAL PAYMENT

The Contractor shall promptly remove from the premises all work condemned by the Architect as failing to conform to the Contract, whether incorporated or not, and the Contractor shall promptly replace and re-execute his own work in accordance with the Contract and without expense to the Owner and shall bear the expense of making good all work of other contractors destroyed or damaged by such removal or replacement.

If the Contractor does not remove such condemned work within a reasonable time, fixed by written notice, the Owner may remove it and may store the material at the expense of the Contractor. If the Contractor does not pay the expenses of such removal within ten days' time thereafter, the Owner may, upon ten days' written notice, sell such materials at auction or at private sale and shall account for the net proceeds thereof, after deducting all the costs and expenses that should have been borne by the Contractor.

ARTICLE 20

CORRECTION OF WORK AFTER FINAL PAYMENT

The Contractor shall remedy any defects due to faulty materials or workmanship and pay for any damage to other work resulting therefrom, which shall appear within a period of one year from the date of final payment, or from the date of the Owner's substantial usage or occupancy of the project, whichever is earlier, and in accordance with the terms of any special guarantees provided in the contract. Neither the foregoing nor any provision in the contract documents, nor any special guarantee time limit, shall be held to limit the Contractor's liability for defects, to less than the legal limit of liability in accordance with the law of the place of building. The Owner shall give notice of observed defects with reasonable promptness. All questions arising under this Article shall be decided by the Architect subject to arbitration, notwithstanding final payment.

ARTICLE 21

THE OWNER'S RIGHT TO DO WORK

If the Contractor should neglect to prosecute the work

properly or fail to perform any provision of this contract, the Owner, after three days' written notice to the Contractor may, without prejudice to any other remedy he may have, make good such deficiencies and may deduct the cost thereof from the payment then or thereafter due the Contractor, provided, however, that the Architect shall approve both such action and the amount charged to the Contractor.

ARTICLE 22

OWNER'S RIGHT TO TERMINATE CONTRACT

If the Contractor should be adjudged a bankrupt, or if he should make a general assignment for the benefit of his creditors, or if a receiver should be appointed on account of his insolvency, or if he should persistently or repeatedly refuse or should fail, except in cases for which extension of time is provided, to supply enough properly skilled workmen or proper materials, or if he should fail to make prompt payment to subcontractors or for material or labor, or persistently disregard laws, ordinances or the instructions of the Architect, or otherwise be guilty of a substantial violation of any provision of the contract, then the Owner, upon the certificate of the Architect that sufficient cause exists to justify such action, may, without prejudice to any other right or remedy and after giving the Contractor, and his surety if any, seven days' written notice, terminate the employment of the Contractor and take possession of the premises and of all materials, tools and appliances thereon and finish the work by whatever method he may deem expedient. In such case the Contractor shall not be entitled to receive any further payment until the work is finished. If the unpaid balance of the contract price shall exceed the expense of finishing the work including compensation for additional architectural, managerial and administrative services, such excess shall be paid to the Contractor. If such expense shall exceed such unpaid balance, the Contractor shall pay the difference to the Owner. The expense incurred by the Owner as herein provided, and the damage incurred through the Contractor's default, shall be certified by the Architect.

ARTICLE 23

THE CONTRACTOR'S RIGHT TO STOP WORK OR TERMINATE CONTRACT

If the work should be stopped under an order of any court, or other public authority, for a period of thirty days, through no act or fault of the Contractor or of anyone employed by him, then the Contractor may, upon seven days' written notice to the Owner and the Architect, terminate this Contract and recover from the Owner payment for all work executed and any proven loss sustained upon any plant or materials and reasonable profit and damages.

Should the Architect fail to issue any certificate for payment, through no fault of the Contractor, within seven days after the Contractor's formal request for payment or if the Owner should fail to pay to the Contractor within seven days of its maturity and presenta-

GENERAL CONDITIONS. 1958 EDITION.
Ten pages / Page 5

tion, any sum certified by the Architect or awarded by arbitrators, then the Contractor may, upon seven days' written notice to the Owner and the Architect, stop the work or terminate this Contract as set out in the preceding paragraph.

ARTICLE 24

APPLICATIONS FOR PAYMENTS

At least ten days before each payment falls due, the Contractor shall submit to the Architect an itemized application for payment, supported to the extent required by the Architect by receipts or other vouchers, showing payments for materials and labor, payments to subcontractors and such other evidence of the Contractor's right to payment as the Architect may direct.

If payments are made on valuation of work done, the Contractor shall, before the first application, submit to the Architect a schedule of values of the various parts of the work, including quantities, aggregating the total sum of the contract, divided so as to facilitate payments to subcontractors in accordance with Article 37(e), made out in such form as the Architect and the Contractor may agree upon, and, if required, supported by such evidence as to its correctness as the Architect may direct. This schedule, when approved by the Architect, shall be used as a basis for certificates for payment, unless it be found to be in error. In applying for payments, the Contractor shall submit a statement based upon this schedule.

If payments are made on account of materials not incorporated in the work but delivered and suitably stored at the site, or at some other location agreed upon in writing, such payments shall be conditioned upon submission by the Contractor of bills of sale or such other procedure as will establish the Owner's title to such material or otherwise adequately protect the Owner's interest including applicable insurance.

ARTICLE 25

CERTIFICATES FOR PAYMENTS

If the Contractor has made application for payment as above, the Architect shall, not later than the date when each payment falls due, issue a certificate for payment to the Contractor for such amount as he decides to be properly due, or state in writing his reasons for withholding a certificate.

No certificate issued nor payment made to the Contractor, nor partial or entire use or occupancy of the work by the Owner, shall be an acceptance of any work or materials not in accordance with this contract. The making and acceptance of the final payment shall constitute a waiver of all claims by the Owner, other than those arising from unsettled liens, from faulty work appearing after final payment or from requirement of drawings or specifications, and of all claims by the Contractor, except those previously made and still unsettled.

Should the Owner fail to pay the sum named in any certificate for payment issued by the Architect or in any award by arbitration, upon demand when due, the Con-

tractor shall receive, in addition to the sum named in the certificate, interest thereon at the legal rate in force at the place of building.

ARTICLE 26

PAYMENTS WITHHELD

The Architect may withhold or, on account of subsequently discovered evidence, nullify the whole or a part of any certificate to such extent as may be necessary to protect the Owner from loss on account of:

a) Defective work not remedied.

b) Claims filed or reasonable evidence indicating probable filing of claims.

c) Failure of the Contractor to make payments properly to subcontractors or for material or labor.

d) A reasonable doubt that the contract can be completed for the balance then unpaid.

e) Damage to another Contractor.

When the above grounds are removed payment shall be made for amounts withheld because of them.

ARTICLE 27

CONTRACTOR'S LIABILITY INSURANCE

The Contractor shall maintain such insurance as will protect him from claims under workmen's compensation acts and other employee benefits acts, from claims for damages because of bodily injury, including death, and from claims for damages to property which may arise both out of and during operations under this Contract, whether such operations be by himself or by any subcontractor or anyone directly or indirectly employed by either of them. This insurance shall be written for not less than any limits of liability specified as part of this Contract. Certificates of such insurance shall be filed with the Owner and Architect.

ARTICLE 28

OWNER'S LIABILITY INSURANCE

The Owner shall be responsible for and at his option may maintain such insurance as will protect him from his contingent liability to others for damages because of bodily injury, including death, which may arise from operations under this contract, and any other liability for damages which the Contractor is required to insure under any provision of this contract.

ARTICLE 29

FIRE INSURANCE WITH EXTENDED COVERAGE

Unless otherwise provided, the Owner shall effect and maintain fire insurance with extended coverage upon the entire structure on which the work of this contract is to be done to one hundred per cent of the insurable value thereof, including items of labor and materials connected therewith whether in or adjacent to the structure insured, materials in place or to be used as part of the permanent construction including surplus materials, shanties, protective fences, bridges, temporary structures, miscellaneous materials and supplies incident to the work, and such scaffoldings, stagings, towers, forms, and equipment as are not owned or rented by the contractor, the cost of which is included in the cost of the work. EXCLUSIONS: This insurance does not cover any tools owned by mechanics, any tools, equipment, scaffolding, staging, towers, and forms owned or rented by the Contractor, the capital value of which is not included in the cost of the work, or any cook shanties, bunk houses or other structures erected for housing the workmen. The loss, if any, is to be made adjustable with and payable to the Owner as Trustee for the insureds and contractors and subcontractors as their interests may appear, except in such cases as may require payment of all or a proportion of said insurance to be made to a mortgagee as his interests may appear.

Certificates of such insurance shall be filed with the Contractor if he so requires. If the Owner fails to effect or maintain insurance as above and so notifies the Contractor, the Contractor may insure his own interests and that of the subcontractors and charge the cost thereof to the Owner. If the Contractor is damaged by failure of the Owner to maintain such insurance or to so notify the Contractor, he may recover as stipulated in the contract for recovery of damages. If other special insurance not herein provided for is required by the Contractor, the Owner shall effect such insurance at the Contractor's expense by appropriate riders to his fire insurance policy. The Owner, Contractor, and all subcontractors waive all rights, each against the others, for damages caused by fire or other perils covered by insurance provided for under the terms of this contract, except such rights as they may have to the proceeds of insurance held by the Owner as Trustee.

The Owner shall be responsible for and at his option may insure against loss of use of his existing property, due to fire or otherwise, however caused. If required in writing by any party in interest, the Owner as Trustee shall, upon the occurrence of loss, give bond for the proper performance of his duties. He shall deposit any money received from insurance in an account separate from all his other funds and he shall distribute it in accordance with such agreement as the parties in interest may reach, or under an award of arbitrators appointed, one by the Owner, another by joint action of the other parties in interest, all other procedure being as provided elsewhere in the contract for arbitration. If after loss no special agreement is made, replacement of injured work shall be ordered and executed as provided for changes in the work.

The Trustee shall have power to adjust and settle any loss with the insurers unless one of the Contractors interested shall object in writing within three working days of the occurrence of loss, and thereupon arbitrators shall be chosen as above. The Trustee shall in that case make settlement with the insurers in accordance with the directions of such arbitrators, who shall also, if distribution by arbitration is required, direct such distribution.

ARTICLE 30

GUARANTY BONDS

The Owner shall have the right, prior to the signing of the Contract, to require the Contractor to furnish bond covering the faithful performance of the Contract and the payment of all obligations arising thereunder, in such form as the Owner may prescribe and with such sureties as he may approve. If such bond is required by instructions given previous to the submission of bids, the premium shall be paid by the Contractor; if subsequent thereto, it shall be paid by the Owner.

ARTICLE 31

DAMAGES

Should either party to this Contract suffer damages because of any wrongful act or neglect of the other party or of anyone employed by him, claim shall be made in writing to the party liable within a reasonable time of the first observance of such damage and not later than the final payment, except as expressly stipulated otherwise in the case of faulty work or materials, and shall be adjusted by agreement or arbitration.

ARTICLE 32

LIENS

Neither the final payment nor any part of the retained percentage shall become due until the Contractor, if required, shall deliver to the Owner a complete release of all liens arising out of this Contract, or receipts in full in lieu thereof and, if required in either case, an affidavit that so far as he has knowledge or information the releases and receipts include all the labor and material for which a lien could be filed; but the Contractor may, if any subcontractor refuses to furnish a release or receipt in full, furnish a bond satisfactory to the Owner, to indemnify him against any lien. If any lien remains unsatisfied after all payments are made, the Contractor shall refund to the Owner all moneys that the latter may be compelled to pay in discharging such a lien, including all costs and a reasonable attorney's fee.

ARTICLE 33

ASSIGNMENT

Neither party to the Contract shall assign the Contract or sublet it as a whole without the written consent of the other, nor shall the Contractor assign any moneys due or to become due to him hereunder, without the previous written consent of the Owner.

ARTICLE 34

MUTUAL RESPONSIBILITY OF CONTRACTORS

Should the Contractor cause damage to any separate contractor on the work the Contractor agrees, upon due

384

notice, to settle with such contractor by agreement or arbitration, if he will so settle. If such separate contractor sues the Owner on account of any damage alleged to have been so sustained, the Owner shall notify the Contractor, who shall defend such proceedings at the Owner's expense and, if any judgment against the Owner arise therefrom, the Contractor shall pay or satisfy it and pay all costs incurred by the Owner.

ARTICLE 35

SEPARATE CONTRACTS

The Owner reserves the right to let other contracts in connection with this work under similar General Conditions. The Contractor shall afford other contractors reasonable opportunity for the introduction and storage of their materials and the execution of their work, and shall properly connect and coordinate his work with theirs.

If any part of the Contractor's work depends for proper execution or results upon the work of any other contractor, the Contractor shall inspect and promptly report to the Architect any defects in such work that render it unsuitable for such proper execution and results. His failure so to inspect and report shall constitute an acceptance of the other contractor's work as fit and proper for the reception of his work, except as to defects which may develop in the other contractor's work after the execution of his work.

To insure the proper execution of his subsequent work the Contractor shall measure work already in place and shall at once report to the Architect any discrepancy between the executed work and the drawings.

ARTICLE 36

SUBCONTRACTS

As soon as practicable and before awarding any subcontracts, the Contractor shall notify the Architect in writing of the names of the subcontractors proposed for the principal parts of the work, and for such other parts as the Architect may direct, and shall not employ any to whom the Architect may have a reasonable objection.

If before or after the execution of the Contract, the Contractor has submitted a list of subcontractors which has been approved by the Architect, and the change of any subcontractor on such list is required by the Owner after such approval, the contract price shall be increased or decreased by the difference in cost occasioned by such change.

The Contractor shall not be required to employ any subcontractor against whom he has a reasonable objection.

The Architect shall, on request, furnish to any subcontractor, wherever practicable, evidence of the amounts certified on his account.

The Contractor agrees that he is as fully responsible to the Owner for the acts and omissions of his subcontractors and of persons either directly or indirectly employed by them, as he is for the acts and ommissions of persons directly employed by him.

GENERAL CONDITIONS. 1958 EDITION.
Ten pages / Page 8

Nothing contained in the contract documents shall create any contractual relation between any subcontractor and the Owner.

ARTICLE 37

RELATIONS OF CONTRACTOR AND SUBCONTRACTOR

The Contractor agrees to bind every Subcontractor and every Subcontractor agrees to be bound by the terms of the Agreement, the General Conditions of the Contract, the Supplementary General Conditions, the Drawings and Specifications, as far as applicable to his work, including the following provisions of this article, unless specifically noted to the contrary in a subcontract approved in writing as adequate by the Owner or Architect.

The Subcontractor agrees—

a) To be bound to the Contractor by the terms of the Agreement, General Conditions of the Contract, the Supplementary General Conditions, the Drawings and Specifications, and to assume toward him all the obligations and responsibilities that he, by those documents, assumes toward the Owner.

b) To submit to the Contractor applications for payment in such reasonable time as to enable the Contractor to apply for payment under Article 24 of the General Conditions.

c) To make all claims for extras, for extensions of time and for damages for delays or otherwise, to the Contractor in the manner provided in the General Conditions of the Contract and the Supplementary General Conditions for like claims by the Contractor upon the Owner, except that the time for making claims for extra cost is one week.

The Contractor agrees—

d) To be bound to the Subcontractor by all the obligations that the Owner assumes to the Contractor under the Agreement, General Conditions of the Contract, the Supplementary General Conditions, the Drawings and Specifications, and by all the provisions thereof affording remedies and redress to the Contractor from the Owner.

e) To pay the Subcontractor, upon the payment of certificates, if issued under the schedule of values described in Article 24 of the General Conditions, the amount allowed to the Contractor on account of the Subcontractor's work to the extent of the Subcontractor's interest therein.

f) To pay the Subcontractor, upon the payment of certificates, if issued otherwise than as in (e), so that at all times his total payments shall be as large in proportion to the value of the work done by him as the total amount certified to the Contractor is to the value of the work done by him.

g) To pay the Subcontractor to such extent as may be provided by the Contract Documents or the subcontract, if either of these provides for earlier or larger payments than the above.

h) To pay the Subcontractor on demand for his work or materials as far as executed and fixed in place, less the retained percentage, at the time the certificate should issue, even though the Architect fails to issue it for any cause not the fault of the Subcontractor.

j) To pay the Subcontractor a just share of any fire insurance money received by him, the Contractor, under Article 29 of the General Conditions.

k) To make no demand for liquidated damages or penalty for delay in any sum in excess of such amount as may be specifically named in the subcontract.

l) That no claim for services rendered or materials furnished by the Contractor to the Subcontractor shall be valid unless written notice thereof is given by the Contractor to the Subcontractor during the first ten days of the calendar month following that in which the claim originated.

m) To give the Subcontractor an opportunity to be present and to submit evidence in any arbitration involving his rights.

n) To name as arbitrator under arbitration proceedings as provided in the General Conditions the person nominated by the Subcontractor, if the sole cause of dispute is the work, materials, rights or responsibilities of the Subcontractor; or, if of the Subcontractor and any other subcontractor jointly, to name as such arbitrator the person upon whom they agree.

The Contractor and the Subcontractor agree that—

o) In the matter of arbitration, their rights and obligations and all procedure shall be analogous to those set forth in this contract; provided, however, that a decision by the Architect shall not be a condition precedent to arbitration.

Nothing in this article shall create any obligation on the part of the Owner to pay or to see to the payment of any sums to any subcontractor.

ARTICLE 38

ARCHITECT'S STATUS

The Architect shall have general supervision and direction of the work. He is the agent of the Owner only to the extent provided in the Contract Documents and when in special instances he is authorized by the Owner so to act, and in such instances he shall, upon request, show the Contractor written authority. He has authority to stop the work whenever such stoppage may be necessary to insure the proper execution of the Contract.

As the Architect is, in the first instance, the interpreter of the conditions of the Contract and the judge of its performance, he shall side neither with the Owner nor with the Contractor, but shall use his powers under the contract to enforce its faithful performance by both.

In case of the termination of the employment of the Architect, the Owner shall appoint a capable and reputable Architect against whom the Contractor makes no reasonable objection, whose status under the contract shall be that of the former Architect; any dispute in connection with such appointment shall be subject to arbitration.

GENERAL CONDITIONS. 1958 EDITION.
Ten pages / Page 9

ARTICLE 39

ARCHITECT'S DECISIONS

The Architect shall, within a reasonable time, make decisions on all claims of the Owner or Contractor and on all other matters relating to the execution and progress of the work or the interpretation of the Contract Documents.

The Architect's decisions, in matters relating to artistic effect, shall be final, if within the terms of the Contract Documents.

Except as above or as otherwise expressly provided in the Contract Documents, all the Architect's decisions are subject to arbitration.

If, however, the Architect fails to render a decision within ten days after the parties have presented their evidence, either party may then demand arbitration. If the Architect renders a decision after arbitration proceedings have been initiated, such decision may be entered as evidence but shall not disturb or interrupt such proceedings except where such decision is acceptable to the parties concerned.

ARTICLE 40

ARBITRATION

All disputes, claims or questions subject to arbitration under this contract shall be submitted to arbitration in accordance with the provisions, then obtaining, of the Standard Form of Arbitration Procedure of The American Institute of Architects, and this agreement shall be specifically enforceable under the prevailing arbitration law, and judgment upon the award rendered may be entered in the court of the forum, state or federal, having jurisdiction. It is mutually agreed that the decision of the arbitrators shall be a condition precedent to any right of legal action that either party may have against the other.

The Contractor shall not cause a delay of the work during any arbitration proceedings, except by agreement with the Owner.

Notice of the demand for arbitration of a dispute shall be filed in writing with the other party to the contract, and a copy filed with the Architect. The demand for arbitration shall be made within a reasonable time after the dispute has arisen; in no case, however, shall the demand be made later than the time of final payment, except as otherwise expressly stipulated in the contract.

The arbitrators, if they deem that the case requires it, are authorized to award to the party whose contention is sustained, such sums as they or a majority of them shall deem proper to compensate him for the time and expense incident to the proceeding and, if the arbitration was demanded without reasonable cause, they may also award damages for delay. The arbitrators shall fix their own compensation, unless otherwise provided by agreement, and shall assess the costs and charges of the proceedings upon either or both parties.

CASH ALLOWANCES

The Contractor shall include in the contract sum all allowances named in the Contract Documents and shall cause the work so covered to be done by such contractors and for such sums as the Architect may direct, the contract sum being adjusted in conformity therewith. The Contractor declares that the contract sum includes such sums for expenses and profit on account of cash allowances as he deems proper. No demand for expenses or profit other than those included in the contract sum shall be allowed. The Contractor shall not be required to employ for any such work persons against whom he has a reasonable objection.

USE OF PREMISES

The Contractor shall confine his apparatus, the storage of materials and the operations of his workmen to limits indicated by law, ordinances, permits or directions of the Architect and shall not unreasonably encumber the premises with his materials.

The Contractor shall not load or permit any part of the structure to be loaded with a weight that will endanger its safety.

The Contractor shall enforce the Architect's instructions regarding signs, advertisements, fires and smoking.

CUTTING, PATCHING

The Contractor shall do all cutting, fitting or patching of his work that may be required to make its several parts come together properly and fit it to receive or be received by work of other contractors shown upon, or reasonably implied by, the Drawings and Specifications for the completed structure, and he shall make good after them as the Architect may direct.

Any cost caused by defective or ill-timed work shall be borne by the party responsible therefor.

The Contractor shall not endanger any work by cutting, excavating or otherwise altering the work and shall not cut or alter the work of any other contractor save with the consent of the Architect.

CLEANING UP

The Contractor shall at all times keep the premises free from accumulations of waste materials or rubbish caused by his employees or work, and at the completion of the work he shall remove all his rubbish from and about the building and all his tools, scaffolding and surplus materials and shall leave his work "broom-clean" or its equivalent, unless more exactly specified. In case of dispute the Owner may remove the rubbish and charge the cost to the several contractors as the Architect shall determine to be just.

INDEX